THE
CYPRUS TAPES

BY
DAVID MATTHEWS

Published by Downlow Productions

ABOUT THE AUTHOR

THE author (David Carter/David Matthews) was born in Pakistan, educated in the United States and served as a commissioned officer in the Royal Corps of Signals. In the mid-sixties, he joined the British Broadcasting Corporation as a writer-producer, working for both radio and television. He later anchored major documentaries.

During his broadcasting career he was responsible for a wide range of documentary and feature programmes for the BBC and ITV, several of which received awards in Britain and the United States.

He has travelled extensively, reporting from several 'sensitive' areas, including The Gulf, the Lebanon, southern Turkey, the Black Sea, India, Pakistan, Hong Kong, East Germany and The Falklands.

Aside from his journalistic activities, the author has written several plays which have been broadcast in the United Kingdom.

Before his recent retirement, he worked on the defence side of a major UK aerospace organization in an executive capacity.

He is married to a former stage and television actress. They have two grown-up children. The family lives in Hertfordshire, England.

First published 1987 by Kemal Rüstem & Brother, London

This edition published 1999 by Downlow Productions, 8 The Old Drive, Welwyn Garden City, Hertfordshire, England. Distributed by Fresh Publications, PO Box 48, Girne, Mersin 10, Turkey.

A catalogue record for this book is available from the British Library.

ISBN 0 9537170 0 3

Printed in the TRNC by A-N Graphics (Kıbrıs) Ltd, Lefkoşa

CONTENTS

'Sana söylerim kızım, sen işit gelinim'

I tell it to you, my daughter, so that my daughter-in-law may hear it.

Turkish Cypriot saying

'A man who is three feet tall has just the same rights as one who is six feet tall.'

President Rauf Denktaş of the
Turkish Republic of Northern Cyprus

This book is dedicated to my wife, Wendy,
and our children, Sheryl and Matthew,
whose love for Cyprus is as great as mine.

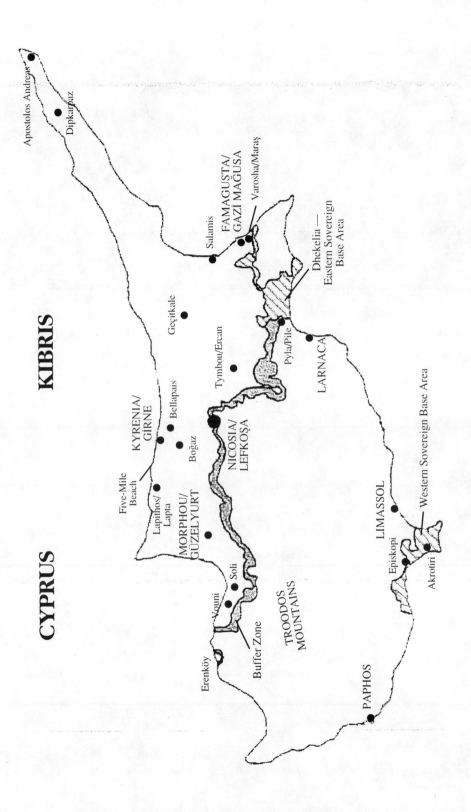

CYPRUS

KIBRIS

Apostolos Andreas

Dipkarpaz

FAMAGUSTA/
GAZİ MAĞUSA

Varosha/Maraş

Salamis

Dhekelia —
Eastern Sovereign
Base Area

Geçitkale

Tymbou/Ercan

Pyla/Pile

LARNACA

KYRENIA/
GIRNE

Bellapais

Boğaz

NICOSIA/
LEFKOŞA

Western Sovereign Base Area

Five-Mile
Beach

Lapithos/
Lapta

MORPHOU/
GÜZELYURT

LIMASSOL

Soli

Episkopi

Vouni

Akrotiri

Erenköy

TROODOS
MOUNTAINS

Buffer Zone

PAPHOS

INTRODUCTION

WHEN Gill Fraser, the energetic editor of *Cyprus Today*, the English-language newspaper of the Turkish Republic of Northern Cyprus, told me that she had received several inquiries about *The Cyprus Tapes* and suggested my book be republished, I was delighted and jumped at the idea.

Much has happened to Cyprus — and to myself and my family — since the book first appeared in 1987 and so I wondered if I should, with the benefits of hindsight, rewrite the edition you have in your hands today.

After some thought, I opted for a compromise.

I decided, obviously, to correct mistakes which readers had drawn to my attention, but not to change the thoughts I had expressed 11 years ago. They were true then and I felt they should be left untouched.

But with the chance to improve this work, I chose to re-arrange some chapters and to put back material from my original type-script. Kemal Rüstem, the first publisher, made cuts for reasons of space. This time, I am leaving it once again to my current editor to decide what is excluded, if anything.

Some readers of the first edition told me they would have welcomed a map of Cyprus to help them locate the places I mention — and they thought some photographs ought to have been included as well.

The new publisher has put right these shortcomings.

Otherwise, it is the same book as before. It is not a scholarly work nor a comprehensive study of historical events intended to add to the knowledge of historians, rather it is simply a story — or dramatized documentary — about some Cypriots, Greek and Turkish, UN soldiers and British expatriates, all ordinary people caught up in extraordinary situations, rarely of their own making. Without apology I point out that I have relied on their memories of events, their perception of the truth and my own observations.

To the best of my knowledge, all the incidents related are factual.

Where there has been a need for statistics, I have drawn on figures provided by both sides, divided by common sense, and compared the answer against UN source material.

In the chapters devoted to UNFICYP I have compressed material gathered over an extended period to describe what was a typical 24-hour period in the Buffer Zone during the mid-'80s. Thus, some of the people mentioned — and many of the military units — were not present in Cyprus at the same time. Since then, too, several national contingents have been replaced by others.

The names of some of the book's characters have been changed, and one is a composite based on two real people. I did this to prevent embarrassment and to avoid facing litigation. In this, I partly failed because a person did try to sue me for libel, but gave up for fear of having more of his past exposed in a court of law.

For convenience, I continue to write in the third person. There are no hidden reasons for this device. It allows me simply to be more objective about myself.

If there are errors of fact or judgement in the pages which follow, I am alone to blame, but if you are left with a better understanding of Cyprus, then that will be due entirely to the people, friends and critics alike, on both sides of the island, whose contributions make up this book.

I tried never to breach their trust, but if I have by quoting their unguarded moments, I hope they will be as forgiving as they were helpful and hospitable. Unfortunately a few of them are no longer with us, but they continue to live in my memory.

Scores of individuals supported this project and all know who they are. But in particular I owe a great deal to the late Nancy Crawshaw, who spent many years of her life creating a better understanding of the peoples of Cyprus by her dedication to factual reporting and careful analysis of Cypriot affairs. It was she who suggested I write this book, although I suspect it turned out very different from what she had expected.

I am also indebted to several other writers on Cyprus whose works I studied and absorbed to learn the background to events I describe. These include *The Road to Bellapais* by Dr Pierre Oberling, Mehmet Ali Birand's *Thirty Hot Days*, H. Scott Gibbons's *Peace Without Honour*, John Reddaway's *Burdened With Cyprus* and *The Enchanted Land* by Professor Noel Kennedy Thomas, who describes his journey to the Karpas which I arranged so that he could be my witness of how Greek Cypriots there were faring, and to confirm or deny allegations that their holy places were being systematically destroyed.

Nor would I have been able to complete this book without practical help from several public information officers in south and north Cyprus. Oktay Oksuzoğlu often bent the rules to provide assistance. He retired from TRNC government service some years ago to devote his life to writing poetry with Muslim themes.

UNFICYP military staff, the British Ministry of Defence and the Turkish army in northern Cyprus were always quick to answer my questions, too. I wish the same could be said of the civilian branch of the UN mission, whose staff tried to bend me to their point of view, change parts of what I had written and disagreed with most of my conclusions.

Except for them, nobody else from any government agency, anywhere, has attempted, let alone succeeded, in limiting my freedom of expression, although they often provided assistance to make my visits to Cyprus possible.

As with the first edition, today's publishers have once again agreed to distribute among TRNC children's charities any royalties due to the author. For that, alone, thank you for buying this new edition of *The Cyprus Tapes*.

David Carter
June 1999

CHAPTER ONE

FIVE DAYS TO WAR

Summer 1974

TURKISH paratroopers, stooping under the weight of military equipment strapped to their bodies, queued in the belly of an American-built C-130 Hercules. They were over Morphou and heading towards Nicosia. On a barked command they stepped forward and jumped through the open tail-gate of the rumbling aircraft, pulled their ripcords and floated through the sky like a shower of psychedelic mushrooms. To their left and right, DC-3 Dakotas were also spewing their contents on to the parched plains north of Nicosia, just as dawn light began to filter through the jagged edges of the Pentadaktylos range of mountains.

So began another war in Cyprus, the latest in a long line stretching back to the start of recorded time. Within four weeks the island would be partitioned, entire populations of towns and villages uprooted and moved from one side of the island to the other. None of them would be able to return to the place of their birth.

Turks would call the action a 'Peace Operation', the Greeks an 'invasion'.

It was 05.00, Saturday, 20 July 1974.

Julia Sinclair pulled the bed-sheet over her head and tried vainly to hide from the sound of the ringing telephone. If she stayed still long enough perhaps Bill, her husband, would get out of bed and deal with the inconsiderate early-morning caller. She knew there was no possibility of her daughter, Susie, raising herself and staggering the six short steps to the hallway to pick up the receiver.

Cyprus was not Julia's favourite place.

Certainly the cost of living was far lower than back home in England, and Susie was able to enjoy a way of life which the family could never afford elsewhere, but Julia had never felt settled since her husband had resigned his staff post at the Central Office of Information in London.

Realizing that she was on her own again and losing the battle of the ringing bell, Julia rolled off the mattress and plopped her feet into a pair of slippers by the side of her bed, more an automatic reflex than a conscious act. Stretching her neck and exercising her shoulders, she walked wearily to the hall and picked up the receiver.

A curt voice crackled on the far end of the line. 'Look out of the window, Julia,' the speaker ordered. It was a journalist friend of theirs who worked for *The Cyprus Mail*, the English-language daily newspaper. 'The Turks have finally done it,' he continued, 'they're invading. Their paratroops are dropping near Kythrea and the airport.'

'Perhaps it's an exercise. Something to do with NATO.'

'No,' the journalist stressed. 'Cyprus has nothing to do with NATO, yet. And this can't be an exercise. Look, I can't stop to talk. I'll phone you back as soon as I have any more information.'

Stunned into silence by the news, Julia replaced the receiver slowly. During the past five days her dislike for Cyprus had changed to fear, but Bill had been deaf to her worries. Now they were all caught up in a war.

Ever since the family settled in Cyprus in 1970, Julia had ignored local politics and reports of inter-communal fighting. It was not her concern that Greek and Turkish Cypriots allowed their prejudices to get the better of them. If she had doubts about her role, they were kept in check in the back of her mind, helped occasionally by five milligrams of Valium.

A thousand feet above sea-level, at their home in Tjiklos, Major Phyllis Heymann, MBE, and Major Betty Hunter Cowan, TD, were awake too; their sleep disturbed by the sound of steady flapping from the rotor-blades of giant helicopters which were ferrying the Turkish Special Forces from their mainland bases to their designated landing zones on the island.

The two retired majors were known as 'The Cave Ladies', a nickname given to them by members of the Canadian contingent of the United Nations Force in Cyprus who had been camped in their grounds. Although the Canadians had been replaced by Finns, the name stuck.

'Well, the Turks have arrived,' Betty remarked, her voice a mixture of cool detachment and disappointment. 'What a bore. We won't be able to go out today for our shopping.'

'Nonsense,' Phyllis chided her friend, adding, 'I'm sure it will be over quickly.'

Determined that the events unfolding outside were not going to upset their normal routine, they made themselves a light breakfast and sat eating in their dining-room. After a life of service in the cause of 'Empire', represented by the jumble of memorabilia stored in their home in Tjiklos, they were well used to handling the unexpected; as far as they were concerned, the arrival of the Turkish army to the shores of Cyprus should have been expected by intelligent people at any time during the past few days.

Since 1959 Cyprus had been their home. They called it their *beloved* island, a small place on *the edge of heaven*, bedevilled sadly by 'a handful of trouble-makers'. At the moment, however, the two majors were only mildly annoyed by having their weekend disrupted. For they enjoyed getting out and about, including visiting the Sovereign Base Areas, which, by right of treaty, were forever a little bit of Britain. One of these Bases was Episkopi-Akrotiri, the other Dhekelia.

With their rows of neat semi-detached houses, red pillar boxes, polo grounds, and streets named after English counties, the Bases could have been mistaken for Catterick-in-the-sun or Aldershot-by-the-sea. Parade squares echoed to the blasts of sergeant-majors and police were always ready to issue speeding tickets to motorists. Sleepy officers' messes only added to the peculiarly British atmosphere. Here many expatriates revived their sterling qualities, eavesdropped on the freshest military gossip and borrowed the latest editions of *Punch*, *The Tatler*, and *The Illustrated London News*. But when UN soldiers posted to camps in the Kyrenia mountains wanted a change of scenery, they visited Phyllis and Betty, a couple known throughout Cyprus for their generosity of spirit, mainly poured from a bottle. Newcomers to the island were warned invariably to beware the large 'sundowners' that 'The Cave Ladies' poured their guests on the porch of their Tjiklos home. Surviving hangovers was the toughest part of UN service for these young soldiers.

As the Turkish aircraft flew over, the two women went outside to see for themselves how the Turks were managing their military operation. Betty carried a portable wireless and she searched the dial for a news bulletin. Eventually she tuned into the local British Forces Broadcasting Service in Dhekelia, although both she and her partner preferred the BBC's World Service. 'It's so much more to our taste, don't you know,' Betty had often been heard to remark. But, in common with other Britons in Cyprus, they had been advised by Her Majesty's High Commission in Nicosia to listen to the BFBS for instructions in the event of trouble. What they picked up was the forced enthusiasm of a disc-jockey using the slang of an American B-picture script and delivering his lines in the accent of a Londoner.

The disc-jockey was giving the weather forecast for Cyprus, based on material gathered from the Royal Air Force meteorological station on top of Mount Olympus. He was predicting a temperature in excess of 100 degrees. There was no other information before he spun his next pop disc. This style of broadcasting did not find favour amongst the officer corps and the island's elderly ex-colonials who felt strongly that standards were falling everywhere.

'If he hasn't got The News dear, switch him off,' Phyllis commanded, and Betty did as she was told as they continued to stroll their 'wild Cyprus' garden, half a mile in circumference, filled with trees bearing carobs and olives. They were not in the least frightened. They had survived many military campaigns between 1939 and 1956, and they were convinced that what was taking place now would only be a minor interruption in *their* way of life; they were less certain how others would react.

'We'll have to conserve our precious water now because the electricity is sure to fail,' Betty commented. Their water came from a communal tank, pumped by an electrically-powered motor. 'I think we're going to have a lot of very frightened people dashing up here.' She glanced in the direction of Kyrenia, far below them.

In the thirties Kyrenia was known as the island's honeymoon resort.

When summer heat and humidity made the capital, Nicosia, impossible to bear, young colonial officers and their wives packed their bags and drove to this small port on the northern coast to enjoy its cooler, more romantic atmosphere.

Despite the growth of modern tourism, the town had changed little from those days, except now the crowds were from all parts of Europe. They spilled off the elevated pavements to meander along the town's narrow main street much to the annoyance of motorists.

Cars travelled at a crawl on the left sides of the packed streets, hooting and honking on their way. This cacophony of sound was mainly caused by irritable foreigners unused to the easy tempo of Cypriot life and the strange habits of local drivers, who stuck their right arms through the windows of the driver's sides of their vehicles. Only occasionally was this their signal for turning. More often than not the drivers were simply cooling their hands. Frequently, too, they stopped in Hellas Street, stepped out, did their shopping at the Neocles supermarket, returned, and then allowed the procession to move on slowly.

On holidays and weekends the streets were even more congested as the people of Nicosia came to Kyrenia for a breath of sea air. They would swing right at the bottom of Catsellis Street for the harbour, or left, past the Barclays Bank opposite The Dome Hotel, to travel along the coast road to Five-Mile Beach and Snake Island.

In the Lilliputian harbour there were always fishing boats and yachts that flew the flags of many nations. They were protected from the Mediterranean's sudden storms by a thick harbour wall, which curved like a horseshoe from a Byzantine castle to a miniature lighthouse. It had become a familiar scene to British television viewers as the setting for a glossy Benson & Hedges' commercial for cigarettes.

Every day from noon till late at night, the water-side restaurants were packed with tourists. Young waiters scurried in all directions, relying for their wages on tips from their customers. There were the Marabou and Galleon owned by Peter Christodoulou, and The Harbour Club, a particular focus of attention. Here, Judy Findlay was the hostess and entertained British guests with her versions of forties' songs which had helped make her a minor star, in London. From 1950 she had run the restaurant with her husband, Roy. Their visitors' book held the signatures of the rich and famous from the worlds of showbusiness and politics, people like Tommy Handley, Elsie and Doris Waters, and Duncan Sandys.

Over the centuries Kyrenia castle had guarded the harbour's narrow entrance with varying degrees of effectiveness. During World War II its north-east corner tower had been used by local militia as a look-out for enemy aircraft. If any were observed the soldiers would crank the handle of a field telephone connected to flight controllers at the RAF station at Timbou. From there, Spitfires and Hurricanes of Flight 259 were scrambled, roared along the grass strip, and aimed to catch the Germans far out at sea. They were commanded in 1941 by ex-Battle of Britain pilot 'Tubby' Mermagen.

On this Saturday morning Greek Cypriot militia men held Kyrenia castle and the aircraft they sighted were Turkish. The first were at 05.18 exactly, a flight of Phantoms that screamed along the coastline, firing their missiles at a National Guard camp near Snake Island. The Greek Cypriots counted the planes and fired their rifles and light machine-guns skywards. Theirs was a gesture of defiance only, for their weapons were too light to stop the formations on their way to Nicosia. Nor did the defenders have aircraft of their own to call up. Total air superiority belonged to the Turks. They watched impotently as two Greek Cypriot gunboats tried to slip harbour only to be sunk in the open sea by the Turkish air force.

In Nicosia, Julia Sinclair sighed and walked into the kitchen, unsure whether to pour herself a large brandy or make coffee. Until she collected her thoughts, there was no point in waking Bill or Susie. When she did, she was determined to make them listen to her voice; they had to leave Nicosia as soon as possible; if they refused then she would leave without them.

Because there was a tumbler on the draining-board and a bottle of Three Kings brandy on the kitchen table, Julia decided that coffee could wait. Alcohol, she reasoned, would stiffen her resolve and prepare her for the confrontation with Bill and Susie. She was certain that they would challenge all her points. To make sure she remembered what needed to be said, she began writing down her points, using a blunt pencil.

Failing to mark the paper of her note-pad clearly, she threw the pencil on the floor and pulled open kitchen drawers, scattering bills in unopened envelopes, crumpled receipts and old recipes clipped from magazines.

At the bottom of the second drawer Julia found her diary, a large leather-bound volume of lined pages. It was her handwritten record of daily life in Cyprus, each entry carefully dated. Placing the volume on the table next to her brandy glass, she flipped it open to where the barrel of a fountain pen acted as a marker for her most recent entry. She began to read.

15 July 1974

There was a coup in Cyprus today and the president, Archbishop Makarios, was overthrown. It began at eight o'clock in the morning when I switched on my vacuum cleaner. I thought I had been the cause of something awful because at that moment there were lots of explosions outside.

Bill was having a cup of coffee with a friend at a restaurant near

Metokhi monastery, waiting to drive to the Nicosia racecourse where Susie was exercising her chum's horses. When he heard the gun-fire, he dropped his coffee and stained his trousers (I don't think I'll be able to get the stains out). He says that Cypriots were running in all directions trying to escape bullets fired by the Greek Cypriot National Guard. They were aiming at some tanks which were coming from an olive grove. He didn't stop to count them, but jumped into our car and drove like mad through the back streets to collect Susie.

Thank goodness he got to her safely, but she was very silly, refusing to leave until she had returned the horses to their stables. Needless to say, the horses were very frightened by the sound of the gun-fire.

The only way home for Bill and Susie was through the Turkish side of Nicosia via the Ledra Palace checkpoint where the UN has a position. They were waved through without difficulties, but when they reached Archbishop Makarios Avenue, the firing was so bad that he had to tell Susie to lie flat on the car floor. Then he put his foot down and raced for home.

Bill says that there were lots of Cypriots lying under their cars, holding their hands over their eyes and ears.

I was worried stiff and spent my time, quite irrationally, rushing from the front to the back balcony trying to work out the direction of the shooting. I saw thick black smoke coming from the Presidential Palace. I heard bursts of machine-gun fire and the crack of rifle shots. The dull thuds I expect were mortar bombs exploding.

At last Bill and Susie arrived back and Bill said we ought to go immediately to the British High Commission for instructions; perhaps get a Union Jack for our car so that everybody would know we were English. 'Don't be so old fashioned,' Susie said. 'What can the High Commission do? Send for a gunboat to take us home?' I must say she had a point although what she really wanted was a swim at the Nicosia Club. Bill agreed to go there because, he said, the Club would be as safe as the High Commission on 'The Green Line', which keeps the Turks apart from the Greeks. Personally I think Bill wanted to have a drink. Neither of them asked my opinion.

We reached the club without incident and found we were the only members there, except for a woman in a bikini by the pool. Bill couldn't keep his eyes off her.

The club's manager was very worked up. He charged at us shouting 'Makarios is dead. Makarios is dead.' He said the National Guard had taken over the government; the news was broadcast on the radio. He asked us to leave so that he could shut the club. 'Not before I've had a drink,' Bill told him. The manager replied that that was impossible as all his staff had run away. But I saw three waiters and asked him who they were. He replied that they were Turks. Bill said that they should go home as well, and that if the manager handed us the keys, we would lock up. Surprisingly the manager agreed.

During the morning Nicosia prison, just up the road from the club, was attacked by the National Guard, who released all the prisoners. I certainly wouldn't want to be in the shoes of the former prison guards tonight . . .

In the middle of the afternoon the firing died down and we decided to leave the club and return home. On the way we passed the Paphos Gate police station. It had a hole blown in its side by a Russian tank that was parked in the centre of the road. Bill said it was a T-34, but whatever it was, it hadn't done a very good job because the police station was still open for business; which was more than could be said for the shops. We didn't realize there was a curfew in force.

A few hours ago we watched a special programme on television from the Cyprus Broadcasting Corporation. We were introduced to the new President, who read a prepared speech. His name is Nicos Sampson. His eyes were glazed and his face twitched. Bill said the new President would have to improve his image if he is to bolster the confidence of the people.

I'm writing these lines in semi-darkness as I sit on the balcony. It's very, very hot and I can tell that our neighbours in the nearby flats are trying to get some fresh air too. Despite the curfew, I know they're there, because from time to time I see the flare of a match being lit and the glow of cigarettes.

Occasionally there's a burst of tracer which cuts through the blackness. Somebody is continuing to fight. Although I can't see them, I can hear tanks manoeuvring. But nothing seems to frighten the crickets; they're still chattering.

16 July 1974

The new administration lifted the curfew for a couple of hours this afternoon and we tried to do some shopping. We weren't very successful. There's been a lot of panic-buying and some shopkeepers told us a lot had been stolen during the street fighting yesterday. I suppose looting is to be expected in circumstances like these.

Susie suggested that we should drive to the Turkish quarter of Nicosia and see what was on offer there. Their area is so scruffy in comparison with the Greek Cypriot side of town. They don't appear as industrious as the Greeks. No wonder Bill's friends say the Turks are a burden on Cyprus, always demanding a great deal and giving very little in return. I've heard that Turks have been leaving Cyprus for years, and somebody, I forget who, said the other day that before long, there won't be any left.

There's been nothing on the radio except martial music and stirring announcements about Mr Sampson and his new government. But not everybody's happy about the man. Annie Barrett telephoned from Kyrenia and called him 'The Butcher of Ledra Street'. She said that he used to murder English civilians during the fifties when Cyprus was ours. Nobody thinks the Turks will stand for him and that the coup is only the start of more trouble. Annie was damned upset about the way the CBC cancelled *Upstairs Downstairs* last night. I must say I missed the programme, too. Listening to the CBC today I couldn't help thinking how the same announcers used to speak so glowingly about Archbishop Makarios. Now they vilify his name. It doesn't make sense. It's also very confusing to hear talk about all the support Sampson has while there are reports of Greek Cypriots still fighting each other.

17 July 1974

Well, I don't know what to make of things now, but I'm certain we're sitting on a powder-keg about to explode. It turns out that Archbishop Makarios wasn't killed in the coup after all. It seems he escaped to Paphos where he joined some of his supporters, got on a radio, and was rescued by the UN.

Annie was right: the Turks are very cross about President Sampson. According to the BBC, the Turkish Prime Minister has gone to London for talks with our Government. Because of some silly treaty we signed years ago, he wants us to push out Sampson and his men. I don't see why we should get involved, unless it's to help us get out. But there it is.

Bill says it's a storm in a teacup. He calls the BBC reports scare-mongering and accuses the Turks of over-reacting. If there was any danger to us, he says the British Forces Broadcasting Service at the Sovereign Bases would be the first to know. They'd give us specific instructions, not just tell us to stay calm.

We went to the High Commission again today and at last collected a Union Jack to fly from our car. I don't know why because we haven't been stopped by the National Guard on our way backwards and forwards to the club.

Lots of children were packing the club swimming pool. They're still arriving from England to spend school holidays with their parents out here. So I don't suppose there can be any real danger, otherwise they wouldn't have been allowed to come, would they?

In fact all the club staff were back on duty, looking very smart. The manager said that by Friday he would have the restaurant working again and we'll be able to have a cooked lunch. That will make a change because we're all fed up having to pack picnic hampers with sandwiches.

When we returned home we listened to the World Service, because even Bill accepts now that we're not hearing the full story from the BFBS or the CBC. The BBC told us that Makarios had reached London and that there are a lot of talks going on there, and in Athens and Ankara. While life seems to be settling down here, it appears everywhere else they're getting excited. I'll be glad when we know exactly what's happening.

I wish it wasn't so hot. I feel so sticky, and if that wasn't enough, it's that time of the month.

18 July 1974

Nothing's changed. Wake the family, make a light breakfast, cut sandwiches, check the refrigerator, race the cleaner round the flat, make the beds, look in the mirror and start to put on a fresh face to meet the world.

We drove to the High Commission again, but there are no fresh instructions.

I'm writing this by the club swimming pool. The women with the bikini is here again. After chatting her up, Bill says she's a BOAC stewardess.

Most of the same old faces are here. Life must be getting back to normal because our drinks are being mixed with a dash of malice again (At least tomorrow we'll have a proper lunch)

Harry Bowden has driven down from Kyrenia and tells us that Betty and Phyllis are convinced 'Johnny Turk' is planning something. Bill replied that 'The Cave Ladies' are silly. Harry agreed. Perhaps it's because the two old bats out-rank him. He was a captain in the Territorial Army during the War, but likes us to use his rank although we know he's a retired bank manager. Harry's always talking about 'our Sovereign Bases and their importance to maintaining stability in the Middle East'. He's pompous, but can be amusing.

Up in Kyrenia there's been shooting in the streets and the Turks have scuttled off to join their relatives in Nicosia, Harry says. The Brits are buying up everything they can lay hands on in the shops, ignoring orders to stay at home. Last Monday Harry saw President Makarios's summer palace near Bellapais set on fire by his opponents. Harry calls him 'Black Mack'.

Harry's sure that most of the police have been rounded up and imprisoned, and says they'll be released only if they promise to support the new lot. He's particularly worried about his friend, Sergeant Costas Michaelides. Costas is Allan Cavinder's neighbour. I asked how Allan was and Harry replied, 'He's going on about an Anglo-Turkish military operation to clean up the louts and give them short shrift.' That's our Allan!

Susie has introduced her latest UN 'finds', two subalterns from the British contingent. There's never a shortage of handsome young men from the UN. I think they treat service in Cyprus like a well-paid holiday. English girls have premium value here because the locals are kept on a tight rein by their families. Ours can afford to pick and choose their UN officers. Susie's latest are Adrian and Ronnie and they've invited her to spend the weekend with them at Five-Mile Beach, where they're planning a barbecue.

I'm certain that Adrian and Ronnie were very indiscreet in telling us how Makarios was flown by the RAF to Akrotiri. They said that the new Cyprus government was installed by the Greek army. Britain removed Makarios from the island because we feared the National Guard would take their spite out on us if we interfered in the coup.

Harry became very angry and told them they were talking nonsense. Our soldiers could give the Greeks a 'bloody nose' any time we wanted. The National Guard were either 'Nellies' or 'Bubbles and Squeaks'. Adrian and Ronnie weren't sure. They felt there was a real cause for concern over the welfare of British servicemen's families who live off the Bases in places like Limassol. They can't be protected and that's another reason why Turkey won't be supported by our government. Harry blamed everything on the Americans. He bet America would recognize the new government and insisted that the US Ambassador, Roger Davies, was probably having talks already with Sampson's henchmen.

Later

Well, we've listened to the World Service and they're still playing chess with Cyprus; not the BBC but the governments of Britain, America, Turkey and Greece.

I want to scream, do something to escape from this complacency.

19 July 1974

Why I even bothered to put the date down, I can't say. These days have been blurring one into another. I only know it's Friday because of the kitchen calendar and the fact the date matches the space in my packet of contraceptive pills. I don't why I bother with them anymore.

The club manager promised us lunch today and so I didn't make any sandwiches. I decided not to diet. I just wanted to enjoy a properly cooked meal for the first time in a week. But nothing ever works out as planned: The curry didn't materialize. And the reason? Well, because the Greek Cypriot staff ran off again. Lunch was cancelled the minute the radio said the Turks were assembling an invasion fleet at Mersin and Alexandretta.

And what about us, the British?

Nobody tells us what we're supposed to do. Bill just says, 'Don't worry, pet.'

Julia closed her diary and tried to drown her thoughts, impressions, and feelings with another brandy. From the bedroom Bill called out, 'Who was that damned idiot telephoning in the middle of the night?'

'It's not the middle of the night,' Julia replied calmly. 'It's a quarter to six and the invasion you said wouldn't happen, has.'

When the Turks last invaded Cyprus in 1571, they were led by Sultan Selim. He may have been called 'The Fool' and 'The Sot', but he managed to conquer the whole island without undue difficulties and absorbed it into the Ottoman Empire, where it stayed until 1878. Then, strapped for cash, the Turks ceded Cyprus to the British who recognized its strategic importance and were prepared to pay the price.

Before the Turks, the Venetians held Cyprus. They surrendered Kyrenia, or *Corineum* as the Romans called it, without a shot being fired by Sultan Selim's naval commander, Admiral Sadık Paşa. When the latter died, he was buried in the castle where his tomb became a tourist attraction.

As 'The Cave Ladies' considered the military possibilities for the Turks in 1974, they wondered whether history was about to repeat itself and whether Sadık Paşa was trembling in his grave with excitement.

From what was going on above and around the two retired majors, it appeared to them that the Turkish paratroopers were aiming to capture Nicosia International airport to prevent reinforcements from Greece coming to the aid of the Greek Cypriot defenders. Turkey also needed an air base on Cyprus for its own forces. A port facility was required too. Famagusta seemed the obvious choice.

The strength of the opposition was uncertain, but the Turks had to conclude their mission quickly, perhaps within 48 hours. Within that period the major powers would awake to the global implications of the situation in Cyprus and the Turks would be pressurized to stop.

To secure their objectives, the Turkish paratroopers would need the support of additional land forces. These would have to thrust their way up the mountains from Kyrenia and use the pass below St Hilarion castle, which dominated the main road from Nicosia. Turkish Cypriot 'Freedom Fighters' were there already.

For several years 'The Fighters' had controlled this route. Greek Cypriot traffic wanting to use the road had had to form a twice-weekly convoy, which was escorted by UN troops. Even then, movement took place only with the agreement of the Turkish Cypriots.

Greek Cypriots who wished to avoid being tied to a UN schedule had been forced to take the longer route from Nicosia to Kyrenia. This meant travelling east or west by other passes which were controlled by their militia.

It seemed clear to 'The Cave Ladies' that once the Turkish forces established a safe corridor between Kyrenia and Nicosia, they would probably fan out to the east and west, mopping up all pockets of Greek Cypriot resistance.

For the time being, however, the two retired British majors were less interested in Turkey's ultimate objectives and more about the fate of civilians in Kyrenia. They believed that most British residents would stay in place, but not tourists. Even if there were no direct assault on the port, Betty and Phyllis believed there would be panic in the streets as Greek Cypriot civilians and foreign visitors made a headlong dash for the south. But whichever route these people chose, they would not be able to avoid the Turkish army.

Between the two groups sat Tjiklos, 'The Cave Ladies' and a dozen

Finnish soldiers representing the UN. They would have to take charge of the civilians who were rushing to find a safe haven. If Betty and Phyllis had only themselves to feed, their stocks could last for a month at least. At this point, however, they did not know how many others would join them soon and for how long.

Power lines to Tjiklos could be cut at any moment. When that happened, the water-pumps would stop and 'The Cave Ladies" freezer would cease to function. Unless they took urgent action, their meat supplies would rot within hours. The outside temperature was already 103 degrees.

First 'The Cave Ladies' gathered every container that they could find and filled them with water while the pumps worked. Next, drawing on her experience in India before World War II, Phyllis suggested they part-boil all their meat, separating the white from the red. Before serving, they planned to boil it again to destroy any bacteria that may have collected.

'It'll be damned awful to eat,' Betty said, 'but a little curry powder might improve the flavour.'

From vantage points in Kyrenia castle, the Greek Cypriot defenders saw ships of the Turkish fleet heading towards the island and alerted their military positions along the north coast. Unlike the Venetians in 1571, many of the younger Greek soldiers had no intention of giving up without a fight. Some of their officers took a different stance: they stripped themselves of their uniforms, changed into civilian clothes and made a dash to The Dome Hotel, where they mingled with guests and hoped they could escape to safety with them. The officers tore up their military identification papers and, where possible, replaced them with United Kingdom passports. They had been issued with these when Cyprus was still a British colony. Ever since, they had kept their passports up to date. If the Greek Cypriot officers were stopped by the Turkish army, they would claim they were British and, therefore, should not be interned as prisoners of war.

In Tjiklos, Betty and Phyllis went to work confidently, laying down boxes of candles and other provisions on the floor of a cave by the side of their house. They planned to be ready for whatever happened next. The Turkish military action was no surprise to them. By contrast, Greek Cypriots and tourists on the north coast had been caught completely unawares. They oozed the smell of fear and it overwhelmed the scent of lemons and oranges carried on the breeze from the citrus groves on the outskirts of Kyrenia.

CHAPTER 2

THE HOUSE ON FIVE-MILE BEACH

THROUGHOUT Friday night 31 ships of the Turkish navy gathered below the horizon and, as the sky brightened on Saturday morning, they emerged from the sanctuary of darkness and steamed purposefully towards Five-Mile Beach, west of Kyrenia. Their movement was monitored by the US Sixth Fleet and units of the Royal Navy, including the aircraft carrier HMS *Hermes* and the missile-carrying warship HMS *Devonshire*. Under the waves of the eastern Mediterranean there was submarine activity too, presumed Russian. Even at this late stage many observers were convinced they were witnessing the climax of another Turkish naval exercise, not a *real* military operation.

As recently as 17 July American Intelligence had reported to Washington that Turkey, much as it disapproved of what was taking place, did not have the military capability to move against Cyprus. For this reason Secretary of State Henry Kissinger had rejected a proposal to send units of the US Sixth Fleet to Cypriot ports, visits designed to discourage hostile action from any side.

A day later, however, the Turkish Foreign Ministry in Ankara informed the Colonels in Athens, who constituted the government of Greece, that unless their military personnel were withdrawn immediately from Cyprus and Nicos Sampson removed from the Presidential Palace in Nicosia, Turkey would be forced to intervene in accordance with Article 4 of the Treaty of Guarantee, which was signed by Britain, Greece and Turkey when Cyprus became an independent Republic in 1960.

In London, Foreign Secretary James Callaghan had rejected a Turkish request that Britain should participate in a joint military operation against the Sampson regime. Callaghan insisted a political solution had to be found to the problem of Cyprus. That was where the situation rested on Friday evening as British civil servants commuted home. Their views were shared by the US State Department diplomats who were shuttling between Ankara and Athens trying desperately to find a formula to satisfy Greece and Turkey, the two feuding NATO members.

From the sidelines Moscow watched closely. The Soviets knew that whatever the outcome, it would not be helpful to the Western Alliance.

All analysts agreed on one thing: military action by Turkey was not yet on the cards. They argued that its military activity was simply designed to underline the Turkish warning to the Greeks. The ships steaming from the ports of Mersin and Iskenderun were exercising, the experts declared. They maintained the Turks were following precedents set by them when their interests in Cyprus had been threatened before. The Turks had always worked up a fine head of steam and then settled for a minimum show of force. Twice before, in 1964 and 1967, they had held back from all-out war by using their air force only to fly a few sorties against the extremists in the Greek Cypriot National Guard.

As only four days had passed since the coup, Western authorities claimed there were many practical reasons, too, why the Turks *could not* mount a large-scale land, sea and air operation against Cyprus; even a major power would find the problem difficult to solve within such a narrow time frame. Furthermore, Britain had refused help and there was no moral backing from the United States, on whom Turkey relied for much of its military hardware.

Unfortunately for Western experts, none of these views were held by Admiral Kayracan, the overall commander of the operation, nor by General Sancar, the Chief of the Turkish General Staff. As far as they were concerned, rather than being inconceivable, action had been inevitable from the moment the coup succeeded. With or without the support of Britain and the United States, they were determined to bring an end to the problem.

For years, Turkey had been drawing up contingency plans to counter Greek threats in Cyprus and elsewhere; these plans were frequently rehearsed and adjusted. Now the time had come for them to be tested.

At the main building of the Ministry of Defence in London's Whitehall, Colonel Derrick Knight, a press and information officer, was looking forward to the end of his spell of night duty. It had been a very busy week for him and his colleagues. They had dealt with hundreds of enquiries by the media about what UK military actions were planned and the role of the 8,043 British military personnel at the Sovereign Bases and the Royal Navy off-shore.

Following standard civil service policy, Knight's statements were always truthful. How much information journalists drew from his answers depended on the strength and precision of their questions. For experienced correspondents who had gained his trust, Knight often added off-the-record background details to help their coverage of events.

What concerned Knight most of all was how inexperienced journalists accepted rumours as facts. As an old Cyprus hand this bothered him, for he was aware that many of the island's difficulties had been made worse by the spread of misleading information.

With the approach of the weekend, there had been fewer questions because journalists had gathered in Cyprus to file their stories directly from the island. The majority were based at The Ledra Palace Hotel in Nicosia. If they stayed there, it was doubtful they would be any better informed than had they remained in London, close to Whitehall.

Some, of course, like Michael Nicholson of ITN, would be very active and his reports Knight needed to watch.

Nicholson and his camera and sound recording team spent Friday night driving up and down the Nicosia-Kyrenia road. At 05.00 on Saturday they were near Boğaz when the first Turkish paratroopers dropped. As a result, ITN had a world exclusive. Meanwhile, the BBC's Simon Dring and his crew had installed themselves at Dhekelia, keeping their eyes trained on British military activity. At sea, another BBC correspondent, Michael Buerk, had chartered a fishing-boat and was trying to sail through the Turkish fleet. He was intercepted, arrested and held in custody for a night before the Turks sent him on his way.

At The Ledra Palace, Donald Wise was still fast asleep. Recognized as one of the great war correspondents of the 20th century, the urbane former member of the Parachute Regiment had been flown to Cyprus from Hong Kong by the Daily Mirror to cover the coup and its aftermath. Always cool and calm, his style was the envy of the press corps. He claimed he wrote short, simple commentaries because 'my readers move their lips when they read, old boy'.

Down the corridor, Jonathan Dimbleby and a TV documentary crew were checking their video and audio equipment, not knowing that ITN's Nicholson was miles ahead in the news-gathering stakes.

Very early on Saturday morning several London-based correspondents of foreign newspapers telephoned Knight, asking him to confirm or deny claims that a large Turkish fleet was heading towards Cyprus. If these reports were correct, then what counteraction was HM Government planning?

Relying on the facts at his disposal, Knight explained that Turkish ships were always off the coast of Cyprus; after all, only a 40 mile-wide channel separated the north of the island from the Turkish mainland. The Turkish navy, he added, frequently conducted routine exercises in these international waters.

A few hours earlier Whitehall officials had been in contact with the British military headquarters at the Western Sovereign Base, where there was a Joint-Services Public Relations unit in Episkopi. The unit included Anthony Twist, an expert on Cyprus affairs, and Peter Brown, a hard-nosed ex-journalist. In the days ahead, Twist would open his home to a Turkish Cypriot refugee family from Limassol, and, at the height of the war, Brown would help to load food and medical supplies on a Hercules aircraft shuttling between Dhekelia and Akrotiri on mercy missions organized by the RAF.

The Base authorities had confirmed that the Turkish fleet was on the move, but that its course was no different from the one it used during exercises. They were positive the ships would stop on the edge of the territorial waters of Cyprus, and then steam in circles before returning to their home ports. London was assured that Cyprus was returning to normality after the upheavals of the previous days.

Now Knight was having to ring alarm bells in Whitehall and roust his colleagues from their beds: the British bases in Cyprus were confirming a Turkish invasion of the island.

At RAF Akrotiri, the Base commander, Air Marshal Donald Hall, a giant of a pilot at six feet four inches, had a reputation for being able to handle awkward and dangerous situations without ever raising his voice. His abilities would be tested to the full, not just this morning but several times in the weeks ahead. His immediate concern was the security of the Lightning fighters and Vulcan bombers that were there. The Vulcans formed part of the UK's nuclear deterrent. Next he needed to bring the servicemen's families, who lived on the outskirts of Limassol, to the safety of the base.

The commander picked up one of the three telephones on his office desk and called his wife. 'Don't get too hassled,' he said, 'but the Turks have invaded.'

During the next few hours, he organized a fleet of trucks to collect the families, protected by soldiers from the Royal Scots regiment. He also offered civilian tourists refuge at Akrotiri.

At Dhekelia, the Somerset and Cornwall Light Infantry, commanded by Major Gage Williams, took up defensive positions.

Before speculating about what would happen next, Knight, at the Ministry of Defence, wanted a cup of coffee. He reached for his flask. It was empty. The time was 04.00 GMT.

Precisely at that moment, landing-craft were pulling away from the mother ships of the Turkish Task Force, churning their way through the gently rolling sea towards the shallows of Five-Mile Beach. When the boats crunched to a halt, squads of heavily-armed soldiers tumbled out, some falling into the salty slush, knocked off balance by the weight of the equipment strapped to their waists and carried on their shoulders. One of the first casualties was an officer, drowned as his comrades ran over him in their dash to firm ground.

Although the Turkish forces had surprised the Greeks by landing at Five-Mile Beach, the defenders were recovering rapidly. Turkish marines who failed to fan out and find cover quickly ate grit as Greek bullets from Czech-made AK-47 assault-rifles and Vickers machine-guns tore into their flesh. Male nurses and doctors, identified by Red Crescent armbands, found themselves rushing in several directions to deal with the injured and dying. These included Private Kasım Sungar, Private Abdullah Ömür, Lieutenant Celal Bekiroğlu and Medical Orderly Tevfik Uğur. Also mortally wounded that first day was Colonel İbrahim Karaoğlanoğlu, to whom Turkish Cypriots would later dedicate a nearby village.

The day before, European holiday-makers had sunbathed on the fine sands of Five-Mile Beach and splashed in its tepid waters after four days of being confined to their rented homes and hotels. Despite the coup, the Greek Cypriot owners of the two restaurants there were doing brisk business. Both men competed for customers and the freshest fish on sale at the market in Kyrenia, just five miles to the east. Nothing hampered the restaurateurs from providing excellent food and service. For a testimonial they only needed to ask George Tsigarides, an official of the Cyprus Tourism Organization. With friends he dined regularly at their restaurants. In fact, he had booked a table at one of them for this Saturday evening.

George's job took him to the most attractive parts of Cyprus, but there was none he enjoyed more for his own relaxation than Five-Mile Beach. Here, he shed the image he wore in the capital and became his true self.

George was a charming and clever man, but, despite his talents, he had failed to rise higher than the middle ranks of the CTO. Perhaps this was because he had set himself apart from politics, though nobody doubted his integrity or commitment to the Greek cause in Cyprus and his pride in being Greek.

For those lacking gentility George was too pedantic and careful. Even in the most crowded official receptions, he invariably managed to keep space around himself. On the hottest days of summer his cotton shirts remained crisp, clean and free of sweat; his shoes stayed polished on dusty village tracks; and his small leather handbag always contained the right change, pens and pads to deal with any situation.

If there had been a Cypriot aristocracy, George would have belonged. But, like aristocrats elsewhere, he was impoverished and forced to curb his instincts to buy rare Greek artefacts to add to the collection in his family's Nicosia home in Themistocles Dervis Street, just around the corner from the CTO's main office. He lived with his parents.

George was short of funds because he had used his money to realize a dream. For years he had striven to buy a plot of land as close as possible to Five-Mile Beach, where he wanted to a build a home of his own which he could share with friends at weekends. With a loan from his bank, he had succeeded. A house had been built; now only its final decorations awaited approval. He had every right to feel proud because he had dug the foundations, collected the bricks, mixed the mortar and watched the building rise slowly over a period of more than six months. Today he held the deeds of one of the two apartments in the house. The house was on the far west corner of the beach, the very spot the Turkish army had chosen to land.

Earlier in the week George had planned to drive to Kyrenia on Friday evening, using the long route to avoid the Turkish Cypriot checkpoint near St Hilarion castle. He aimed to spend the weekend in his new home, but his mother made him re-think his plans. She wanted her son to visit his father who was in hospital. Because of the civil unrest she also felt nervous and refused to be left on her own in the family home in the heart of Nicosia.

George, therefore, had gone to bed early on Friday night. He was irritated by his mother's demands, little realizing his life may well have been saved by her intervention.

About 10 miles north of where George lived in Nicosia, 37-year-old Vural Türkmen's concerns were different, but nevertheless centred on domestic matters too. The day before the coup, his English wife, Margaret, had been rushed to the British Military Hospital in Dhekelia, where she gave birth. So far Vural had not been able to see his new-born son, named Kerim. On Thursday, Vural had been ordered to re-join his unit in the Turkish Cypriot Defence Force. He held the rank of major and his job was to command a defensive position between the capital and Kyrenia.

Unlike George Tsigarides, Vural Türkmen believed that the safe existence of Turkish Cypriots could only be guaranteed if they managed their own affairs, well away from Greek Cypriot areas. He saw the coup as the final step by which the Greek Cypriots would unite his island with Greece.

On Friday evening, Vural ate dinner with army friends. The atmosphere was less than cheerful; it was a mixture of depression and fatalism. Since Sampson had assumed the Presidency of the Republic, his forces had attacked several Turkish Cypriot villages, massacring their inhabitants.

At 21.20, Vural and the other part-time soldiers finished their meal, still unaware that they would be in the thick of battle within hours. Behind their barricades they wished for the Turkish army to liberate them and provide protection now, but, having listened to the news from the BBC, they had concluded Turkey would only talk about their problems, held back by the major powers from taking decisive military action. Like George, Vural had gone to bed angry.

At 01.20 a radio operator woke Vural to tell him the Turkish army was on its way; the news had been relayed from a Special Forces' unit which had landed already to make contact with its Turkish Cypriot counterparts.

D-Day had arrived.

Vural was frightened, not for himself, but for his wife, their five-day-old son and their daughter, Ayla, aged four.

Northern Nicosia fell silent and still. Tension ran high as the population prepared for war. Every male adult in the Turkish quarter collected arms, many made for use in the first World War, and joined 'The Fighters'.

Nobody knew yet when or where exactly the Turkish army planned to land. That information came an hour later. The military operation would start precisely at 05.00, but did the Turks mean Cyprus time or mainland time? Neither side asked for clarification, each believing the blunt message was perfectly clear despite the fact that a one-hour time difference existed between Turkey and Cyprus. Later this would cause confusion.

For Arif Gürbüz and Ali Özel, both Turkish Cypriot 'Freedom Fighters' in the walled city of Famagusta, where 12,000 Turkish Cypriots lived, that difference in time would not alter their chances of survival at all. Everybody knew that once Turkish forces landed, the Greek Cypriot National Guard would attack Turkish Cypriot villages.

Because of the distance from the Turkish beach-head in the north, and the need for the Turkish army to establish a safe and secure corridor between Kyrenia and Nicosia, the Turkish Cypriots in the south would be left to fend for themselves. At best, the Famagusta defenders could expect no more than limited Turkish air strikes against the Greeks, whose forces already ringed the ancient city. Soon they would start a sustained artillery bombardment.

Arif, a robust, Falstaffian character, was the Turkish Cypriot official responsible for the city's water, and he expected his Greek Cypriot opposite number to cut supplies immediately war broke out. Because it was already one of the hottest summers on record, he found it impossible to calculate when the holding tanks inside the city would run dry. Yet confidence was high, food plentiful, and an underground hospital was standing by to deal with casualties.

Famagusta had experienced sieges before in its turbulent history and was strongly defended today by inhabitants determined to hold their ground until help arrived, but the surrounding villages were less protected. Arif's wife lived in one of them. She was pregnant and their baby was due within six weeks. Her vulnerability had strengthened his resolve to fight to the last bullet. A native of Famagusta, he was not a stranger to death and violence. As a teenager he had witnessed several EOKA terrorist attacks against the British. In the Greek language EOKA stood for *Ethnikí Orgánosis Kiprion Agonistón*, the National Organization of Cypriot Fighters. Arif had seen one of its members, a Greek Cypriot, shoot dead two British housewives near the colonial administration building. Now he never hid his contempt of EOKA and its aims. Arif maintained EOKA needed to be punished; strength was all it respected. As a devout Muslim, he believed a place in heaven was assured for those who fought bravely in the defence of the weak.

Ali Özel was a Muslim too, but he applied his faith in a more pragmatic fashion. Overweight from enjoying good food and drink, he fasted during Ramazan not only to observe the rules of the Koran, but to slim as well. He was a former Customs officer from the port of Limassol and well-versed in the tricks of both the gamekeeper and the poacher. His father was a retired schoolteacher, who lived with his wife in the Turkish quarter of the island's second city. Here Ali had several Greek Cypriot friends, but he doubted they would be able to protect his parents if the worst came.

Ali's uniform was scruffy and his face carried the stubble of several days' growth beneath a thick black moustache, but his appearance belied his true background. He spoke several languages fluently, including Greek; his knowledge of English literature and the history of Cyprus was extensive and objective. It was for these reasons that he acted as a liaison officer for the Turkish Cypriot 'Fighters' in their dealings with the Swedish UN contingent stationed nearby. The Turkish Cypriots were sure that the Swedes' sympathies lay with the Greek Cypriot administration.

Ali was enjoying to the full the role in which fate had cast him. He was an actor at heart and circumstances made him a star player in the place where Shakespeare had set his Othello.

Between 20 July and 16 August, both Ali and Arif would be tested many times under fire. For now, they knew only that the Turkish operation was set for dawn.

Within minutes of the first paratroopers dropping from the sky, both the Cyprus Broadcasting Corporation and Radio Bayrak, 'the voice of the Turkish Fighters', broke the news in varying degrees of hysteria. Depending on the station, Cypriots were either urged to defend themselves against 'the brutal and barbaric aggressors' or fight alongside 'our brothers from the mainland'. The bulletins were confused and served only to spread fear and anger from one side of the island to the other.

At a South Nicosia hospital, Maroulla Siamisi was busy, preparing to receive war casualties. There would be too many arriving too fast to treat satisfactorily. Morgues would run out of space and many Greek Cypriot soldiers would have to be buried in mass graves, her husband among them. There was no time to keep proper records on every case.

Panic became widespread amongst Greek Cypriot civilians who saw the American-built C-130 Hercules every 20 minutes dropping their loads on the northern side of the capital, but even more frightening were the low-flying Phantoms, the F-104s of the Turkish air force. In flights of three, they spiralled away after releasing their rockets and bombs which demolished targets in sheets of flame. The Turkish pilots were very confident of their success. They knew they were unlikely to encounter their enemy's fighter aircraft, because the nearest Greek air base was on Rhodes, at the extreme limit of a fighter aircraft's range.

During the first day Turkish jets destroyed several columns of Greek Cypriot National Guard reinforcements moving towards Kyrenia. They strafed military positions around Nicosia and attacked others on the northern coast, but sometimes pilots missed their targets. Near Athalassa, rockets overshot a Greek military camp and hit a psychiatric hospital. Trying to sink a naval vessel off Paphos, they damaged a valuable excavation site instead.

Although the Turkish air force commanded the skies, not all their pilots returned safely to their bases. Flying an F-84, Lieutenant İlker

Karter was one of those who sacrificed his life that first day. He left a widow and one child. Another Turkish hero was Major Fehmi Ercan, whose love for Cyprus was well known to his colleagues. He died while directing an air attack against a Greek army position. Later the Turkish Cypriots would name their civilian airport after him.

The Turks also used helicopters adventurously. When Vural Türkmen and his soldiers saw them, they thought at first that they were carrying UN observers; nobody believed fully-loaded helicopters could fly from Turkey to Cyprus, and then, without refuelling, return to their home bases on the mainland.

To minimize the risk of accidental aerial attacks on Turkish Cypriot areas, the 'Freedom Fighters' had marked the grounds of their enclaves with large white crescents made from painted boulders. On the flat tops of their buildings in towns they had laid giant Turkish flags, easily visible from the sky.

Several days earlier Turkish Special Forces had begun to operate along the northern coast, identifying the locations of Greek military positions and clearing minefields at sea. Their operations were conducted in complete secrecy; not even Turkish Cypriots knew they were taking place.

Against this all-out attack, the Greek Cypriot defenders and the Greek soldiers from the mainland were finding it very difficult to resist the Turkish drive from Five-Mile Beach to Kyrenia.

The coup had created more than mistrust between the different elements of the Greek Cypriot forces. The 4,000 soldiers of the Tactical Reserve supported Makarios, while the 10,000 men of the Greek Cypriot National Guard, commanded by Greek officers, had been responsible for the Archbishop's overthrow. They had fought and killed each other in the previous five days. Now they were forced to act together against a common threat, but did not know how.

There was no confusion amongst the disciplined ranks of the three Turkish brigades which had come ashore at Five-Mile Beach, from where their soldiers were being rushed by helicopters to support 2,000 paratroopers and the 650 men of the resident Turkish contingent fighting north of Nicosia. For the Turkish Cypriot 'Freedom Fighters' engaged in the battles taking place along the Kyrenia road and in the vicinity of St Hilarion castle, there were no exact figures.

East and west of Kyrenia, Greek Cypriot forces fell back against the weight of the Turkish onslaught. Dhikomo and Trachonas fell swiftly. The Turks were carving a clear path to Nicosia, despite heavy Greek mortar bombardments which caused a considerable number of military and civilian casualties. If a Greek unit did counter, it was taken out from the air immediately afterwards.

Only at Nicosia International airport was the Greek line holding. As the forward elements of the Turkish forces neared the northern perimeter, they were pounded by shells, shot with pin-point accuracy.

Hidden in a civilian bus parked on a high bluff above the runways, Greek artillery spotters could see every move made by the Turks and were able to direct their fire without wasting shells. From the air the Greek vehicle appeared derelict and was therefore safe from counter-attack.

By nightfall, fires raged in the mountains around Tjiklos, started by sparks from tracer bullets used in the fighting. First to burn was the shrubbery, tinder-dry due to the heat of summer. Next to go were the gnarled olive and carob trees, their trunks licked by a carpet of flames that swept relentlessly upwards. Then pine trees exploded like bombs, destroying electricity and 'phone poles. But before the last line fell, the BBC's John Beerman filed a final report from the area, using 'The Cave Ladies" telephone.

Betty and Phyllis were deeply concerned by the loss of power to the water pumps and their telephone line to the outside world. They knew that without pumps nobody could fight the fires, and if the wind changed direction, flames would move towards their home where 150 people had sought sanctuary. Many of them were young children; their safety was paramount.

Most of the displaced were tourists from Kyrenia, fleeing ahead of the Turkish army and not really knowing where they were heading. Neither Phyllis or Betty were 'particularly impressed by the dress or behaviour of these people', many of whom demanded food from the UN soldiers in Tjiklos and safe passage out of the area.

On the way to Tjiklos, several refugees had looted shops for alcohol and cigarettes. Others had arrived running, wearing only swimming costumes, which Betty considered was 'really not quite the right garb at times like these'.

Several were in a state of shock and needed to be organized. The two retired majors took charge of the situation and immediately arranged rations of water and other supplies.

Betty and Phyllis ordered individuals to form groups and stood them in tidy lines. Some civilians were 'trembling a little too damned much', thought Betty, exhorting her friend to 'Keep them busy so that we can build up their morale.' Children were told to search for empty bottles so that a fair distribution of water could begin.

The Finnish contingent was already providing sanctuary for Allan Cavinder, a mechanical services consultant from Kyrenia who, only the day before, had been visiting construction sites and arranging contract labour to start on Monday.

Cavinder drove to the UN camp in his Hillman Husky, followed by a bright orange Mini which carried Len and Maureen Hudson, a honeymoon couple who had been camping at Snake Island. They had been joined by Americans, Armenians and Syrians who worked at the US government's communications monitoring station at Karavas.

That night an open-air dormitory was created in an old Roman road, using the high banks on either side as head rests. 'Not the most comfortable place to sleep, but it's safe,' Phyllis said; the fighting continued around them.

In Famagusta, Arif Gürbüz and Ali Özel heard the Turkish quarter of Limassol had fallen to the Greek Cypriot National Guard after heavy fighting. Both sides had suffered heavy casualties. The Turkish Cypriot survivors had been rounded up and were held prisoner. More than 1,000 men and boys were confined with no protection from the hot sun in the town's football stadium, starved of food and water. Ali did not know the whereabouts of his parents or whether they were still alive.

Meanwhile the Greek Cypriot National Guard continued to pound the interior of the walled city, their shells fired from positions which encircled Famagusta. They were also attacking and destroying Turkish Cypriot villages in nearby areas. Nevertheless survivors got through the Greek Cypriot lines and reached the comparative safety of the ancient fortress. With his mistrust of Greeks, Arif wondered whether these Turkish Cypriots were being herded unwittingly in the direction of Famagusta so that all of them could become easier prey. With water lines cut, the refugees only added to the city's difficulties and the problems of the original 12,000 inhabitants.

Arif decided to raise the matter with the local UN observers, hoping they would use their influence to persuade the Greek Cypriots, on humanitarian grounds, to resume the supply of water.

The Greek Cypriot militia replied that if the Turkish Cypriots were to disarm and surrender, taps would be turned on immediately. The UN officers recommended Arif and the others accept the offer without delay. Their suggestion confirmed his belief that the UN was not impartial. Without discussion the defenders refused, preferring to eke out their existing supplies until they were liberated, whenever that happened.

Back in London, at 148 Warwick Road, W5, Mr and Mrs Griffiths switched on television to hear reports of the war in Cyprus. The Griffithses had escaped from the island the day before on a BOAC Tri-Star which had been diverted to Nicosia International airport from Cairo to pick up stranded holidaymakers. The plane took off again at 15.00 on Friday, the last time the airport was used for civilian traffic. This was also the first and last time the Griffithses vacationed in Cyprus, but for the rest of their lives they would remember the island for their 'memorable holiday'.

On that same Saturday evening, while the Griffithses watched television in Ealing, David Carter, a BBC producer, was having dinner with his actress wife, Wendy, in the La Cucaracha restaurant in London's Soho. They were celebrating the news of her pregnancy. Ten years earlier, she had given birth to a daughter, but nature had not held out the promise of another child until now. Cyprus, therefore, was the very last thing on the couple's minds. Listening to the news bulletins on their drive back to Welwyn Garden City in Hertfordshire, they never imagined that before long their lives would become entangled with the troubled island's problems.

The next day, Sunday, 21 July, the fighting still continued.

As the Turkish forces consolidated their positions between Kyrenia and northern Nicosia, to make matters worse the Greek Cypriot National Guard, the Tactical Reserve Force, and EOKA-B irregulars turned their attentions to civilians, storming Turkish Cypriot enclaves in the south and west of the island.

At Tjiklos, half a mile from where 'The Cave Ladies' lived, Turkish forces were battling still, trying to punch their way from the coast up the mountains while Turkish Cypriot Fighters moved down from St Hilarion, trying to link up.

Greek Cypriot soldiers retreated into the Finnish camp, still shooting, followed by the Turks. 'Stop immediately. This is a United Nations protected area,' a Finnish officer bellowed over the firing. 'We have women and children here.' The Turkish commander responded and ordered his troops to work their way round the camp. The Greeks continued their withdrawal in the opposite direction and, once they were out, began mortaring the UN position. A Finnish soldier, an American civilian and Peter Christodoulou, the Greek Cypriot restaurateur, were wounded during the exchanges of fire.

Two Turkish soldiers tried to escape the flames that were racing along the gullies and ran into a hail of Greek bullets. They fell less than 50 yards from Phyllis and Betty. Rather than be engulfed by the forest fire, one put a rifle to his mouth and squeezed the trigger; the other was already dead. Later their bodies were returned to the Turkish commander by the UN soldiers.

At 13.00 on Monday, 22 July 1974, the Turkish army completed its occupation of Kyrenia. Greek Cypriot resistance was over. The defenders of the Byzantine castle were imprisoned inside. Others were held in The Dome Hotel.

The international community, meanwhile, was trying to evacuate its citizens from the war zone. Britain carried the largest share of the rescue operation.

HMS *Hermes* took up station off Six-and-a-Half-Mile Beach, east of Kyrenia, and one of the ship's officers flew by helicopter to the UN landing site at Tjiklos. His purpose was to arrange a UN convoy to take civilians by road to a collection point on the beach. Everybody waited to see if Turkey would accept a United Nations' call for a cease-fire.

Turkey agreed and the cease-fire went into force at 16.00. By doing so, the Turkish army had lost its opportunity to capture Nicosia International airport, which later became the site of UNFICYP's headquarters and a United Nations' Protected Area.

One hour earlier, the UN buildings at Tjiklos were destroyed by fire started from sparks blown on the wind from the smouldering embers of the surrounding pine trees. The camp was abandoned and many of those there, including Cavinder and the Hudsons, the honeymooning couple, decided to return to Kyrenia which was presumed safer. Forty minutes later their mini-convoy ran into Greek Cypriot sniper fire. The Hudsons' Mini was hit and crashed into the side of the mountain. Maureen Hudson took a bullet in her leg. They were rescued by two UN soldiers in a Land-Rover and all returned to Tjiklos to spend a second night in the open air.

North of Nicosia, at Boğaz where his military position was located, Vural Türkmen unclipped the magazine from his World War II Lee Enfield .303 calibre rifle and stood down from duty. During the previous hour he had received confirmation that his family was safe. His wife remained at the British Military Hospital at Dhekelia with their new-born son. She wanted to rejoin her husband, but the British High Commission said that it could only arrange for her to be escorted as far as the Greek Cypriot quarter of Nicosia.

Three weeks later, however, a member of the Commission staff, acting unofficially, brought her and her son to northern Nicosia, where Vural was waiting in the Turkish Cypriot sector.

The next day, Tuesday, the evacuation of foreigners from northern Cyprus began. It was completed by UNFICYP and British armed forces within 24 hours. Two convoys left Tjiklos; one took people to Six-and-a-Half-Mile Beach where they joined 2,000 other refugees waiting to be picked up by HMS Hermes; the second left for Nicosia, escorted by UN soldiers.

Several tourists and foreign residents were collected from outside The Dome Hotel; they had gathered there on the instructions of the British High Commissioner, broadcast by BFBS. Their evacuation by the Royal Navy took five hours. Amongst them were several 'Ancient Brits' who had chosen to abandon their properties and possessions. Before leaving they handed their car keys for safety to a local artist, William Dreghorn, who had decided to remain.

'Come on, old man, this is the last trip,' an RN officer boomed. 'Aren't you coming with us?'

'No,' replied Dreghorn.

'If you stay, you'll be killed,' warned the officer.

The old-age pensioner pushed the car keys into the pockets of his khaki shorts and, wearing open-toed sandals, walked slowly home through the dusty streets of Kyrenia.

Major Betty Hunter Cowan and Major Phyllis Heymann had helped to provide shelter and food for 150 people during the three preceding days and nights. They had done everything within their limited power to ease the difficulties of the refugees in their charge. Now only their immediate neighbours and UNFICYP personnel remained, all exhausted.

'The Cave Ladies' were pondering their next move when a Turkish army colonel marched towards them at the water-point.

'Can we go home?' Phyllis inquired, not in the least intimidated.

'If you have a home to go to, of course, yes,' he replied, surveying the smoking ashes of several houses. 'You are quite safe now.'

The colonel saluted and turned on his heel.

Betty noted the Turkish officer's remarks on her pad of paper and looked at her watch. It was exactly 17.00, Tuesday, 23 July 1974.

The cease-fire lasted until 14 August, ending only when news came of Turkish Cypriots being massacred in areas still under Greek Cypriot control. Once more the Turkish army moved forward. It stopped on 16 August when a third of Cyprus was under its control.

That was when 16,000 Turkish Cypriots, including Ali Özel and Arif Gürbüz, were liberated in Famagusta. They had survived the Greek Cypriot siege for 21 days. Not until much later did they discover the scale of the Greek Cypriot atrocities and what had happened in the nearby villages of Aloa, Sandallaris and Maratha, where more than 100 unarmed Turkish Cypriot civilians were lined up and shot down in cold blood by EOKA-B gunmen.

Vengeance was meted out swiftly.

Justice was not always done.

At The Dome Hotel in Kyrenia, Greek Cypriots ended their fourth day in detention. Some were Greek officers disguised as civilians. Inside the hotel they were allowed to manage their own affairs, guarded by Turkish Cypriot policemen, not the Turkish army.

At Five-Mile Beach, the sand and scrub-land was littered with empty ammunition boxes and shell cases. Further along the coast there were the charred hulks of Soviet-built T-34 tanks and armoured personnel carriers used by the Greek forces before their defeat. Only a few Turkish soldiers were camped on the sands where they had come ashore just three days before. The rest had moved on to Kyrenia and Nicosia.

George Tsigarides's house, although shaken to its foundations, still stood firm. Even its windows were intact. Some chipped bricks and a few bullet holes in one wall were the only signs it had lived through a battle.

Had George been there when the Turks landed, he would be held captive now in The Dome Hotel. Or dead.

Perhaps the ancient gods of Cyprus, about whom he talked so enthusiastically to tourists, had intervened on his behalf. But they had charged him dearly. For George would never live in his house at the place he called *Pentamili*, and which the Turks were to rename *The Landing Beach*.

CHAPTER 3

'FREEBIE' TO CYPRUS

July 1977

DAVID CARTER stood in the cleanest part of BBC Radio London breathing Dettol fumes in the men's lavatory and watched the remains of an afternoon drinking session trickle away down the hole at the base of a white enamel urinal. He thought it resembled his career at the BBC.

A long time ago, during the middle sixties, he had been called one of the corporation's most promising new producers, a man destined for high office. But somewhere along the line he had made an error of judgement and was paying for it now by doing a job which was taking him nowhere.

Carter had given up being a current affairs television producer in 1970 for no other reason than wanting to be amongst those founding London's first local radio station. Since then his idealism had been dented and so had his bank balance.

But Carter was a fighter of sorts; he had not given up completely trying to re-build his reputation as a good programme-maker, even if those around him were sceptical about his past achievements.

The station's internal loudspeaker system interrupted his thoughts by announcing that he was needed back in his office to take an urgent telephone call.

'Okay,' he sighed. As 'Music Programmes Organizer' for Radio London, Carter was supposed to supervise a small team of producers and presenters, ensuring that their programmes did not infringe any of the countless agreements which the BBC had signed with the Musicians' Union and the record industry. But his impressive title gave him no authority, only responsibilities. BBC rule-books said one thing; Radio London did another. From the very beginning, Local Radio management had operated 'flexible policies', usually by committee.

Carter had argued against the system, but it was pointed out to him, sharply, that because BBC Local Radio in England operated on small budgets, the only way of keeping staff and programme contributors happy was by allowing them to exercise 'personal initiative' and remain 'flexible'.

'Ho hum,' Carter muttered as he walked in the direction of his office. He had crash-landed on a pile of plastic pop produced by plastic people and he knew it. Perhaps it would be better for him if he played the game as others did. Apathy could be contagious.

Carter picked up his telephone. 'Damn,' he exclaimed, knocking over a pile of records on the corner of his desk. 'Hello. Sorry to have kept you waiting.'

'We've never met,' came the reply. 'But your name was given to me by your brother.'

'Which one?' Carter asked cautiously. He had four, all characters searching for a good script.

'Geoffrey,' replied the cultivated voice. 'As you know he's doing a spot of PR for the Cyprus Tourism Organization.'

'No, I didn't,' Carter said. 'I thought he was with British Gas.'

'Well, his work with the CTO is part-time.'

Carter had not seen his brother for at least five years because they had little in common. '. . . and I was hoping that you would be free for a drink this evening,' the caller continued, 'because there's something I'd like to discuss which could be interesting.'

'I'm sorry I didn't catch your name,' Carter replied, convinced the man was an insurance salesman.

'How silly of me. It's Sinclair. Bill Sinclair. I'm a PR consultant and at the moment I'm arranging for a small party of journalists to visit Cyprus. Geoffrey thought you should come with us.'

'Hold on, Mr Sinclair. I'll check my diary.'

Carter looked at the hundreds of records piled in every corner of his office, the green and white station logs in his in-tray, and the stack of listeners' letters awaiting replies. Everything was connected with pop music. Sinclair had called him a 'journalist' and was offering a break from Radio London. What did it matter if he knew little or nothing about Cyprus? He had had only two vague associations with the island. Neither, he considered, were of any significance. As a teenager, during his senior year at high school in California, he had written a pompous letter to the *Oakland Tribune* refuting the Greek Consul's assertions that Cyprus was Greek property and should be freed from British colonial rule. Later, as a junior commissioned officer in the British army, he had undergone training for special operations against EOKA terrorists, but was never sent to the island to test his skills.

'Yes, that's good, there's nothing in the diary this evening. Shall we say five-thirty?'

'Why not? What about us meeting in The Rising Sun. It's your closest pub, isn't it?'

'Fine. See you soon.'

Carter replaced the receiver and wondered if he had made a wise decision. He knew he wanted the trip. Only recently he had left hospital after an operation on his spine and needed a break. It was three years since he had last gone abroad. At the same time he did not want to be placed in a position where he could be criticized. He drummed the desk nervously with his fingers.

Carter was in the BBC's computer as number 025659 Y and that was where he wanted to stay for the time being. The corporation might not pay him a bonus to worry, but he and his family counted on the salary cheque paid into his bank account on the fifteenth day of every month. He would return his staff card to the BBC in his good time, not theirs.

It amused him to think that in the half-century of the BBC's existence, only a tiny handful of people had been 'terminated' and had to face the ultimate indignity of having to return their regulation-size silver stop-watches. It was to the credit of the corporation's personnel selection procedures — and clearance by the resident 'spooks' — that so many of his fellow employees took their responsibilities to inform, educate and entertain the licence fee-payers of the land so seriously.

Before accepting this trip to Cyprus, known in the business as a 'freebie', Carter knew he must get BBC permission. He decided to discuss the matter with Tony Freeman, Radio London's news editor, and Frank Dawes, a senior news producer. They produced the station's weekly half-hour holiday programme which carried consumer advice and reports from foreign parts. Without the support of the travel industry and its offers of 'facility trips' abroad, it was unlikely that the programme could have been made. In other words, force of circumstances made it necessary to accept 'freebies', although the use of the term was avoided. But the two former Fleet Street journalists were committed nevertheless to making certain that their *Holiday Scene* was always honest and objective.

They picked their reporters carefully for assignments abroad. Within the Radio London newsroom, Freeman and Dawes were extremely popular figures, commanding respect from all who worked for them.

As Carter was part of the music side of the station, he had never put himself forward to consumer-test a holiday package, nor had they offered him one, but perhaps the time was now and the place could be Cyprus. He made a note on his blotter to invite Freeman and Dawes for a drink the next day.

Carter reached The Rising Sun very soon after Sinclair's arrival. They found each other without difficulty; they were the only two customers when the doors opened at five-thirty.

'Whisky on the rocks, isn't it, Dave?' Sinclair inquired, extending his hand in greeting. He had been briefed well on what to offer, but nobody had warned him not to shorten Carter's first name.

The PR consultant passed Carter a tumbler of Scotch, a double measure, which was accepted with a nod and a tight smile. Before paying the barman Sinclair counted a sheaf of money in the leather wallet drawn from his hip pocket. He removed a ten-pound note, flicked it to see that no others were stuck to it, and then laid it on the counter. It seemed as if he had designed the gesture to impress; a bit too pointedly, thought the BBC man.

'Cheers,' Carter said, taking a swallow from his glass. 'Sunny days,' Sinclair rejoined, setting aside his gin and tonic. 'What do you think of the suit?' He touched the lapels of his light blue linen jacket. 'Hand-made for just 30 quid. In Cyprus.'

'Let's go outside,' Carter smiled. He disliked instant familiarity as much as dark pub interiors. For a man promoting the pleasures of a sunny island, Sinclair's complexion was remarkably sallow; not a very good advertisement.

Sinclair trailed Carter into Paddington Street, watching him closely. He had expected a taller man, somebody a little more enthusiastic for an expenses-paid trip abroad. Apart from Carter's deep voice, with a trace of a mid-Atlantic accent, he bore no resemblance to Geoffrey, his brother, the man who had brought them together. Nor did Carter look like a pop music broadcaster or somebody who had served as an officer in the British army. Sinclair thought Carter was nondescript in every way and had second thoughts about offering 'the freebie'.

'I always tell friends before they fly off to Cyprus for the first time that they should carry nothing, not even a suitcase. Buy everything out there, shorts, suits, the lot. Even the leather suitcases.' Sinclair raised his right foot. 'See these shoes. A little cobbler by the name of Phillips knocked them up for me in Limassol. Remind me to give you his card before you go. Mention my name and he'll give you a hefty discount on the price.'

Carter concluded Sinclair was a man on the make and take; he would fit into Radio London extremely well. But perhaps two could play the game.

'To what do I owe the invitation of a trip to Cyprus?' Carter asked directly. 'I know absolutely nothing about the place.'

'All the better, coming with an open mind. I'm sure that's the best way to produce a feature for your excellent *Holiday Scene* programme. Care for another Scotch?'

It was obvious Sinclair had researched Radio London thoroughly. He dropped names of producers and presenters as easily as ice-cubes into Carter's glass of whisky. Yet even with this background, he talked as if Carter made the station's important decisions. Carter did not disillusion him; instead he tried to take full advantage of the situation. He wanted an invitation for his wife as well. If she came, the programme would be much improved, Carter suggested. Together they would be able to look at Cyprus through the eyes of a typical couple on holiday.

Sinclair rejected Carter's suggestion. In his judgement, work and play did not blend well, he replied somewhat pompously. To emphasize his point, he told Carter a story of what had happened recently on another CTO sponsored visit.

According to Sinclair's version of events, a Fleet Street journalist, who was well known for his drinking and sexual prowess, returned one evening to his five-star hotel, stripped off his clothes, and when his partner emerged in the nude from the shower, suggested that they play a pre-dinner game.

The journalist persuaded the woman to rest her back against the railings of the bedroom's balcony, her legs spread apart, while he went to the far side of the room and charged.

She, however, became frightened, remembering scenes from old films of castle doors being smashed open by battering rams, and, at the very moment before the man made body-contact, stepped aside. Unable to brake his forward motion, the journalist nose-dived to the concrete edge of the hotel's swimming pool, four floors down.

The incident had caused a lot of problems for the CTO. Not only did the organization fail to get an article published in a national newspaper, it also had to explain to the authorities what had happened. To make matters worse, some weeks later the CTO received a telephone call from the journalist's wife. She wanted to know when her husband could be expected home after his long and exhaustive inquiry into the Cyprus holiday industry.

The CTO had consigned the man's body for return to England to the woman who had travelled with him to Cyprus. She, it turned out to the CTO's horror, was his secretary, faithfully doing her job to the very end. To keep things quiet had cost a lot of time and money, said Sinclair.

Sinclair pointed out that everybody would have a far better time if Carter did not bring his wife. Cyprus was not called the Island of Aphrodite for nothing. Both men watched the office girls of Marylebone High Street heading home in their short summer skirts and high heels.

He agreed, however, that because radio journalists had different working methods from the press, he could arrange for Carter to be separated from the main group and have a personal escort of his own to set up interviews and recordings as required.

'Well,' Sinclair said, satisfied by the arrangements he had outlined, 'all I need from you, Dave, is a scribbled note on Radio London note paper asking the CTO to give you a facility trip. I'll see that you receive your airline tickets and confirmation of your hotel booking a.s.a.p.'

'I write you?' Carter was unsure he had heard Sinclair correctly.

'Yes. It's just part of the routine.'

'No,' said Carter, 'I insist that you, Mr Sinclair, put your proposal to Tony Freeman or Frank Dawes, suggesting that you'd like me to be the Radio London representative. Meanwhile, I'll talk to them both, explaining what we've discussed and how *you* contacted me.'

'What's the difference?'

'A lot to me,' Carter replied sharply. 'My way means that if approval is given the whole deal is up-front. If anybody says later, "Carter, you've broken the rules or bent the guidelines", I can reply, "Balls, the news editor said okay." Do you see what I mean?'

'Well, if you insist, I suppose that's fair enough.'

'I do insist.'

They parted.

Sinclair caught a taxi to Regent Street, while Carter walked to Baker Street tube station to catch a train for King's Cross and his onward journey from there to a semi-detached in Welwyn Garden City.

The next day Carter told Dawes about the invitation and suggested a feature on Cyprus for *Holiday Scene*. Ask Tony Freeman, came the reply. Freeman wanted to know Dawes's reaction before making a decision. Carter only wanted an answer, any kind. Eventually, after moving several times between newsroom and office and back again, Carter was told that they did want a report from the island.

'But, remember that this is a consumers' programme, not a sponsored show,' Freeman warned. 'So you must be critical, get out and about talking to the punters who've paid to be in Cyprus. Find out if they're getting value for money.'

'Sure,' Carter replied. 'Do it a bit like the motoring correspondent who goes to the south of France to test-drive a car and returns complaining about a dirty ash-tray.'

'Very funny,' Freeman said. 'You know what I mean.'

'Is there a check-list that programme contributors follow?' Carter wanted to know.

'Not yet,' replied Dawes. 'Tony and I haven't had time to draft one. We'll get round to it. Just use your common sense and come back with a piece which runs 20 minutes.'

'Of course,' Carter confirmed. 'Anything else?'

'Yes,' Freeman added. 'Lots of colour, sound effects, local music. That sort of thing. Make it sound like a radio programme.'

'No shit,' Carter said. 'Before I leave, will you and Frank show me how to switch on my Uher? But don't tell me where to put the microphone.'

CHAPTER 4

THE GREEKS BORE GIFTS

October 1977

GEORGE TSIGARIDES of the Cyprus Tourism Organization was angry. The scheduled Saturday afternoon flight by Cyprus Airways from London Heathrow to Larnaca was late again. As he stood amongst the impatient crowds outside the Customs Hall he wondered how the 12 travel-writers on board the in-bound aircraft were reacting. All his meticulous planning to impress them would lose its value if they were to return home and write that tourists could not count on reaching their destination on time.

Tourism was vital to the island's economy and favourable press comment in Britain was particularly important at this stage when Cyprus was developing new resorts since losing the traditional and well-known areas of Kyrenia and Famagusta to the Turkish Cypriots.

George could only hope that the press party would forget the inauspicious start to their 'study tour' in the flow of hospitality that would follow their arrival. Fortunately the whole group was not his responsibility, only David Carter, the man from Radio London.

When George first heard he was assigned to act as Carter's personal guide, he was surprised and disappointed. He believed he was being snubbed again by his masters in Nicosia. With his considerable experience and dedication he had expected to be in charge of the main group of journalists.

But George was a professional civil servant and would not allow his feelings to show. He had accepted the decision in apparent good faith and decided that Carter would leave as a committed friend of Cyprus.

In fact, the more George thought about the situation, the more appealing it became. It would give him an opportunity to act independently. From experience he knew how difficult it was to control journalists as a group. Each made different demands, most stayed up late, all refused to rise early and none was ever satisfied.

If Carter were a reasonable sort of chap, then George felt they would get along very well. He was already intrigued by the fact the BBC producer had asked not to be placed alongside his colleagues in a five-star hotel, but had requested a room in a family-run establishment. So while the others would stay at the Amathus Beach, Carter was booked at the Alasia Hotel, close to the centre of Limassol.

George had hoped to spend this Saturday evening getting to know Carter over dinner at the Miramare Hotel, where the owners were long-standing, personal friends. But the Cyprus Airways plane was still far out over the Mediterranean and, as midnight would arrive long before the aircraft, George knew alternative hospitality would have to be arranged. He decided that they should stop for a meal somewhere on the road from Larnaca to Limassol. He had rented a 'Z-car', a self-drive vehicle which would give him flexibility, while his CTO colleagues would have to travel with the other journalists in an air-conditioned coach.

To make certain that he and Carter got away quickly, George spoke to one of his friends, a senior airport official, and received permission to greet his guest inside the Customs area so that baggage could be collected and cleared with a minimum of formalities.

When eventually the aircraft landed, Carter found himself separated from the main body of CTO guests, and so he joined the crowd of other travellers, mainly Greek Cypriots, and followed them through passport checks and immigration controls until they reached the main hall, where passengers' baggage had been deposited.

The other journalists were congregated in the centre as if expecting their cases to find them. But Carter decided to help himself. His bags were marked with Radio London stickers, making them easily recognizable, and within seconds he found them. He adjusted the strap of his Uher tape-recorder, shifted its weight on his shoulder, and carried everything to the Customs officials by the exit. George was waiting there.

'I'm George Tsigarides of the CTO. Welcome to Cyprus,' he smiled. 'Please allow me to take your bags.'

He led the way to the car park. Barely 15 minutes had elapsed since the jet from London touched down.

'I think it will be some more time before the others get away,' George remarked. Carter settled himself into his seat in the rented Renault as his host started the car's engine. 'I'm sorry you were delayed,' George said. He was pleased that his clockwork planning had worked. 'Have you eaten?'

'Yes. On the aircraft,' Carter replied. 'And please call me David.'

'I'm George. I know your brother Geoffrey. He is another good friend of Cyprus.'

Ignoring the mention of his brother, Carter said, 'What a marvellously mellow night.' He had felt a velvet breeze touch his skin the instant he stepped out of the aircraft, and the warm sensation pleased him after the autumnal chill of London. He had glanced upwards and was surprised by the blackness of the sky and the brightness of the stars. He felt he could reach out and touch each one. He could not remember when he had last breathed such clean air.

'Your hotel in Limassol, David, is a good one. I'm sure you'll like it. It's run by my friend, Mr Pipis,' George said, peering into the blackness of the road ahead. They were travelling along the shoreline and Carter saw the moon's reflection rippling in the waves. 'So that I can be of service, I shall be staying at the hotel as well. Perhaps you would like a drink before we get there, if you are not too tired from the journey?'

On arrival in a foreign country, Carter always preferred to unpack and settle in his hotel room before doing anything else, but on this occasion he decided to break his usual pattern. 'I don't imagine there's anywhere left open at this time of night where we could sit outdoors, is there?'

'Of course,' George replied. 'This is Cyprus. We will go to the Miramare Hotel. It's on our way and we will sit in the gardens by the sea.'

'Are you sure, George? I'm not really dressed for drinks in a hotel.' Carter was wearing denim jeans, an open-necked shirt, and a light windcheater. 'Don't worry,' George answered. He wore a dark suit, a tie knotted neatly under his chin. 'I am only wearing a jacket because some visitors prefer formality until they get to know us Cypriots.'

Over drinks at the Miramare, George told Carter that he had drawn up an itinerary which he hoped would satisfy the needs of the *Holiday Scene* programme. They would use Limassol as a base and tour Cyprus from there. Limassol, he said, was the centre of the island's wine trade and its chief port. It had a population of more than 60,000.

Carter glanced at the typewritten sheets and saw that every day of his trip would be filled from dawn till dusk, and even beyond, with visits and meetings. The efficiency of the CTO was to be admired.

'Of course,' George said, trying to judge Carter's reaction, 'we do not have to start working every morning at eight o'clock.' He waited for Carter's reply.

'No, that's okay,' Carter said. 'What's the point of hanging around doing nothing and wasting time? It isn't every day that I get to see new places.'

'Very good,' George said, obviously delighted, now convinced that Carter was a man after his own heart. 'Well let us continue to our hotel. As you will see, I have not made any appointments for the morning and so you will be able to rest after your long flight, or perhaps have a swim. Our lunch is here, in this hotel, in the afternoon.'

'That's great,' said Carter.

George stood up and checked their drinks bill in the light of a lamp hanging from the branch of a small tree.

'Let me pay. Please.' From a shirt pocket, Carter pulled out an envelope containing Cyprus pound notes. 'No, no,' George waved the money away. 'In Cyprus, you are my guest.' He smiled and added, 'You can pay for me in London.'

When Carter and George arrived at the Alasia Hotel, Mr Pipis Thrasyvoulu was waiting behind his leather and wood-panelled reception desk, although it was after two in the morning. He was a tiny man, barely five feet in height; a toy soldier guarding a toy fort.

'Welcome to Limassol, *la petite Paris de Kypros*. Welcome,' he said loudly, shaking Carter's hand vigorously. Then he turned and ordered a night-porter to carry his guests' bags to their rooms. Between phrases in Greek to George, he repeated his welcome in English several times.

'Please, please. Come, sit down. Have a drink. What would you like? Beer? Brandy? Brandy Sour? Whisky? Tea?'

George shook his head. 'I think Mr Carter wishes to rest.' Mr Pipis bowed, snapped to attention, and extended his right arm in the direction of the lift. 'Please. This way. I will show you your rooms.'

'No, thank you,' said Carter. 'It's okay. I'll find my own way.' Mr Pipis smiled again, handed him a key and replied, 'Please, if there is anything you need, let me know immediately. There is a telephone in your room. May I wish you a very good night, and I will see you at breakfast.'

'Perhaps later, Mr Pipis,' George said, trying to be helpful.

'No, I'll be there,' Carter insisted, determined to do everything that was expected of him. 'What time?'

'Any time after seven-thirty o'clock,' replied the energetic Mr Pipis. 'I will serve you some special sausages. They are made in my home village in the mountains. Perhaps Mr George will take you there. You will like the sausages, I am sure.'

'Thank you,' Carter said, trying to smile. Breakfast was not a meal he enjoyed having. 'Good night then.'

Carter's bedroom was spacious, modern and the bathroom was spotless; it was the first place he always looked when he travelled abroad. A bottle of wine and a bowl of fresh fruit stood on the dresser. Even without the gifts, he would have been satisfied. Before going to sleep, he scribbled his first impressions in a small diary. The notes would be useful when the time came for him to write his programme script.

During the next few days Carter filled several pads with facts and figures as George whipped him around Cyprus in the rented Renault. He was taken to all the beach resorts, to Paphos and Ayia Napa at opposite ends of the island; to villages clinging to the sides of the pine-clad Troodos mountains; to castles and to monasteries, stopping here or there to have places of historical interest and legend pointed out. There were so many that Carter found it hard to remember one from another.

Wherever he and George stopped, drinks and food were waiting for them. Sometimes the dishes were Cypriot and the wines locally produced; at other times the meals were European, served by experienced waiters in the luxurious surroundings of large hotels, where the wines and brandies came from France. But whether they ate in a modest taverna or at a five-star hotel, the welcome was always the same.

Never before in his life had Carter experienced such generous hospitality. It was overwhelming and impossible to return. If he saw something and admired it, a carving perhaps, or a particular wine, it was handed to him immediately as a gift.

'George, please tell them I can't accept,' Carter pleaded. 'I was only passing a compliment.'

'No, you must take it,' George replied. 'It is a Cypriot custom.'

'Well, we have a different custom in London,' Carter countered. 'You can admire all you want, and we'll probably charge you for looking.' His joke was intended to purge his feelings of guilt, because many of the gifts had come from villagers whose homes were nothing more than shacks. 'At least let me pay something,' he added, but George always refused.

At Limassol castle Carter met up again with the other journalists. They arrived just as George was about to guide the BBC producer around this thirteenth-century fortress. Here Richard Cœur-de-Lion married Princess Berengaria of Navarre in 1191, after he had conquered Cyprus on his way to the Third Crusade. Soon afterwards the island was transferred to Guy de Lusignan, the dispossessed King of Jerusalem. His family ruled Cyprus for more than 300 years.

At the castle Carter caught sight of Gordon Honeycombe, his giant frame towering above the crowd. 'I think I'll record some interviews,' Carter declared. George welcomed the suggestion. He had been wondering when his BBC companion planned to start working.

Carter's tape-recorder was loaded and ready to use. It had been carried everywhere as Tony Freeman had advised. 'Gather enough actuality to make the feature sound like an entertaining radio portrait of the place,' he had instructed Carter. 'This means you'll have to lug your Uher around with you.'

So far Carter's tapes contained the sound of waves striking shingle on a beach near Limassol, an effect to run under his studio commentary. Now there was an opportunity to record a celebrity, somebody immediately known to Radio London's listeners. Honeycombe could give a very positive start to the programme. As a former ITN newscaster and novelist he would not be short of words. For Carter this was also a major and practical consideration: his script could be shorter and he would need to work less.

Carter switched on his machine, checked to see that it was recording, and moved towards Honeycombe. There were several specific questions to be asked, but the first was designed to draw out a general impression of Cyprus.

'The natives, the Greek Cypriots, are the most friendly people I've come across.' Honeycombe's voice was carefully modulated; his words delivered at exactly the speed Carter needed. There would be no difficulty to edit the piece later. 'The island has great natural beauty and it's not bedevilled by a gross population of British tourists.'

George smiled. These were exactly the kind of sentiments the CTO hoped Carter's programme would contain.

Without prompting, Honeycombe continued: 'The evenings here are fabulous. With the sun setting at some taverna by the sea or some roadside amongst the vineyards, it's most romantic. After all, this is the island of Aphrodite, where she came ashore; and the Greeks and Romans, too, have left their splendid little ruins. I find it all very appealing.

'I've seen as much of the island as one possibly can see and my feelings are best summed up by a poem I've heard sung: *"I asked the moon where I could find you, and the morning star replied, at the edge of heaven."* I think if you are a romantic at heart, then you must discover Cyprus.'

Carter switched off his tape-recorder. The opening of programme was on tape, although Freeman had warned, 'Avoid the "as-the-sun-sinks-slowly-in-the-west-we-say-farewell style". Use the businesslike, un-starry approach of the reporter.'

All right, thought Carter, if that was really what Freeman wanted, then here were reporters to give their opinions. There were no stars in their eyes, only bottles in their plastic carrier bags, their reward for spending a morning at the KEO winery in Limassol. So why not talk about Cypriot wines? Were they any good?

Alan Hall, editor of *The Good Wine Guide* and contributor to the columns of *The Sunday Times*, came forward. 'There used to be a lot of Cypriot rubbish on the British market, but now they are producing wines of distinction.'

Once more George beamed with pleasure.

'For sheer delight,' Hall continued, with barely a pause, 'take back something which will remind you of the sunshine and hospitality of the island. Take back a bottle of a delightful light wine called *Bellapais*. It will give you just the suspicion of a prickle on the tongue. And then there's *Othello*. Look for a bottle of the '52, but open it only when you are with one other person, a special friend with whom to share it.'

Time passed quickly. More recordings were made and the tapes piled up. They covered the practical and romantic aspects of a holiday on the island, and Carter was fairly certain Freeman would be pleased by the results.

In the remote village of Phiti, Carter came across a troop of English ladies captained by Mrs Joan Marsh-Jones, a leading light in the Embroiderers' Guild of Great Britain. She stamped her authority on his tapes by explaining that her group had come to Cyprus to learn traditional weaving skills from the local people. They wanted to know more about the region's lace, *Lefkaritika*, which was exported world-wide. This was another type of holiday.

At the Phillips's shoe shop in Limassol, the place recommended by Bill Sinclair in London, the cobbler's daughter, Lydia, declared that 'most people who write with their left hands have large left feet'. Useless information perhaps, but it would lighten that part of the script where Carter quoted prices and listed cold facts and figures.

From the experts at the KEO winery Carter heard about the 100 varieties of grape grown on the island; the two, *Mavro* and *Xinisteri*, used to make wine; and drank in the history of *Commandaria*, described by them as 'a delicious dessert wine of nobility, with an unrivalled bouquet of its own and a luscious honey sweetness'. It had been first produced at Kolossi castle by the Knights Hospitaller of the Order of St John of Jerusalem at the time of the Crusades. Now 180,000 gallons of the wine were produced each year, but a bottle of 100-year-old Commandaria could cost more than £1,000, they told him, pressing a bottle marked 1927 into his hands.

Sinclair was correct when he had said that visitors returned fully laden from a stay in Cyprus.

Pavlina Tsirides, the attractive and charming owner of the Miramare Hotel, gave Carter advice on how tourists should spend their evenings. 'I would not recommend the night-clubs with the cabarets,' she said sweetly, warning against visits to a notorious red-light square off Zenon Street in Limassol.

'When you come to Cyprus you want to see how the Greeks are enjoying themselves, having a lovely time. Bazouki tavernas are the night-life of Cyprus, with their dancers. Not the Cyprus ones, but the Greek dancers.'

How all this material could be compressed into a 20-minute radio programme baffled George, but he was sure that whichever parts were included, they would paint a most attractive portrait of Cyprus as a holiday island and, after all, that was why the CTO had paid the cost of the Radio London producer's visit.

Cyprus was being taped successfully and Carter could hear his programme taking shape, but something in the back of his mind was nagging him. Was it the Greek Cypriots' overwhelming hospitality? There was after all the old saying, 'Beware Greeks bearing gifts'. He hoped he was not being churlish.

Clearly Cyprus was Greek because everywhere Carter went, he saw only the blue and white flag of Greece and heard only the Greek language being spoken.

On their drive towards Ayia Napa, eastwards from Larnaca, Carter asked, 'George, is there a flag for Cyprus?'

'Yes, of course there is,' the CTO representative replied.

'Is there a Cypriot language?'

'No. We speak Greek and English. Some of the Cypriots who are originally from Turkey speak their own language.'

'What are those large white crescent moons and stars on the side of those hills over there?' Carter asked. Each peak carried a watch-tower and flew the red and white flag of Turkey.

'That's the boundary of the Turkish occupation of Cyprus,' George replied. 'We have to be careful to stay well away from them.'

Returning to Limassol that evening George drew Carter's attention to a large area on the outskirts of the town. It was littered with rows of tents and lines of prefabricated houses. 'That is one of our refugee camps. Those people lost their homes, everything, when we were invaded by Turkey in 1974. There are thousands of these poor people. Perhaps one day you will make another programme about their suffering, and what a tragedy has befallen Cyprus.'

Now Carter knew what had been troubling him during the past few days. George had talked a great deal about the history of Cyprus, from its earliest times when Greeks had settled on the island after the Trojan wars up to 1960, when Britain gave Cypriots their independence. But he had never mentioned the years from 1960 to the present. It was as if George had blanked out that period from his consciousness.

Although his programme was nothing to do with politics, Carter wanted to hear for his own benefit more about recent events and why they had taken place. He was inquisitive by nature, not only because he was a journalist. During the few days left of his official CTO stay in Cyprus, he was determined to press George for detailed information.

Although George was growing more relaxed, he still avoided political discussions and stopped short of commenting on the island's recent history. Even so, there were a number of clues to his attitudes.

On the way to Paphos, they travelled a stretch of road which was extremely well maintained by contrast with others that they had used. On one side, in a valley, there were neat polo grounds, well-watered sports fields and clusters of small houses. Carter had not seen anything like this elsewhere in Cyprus and asked George for an explanation.

'Oh, that is called *Happy Valley*, part of the British Sovereign Base,' he replied with indifference, adding almost casually, 'One day we hope it will become the campus for the University of Cyprus.'

They stopped briefly at the *Temple of Apollo Hylates* at Curium, a religious and political centre founded in 1200 BC by colonists from Argos in the Peleponnese in Greece. George stressed this ancient Greek connection. In 1865, excavations began here under the direction of the American Consul in Cyprus who took many treasures to the Metropolitan Museum in New York.

As they neared Paphos they saw the vine-clad slopes of the Troodos and signs warning motorists to drive carefully because the road became slippery with grape juice during certain seasons of the year. At the time of the Crusades, the Templars owned these vineyards and they were worked by more than 1,000 Muslims, Saracen prisoners of war.

Ten miles to the east of Paphos they came to the *Temple of Aphrodite*, the goddess of love, who, according to legend, was born in the foam where the nearby sea breaks on a small group of rocks. George reminded Carter that Homer had written about this place; today it was exploited by the CTO in all its publicity.

George revealed more of his way of thinking when they reached Paphos. They were there to see the mosaics found in 1962 by a local farmer in the remains of a large Roman villa situated half-way between the harbour and the port's modern lighthouse. Later, while experts from the Cyprus Department of Antiquities were erecting roofs in 1964 to protect the site, more than 2,000 Ptolemaic silver coins were unearthed. They were contained in an Hellenistic jar from the first century BC. The coins had been produced by the mints at Salamis, Kition and Paphos.

Carter decided to photograph these magnificent multicoloured mosaics that depicted characters from Greek mythology and carried images associated with the cult of *Dionysos*, *Bacchus* the god of wine. He raised his cine camera, but George told him to wait.

'Why?' Carter asked.

'Because there will be UN soldiers in your picture,' George replied. 'Holiday-makers do not like to see military people. Wait for them to leave, please.'

This brief exchange led to a conversation about the UN in Cyprus and some of the events of 1974. When it was over, George looked across the excavations and remarked in a voice tinged with disgust, 'The Turkish air force bombed this place. They caused irreparable damage. How could they mistake this for a military target, I ask you?' He shrugged his shoulders. 'They are so stupid. The planes even sank one of their own warships. Over there.' He pointed to the sea just 100 yards away.

How much George admired Archbishop Makarios III, the first President of Cyprus, came to the fore the day they were driving through the Troodos mountains. Close by was Mount Olympus, towering 6,401 feet above sea-level and capped by a giant radar dome. George pointed out that it was listening-post operated by the RAF. Not far away was the twelfth century Kykko monastery, the largest and most famous in Cyprus. 'That was where Archbishop Makarios, at the age of 13, became a novice monk in 1926,' George said, adding quite unexpectedly, 'David, would you like to see where our President is buried?'

At the burial site, red and gold leaves were dropping from the trees. Although it was autumn, the air was filled with the fragrance of spring flowers. The sound of ringing bells came from the monastery, while builders nearby dug the ground and mixed concrete, the noise of their machines at odds with their tranquil surroundings. Two Greek Cypriot soldiers stood guard by the grave.

'The whole of Cyprus visits this place,' George said in a whisper. 'As you can see, they are still completing the construction of the tomb, because when he died, the construction was only halfway through.'

Carter's tape-recorder was running, the microphone was a spear probing George's personal grief. 'Actually he could foresee his death and so, very confidentially, he called his architect and told him what he wanted. But before the tomb was complete, the President died.' The words choked in George's throat.

George and Carter did not speak again until they stopped for coffee in the mountain village of Moutoullas. Greek Cypriots called this coffee *Oriental* although it tasted exactly like the Turkish variety the BBC broadcaster had sampled in a restaurant in Marylebone High Street; but then George had also spoken about *Oriental* Delight.

They sat on the veranda of the village's one and only cafe. Around them vines dripped grapes and orange candle-like objects hung limply from the windows of nearby houses. They were too large to be chillies and Carter asked what they were. 'That's Soujoukko,' George explained. 'Villagers take a piece of string and attach a lot of nuts. Then they dip the string into grape juice which has been boiled. The juice thickens and collects around the nuts like wax. Then it is removed and dried in the sun. It is a very good health food for eating in the winter. Nothing artificial, you see.' He ordered some, chewed a piece and then offered the remainder to Carter. It tasted like sweetened rubber.

While Carter chewed gamely, George said, 'We have to go to Nicosia tomorrow. At the end of your visit the Director of the CTO wishes to discuss with you your views on Cyprus. If you have enjoyed your stay, would you like to remain longer?'

Now that Carter had completed his recordings, George thought he would invite the BBC producer to remain on the island for a few extra days so that the two of them could cover aspects of life which had not been included in the official CTO itinerary.

'At my house I have an extra room for guests, and my mother would be very pleased to meet you,' George said.

Carter thought for a moment. 'Remember all these trips are done in your own time,' Radio London's Tony Freeman had warned. 'You must not charge any expenses in connection with them.'

If that were the case, then Carter was his own master, and whether he stayed or went should not be the BBC's concern. Yes, he decided, he would extend his visit; the extra days in Cyprus would mean fewer at Radio London. 'I'd love to accept your invitation,' he replied.

'Good,' George smiled. 'I will take a short holiday from the office and then I will show you many parts of Cyprus that you have not seen.'

CHAPTER 5

THE EDGE OF HEAVEN

STANDING on the corner of a tree-lined street named after a former mayor, Dr Themistocles Dervis, a man with outspoken contempt for Turks, George's house in Nicosia was a handsome place. It had been built at the turn of the century when British colonial rule gripped Cyprus. Marble steps led to an elevated veranda. The front door was made of polished wood, carved with intricate patterns. Green shutters covered the windows, locking out heat and dust from the outside world. They protected the very best of Cypriot arts and crafts collected in the cool interior. First editions in Greek and English filled the shelves of two front rooms, and fine cut-glass goblets rested on tiny tables covered in delicate Lefkara lace.

Here Carter met some of George's friends. They represented most professions. While they talked on a wide range of subjects and enjoyed George's genteel hospitality, his mother sat watching and listening like a latter-day Queen Victoria holding court. Her wishes demanded immediate attention and visitors paid her homage. Discreetly George offered his guests crystallized fruits and 100-year-old *Commandaria*. Out of courtesy to Carter, everybody spoke English or made a point of translating anything said in Greek.

Amongst those who called were two Englishmen who managed a hotel in London's Kensington. They spent their annual holidays in Cyprus. George had met them in Kyrenia long before the war, and it was from them that Carter heard how his Cypriot friend had lost his home in the north. It was a good enough reason for the man's hostility towards Turks.

Discovering that Carter's birthday fell during his stay, George suggested they should celebrate the occasion by spending the day at Ayia Napa on the south-east coast, where the sea was still warm enough for swimming.

On the way, George and the two English friends talked about the many places in Cyprus which were now impossible for them to visit. They mentioned St Hilarion castle on the Kyrenia road, the ruins at Salamis, and the beautiful beaches of Famagusta, not far from Ayia Napa.

Before reaching their destination, George parked his car on top of a hill and pointed in the direction of a city about four miles away. Somebody produced binoculars and suggested Carter look closely at the place. He saw tall buildings and wide avenues along which nothing was moving.

'That's Varosha, the new town of Famagusta, with Glossa, which used to be the best beach in the Middle East,' one of the Englishman said. 'Thirty-five thousand people used to live there until the Turks forced them to flee. It's deserted now. Everything's been vandalized since the occupation. It's a terrible waste.'

George directed Carter's gaze away from the city to a patchwork of green and red fields below them. 'Look over there, David,' he said. 'See those tractors at work and the water-sprays. That is how we do our farming. Now look ahead of those fields. What do you see?'

The neat cultivation came suddenly to an abrupt end, replaced by yellow and brown vegetation, dry and dead. Windmills stood motionless.

'Some of the best potatoes grew in those fields and beyond them were flourishing orange groves. All that area is under the control of the Turks. They don't even know how to use the land that they have taken.'

One of the Englishmen remarked, 'Because the Turks don't have the farming skills of the Greek Cypriots, they're turning half of Cyprus into a wasteland. Do you know, in the space of three years the Turks have destroyed the work of generations of Greek farmers? Some of the best citrus plantations have been allowed to wither and die. It's frankly disgusting.'

Moving his finger through the air, George traced the outline of the coast as it moved eastwards into the heat-haze of mid-morning. 'Over there, where Cyprus becomes the Karpas, what the English call *The Pan-Handle*, there are still many Greeks held captive, forced to work their farms for the Turks.'

There was no attempt to disguise his anger. George's mood was matched by the two Englishmen. They claimed that not only was there human suffering in the north, but that all Greek churches had been desecrated, their contents looted; whole villages had been destroyed, entire populations exiled.

They were very bitter about Britain's role of not doing anything to rid Cyprus of the Turks. They thought Carter and other journalists ought to do more to expose what was happening. 'It's a disgrace how the BBC and the rest of the media ignore the plight of the Greek Cypriot people,' one of them said.

Carter was spending his 40th birthday hearing about a side of Cyprus which could never be covered by his holiday programme. He would not forget it.

Later, to underline his points, George took Carter for a walk down Ledra Street, a bustling thoroughfare of small shops, crowded pavements and paralysed traffic within the old, walled city of Nicosia known by Greeks as Lefkosia.

Suddenly their path was blocked by a wall of concrete blocks, sandbags and coils of barbed wire. Its height prevented a view of the other side.

This was part of 'The Green Line', the physical partition of the northern and southern halves of the capital. Somewhere on the far side of the wall from where Carter and George stood, there were Turks.

Returning to George's house, they passed through Metaxas Square. Here a small group of women dressed in black stood silently, each carrying a placard filled with Greek lettering. George explained that these were wives and mothers of Greek Cypriots still missing as a result of the war. Nobody knew whether they were dead or alive. The Red Cross and other international organizations had drawn up lists of those killed or captured by the Turks, but more than 2,000 still remained unaccounted.

The Turks, George said, denied all knowledge of their whereabouts, despite the fact that journalists and others had photographed some of the missing individuals in POW camps on the Turkish mainland. He insisted that the Turks should reveal what they knew; to keep the women of Metaxas Square in misery, not knowing whether to hope or mourn, was cruelty in the extreme.

From George's friends, Carter heard a catalogue of accusations against the Turks. Based on this information, he concluded that the partition of Cyprus, and Nicosia in particular, was comparable to the situation in Berlin.

'It's far worse,' said of the Greeks. 'Here there is absolutely no freedom of movement between one side and the other for Cypriot people, not even under very controlled conditions. Not even objective information is allowed to come out. International journalists are certainly not welcome in the occupied areas.

'By the way, have you seen our Checkpoint Charlie? It's located at the Ledra Palace Hotel.'

'No.'

'I will take you,' said George's friend. 'I think you will find it interesting. Foreign officials and the UN cross there to enter the occupied zone. Sometimes journalists, too. Come.'

The traffic became less and the properties more run down the nearer they came to the Ledra Palace. Unlike other parts of Nicosia, the area looked as if it had been left to die slowly and on purpose.

Turning a bend in the road, they reached a barricade consisting of a white pole resting on oil drums. It was connected to ropes and pulleys which allowed it to be raised and lowered without effort by the occupants of two huts, one on either side of the road. A pair of dark blue police vans were parked nearby.

On the left, beyond the barrier, there was a line of UN vehicles, all painted brilliant white. A few yards later the road became a boulder-strewn track which continued until it reached another barricade. Between the two, there were sand-bagged emplacements manned by armed soldiers, weapons pointing at each other.

On the far side, a Turkish flag drooped from a pole stuck in the ground. Close to it was a hoarding covered in Turkish words, crudely written. Where Carter stood with George's friend, the flag was Greek.

'This is free Cyprus,' the Greek said. 'Over there it is occupied Cyprus. Here we are Christian. Over there it is Muslim.'

A few cars were crossing between the two sides. After a cursory glance at their drivers' documents, the Greek Cypriots waved them on. From his position, Carter could not see how the Turks handled these movements.

'Sometimes you can see UN trucks taking food supplies to the Greek Cypriots held captive in the north,' Carter's escort remarked. 'Without this aid, they would die. You should hear some of the stories the drivers tell of what they have seen. Of course, their reports must be kept confidential. If they were published, it is likely the Turks would stop the little aid they allow for our people.

'If you like our country and are a friend of Cyprus, then, David, you should tell people in England what is going on. We only have public opinion in our battle against the Turkish occupying forces.

'You must try to visit the north and see for yourself, but I do not think that they will allow you to enter.'

If that were true, Carter thought, then he must take up the challenge. It seemed to him that there was a lot more to the Cyprus story than he had heard so far.

Despite the great affection he felt for the Greek Cypriots he had met, and his appreciation of their courtesy and generosity, Carter was finding it increasingly difficult to believe that in this day and age any nation, especially a NATO member, would be allowed to simply invade another country on a whim of its leaders and not suffer some form of retribution from the western allies. Surely there were too many interlocking political and military alliances in existence to prevent aggression by a single state.

Then and there he decided to study the whole subject immediately he returned to Radio London.

Carter caught the Cyprus Airways flight back to London, weighed down by two more suitcases than he had carried on his outward journey. They carried much more than his Cyprus tapes. They contained the gifts from his new Greek Cypriot friends.

Carter agreed with Gordon Honeycombe, Cyprus was a place at 'the edge of heaven'.

CHAPTER 6

NORTH CYPRUS RULES

EVERYBODY was satisfied by David Carter's travel programme on Cyprus. Tony Freeman and Frank Dawes, as the producers of Radio London's *Holiday Scene*, gave it warm approval, broadcast it without a single edit, and even suggested that the station's music organizer should do other features for them. Bill Sinclair telephoned to praise the feature's 'objectivity', took credit for suggesting the idea in the first place, and promised to meet Carter in the New Year for 'a drink and a chat'.

From Nicosia came an enthusiastic letter written by the CTO's Director-General, Antonios Andronicou. It began: 'I hasten to congratulate you on this excellent production which constitutes a most positive contribution to our serious efforts to inform the British travelling public about the tourist attractions of Cyprus.

'It was really not only delightful but also interesting listening to all the points which were so ably arranged to be answered in a most convincing and honest manner by ordinary visitors as well as celebrities such as our common friend Gordon Honeycombe.'

Andronicou concluded: 'Needless to say that I was especially impressed by your conclusion and enthusiastic call to Britons to visit Cyprus at least seven times each. I look forward to welcoming you to Cyprus at all times.'

As a token of the CTO's appreciation, a case of Cypriot grapefruit was air-freighted to London and dispatched to the Carter household in Welwyn Garden City, where it arrived on Christmas Eve. But while his family and his neighbours enjoyed the fruit throughout the holiday and well into January, Carter spent his time away from Radio London reading everything his library had to offer on Cyprus.

The first book Carter read was *The Cyprus Revolt* by Nancy Crawshaw. Her knowledge of the subject was considerable, gained from a lifetime reporting the politics of the region. For more than a decade she had worked for *The Guardian*, when that paper was famed more for its informative articles and less for its idiosyncratic opinions and misprints.

Crawshaw's book traced the recent history of the island, told how independence had been achieved, and explained the differences which existed between the Turkish and Greek Cypriot communities. Although it stopped short of the Turkish intervention of 1974, it gave Carter a fresh perspective on the island's difficulties.

Carter decided a direct approach was worth trying. If it failed, he could always try other means. Without discussing his ideas with anybody at the BBC, he telephoned the Turkish Embassy in London and spoke to a press attaché.

Carter had rehearsed his arguments carefully and they flowed easily while the Turk listened patiently. When Carter stopped, the embassy official replied politely, 'Forgive me, sir, but I don't think I can be of very much help. Whether you are permitted or not to enter northern Cyprus must be a decision for the administration of the TFSC, the Turkish Federated State of Cyprus.'

'Who?' Carter asked, surprised.

'The TFSC,' the far voice repeated. 'May I suggest that you contact their representatives. They have offices in London. Please ask to speak to Mr Mustafa Adiloğlu.'

'How do you spell the name?' Carter reached for a note pad and scribbled the answer twice, once phonetically, adding the two telephone numbers given him by the press attaché.

For the next hour Carter dialled and re-dialled the numbers, always finding the lines busy. Eventually, just as he was about to call it a day, he got through to Adiloğlu, who suggested a meeting as soon as possible.

Carter walked past the entrance to the London offices of the Turkish Federated State of Cyprus twice before realizing that the tiny door sandwiched between an airline sales-room and a wine bar in Cockspur Street was where he was supposed to be. To gain entry he had to push a bell by the side of an intercom system. Before the door opened, a small closed-circuit TV camera scanned him. A few seconds later, the door buzzed ajar, revealing a staircase.

The interior of the hallway was dark; the only decorations were a few framed posters of the leaders of the Turkish Cypriot administration; it was all very different from the plush and expensive offices of the CTO in Regent Street.

Carter climbed the stairs and reached the first floor where a plump Turkish Cypriot girl greeted him from behind her typewriter and a small telephone switchboard. There were three telephones on her desk, all buzzing, which she ignored as she said in a bright cockney accent, 'Good morning, Mr Carter. It is, isn't it?'

'Yes,' Carter replied, casting his eyes around the room quickly. A hand-operated duplicator was being cranked by an elderly man in need of a shave; both the machine and its operator had obviously seen a lot of service in their time and were in need of retirement. Newspapers were piled in corners; an electric kettle was bubbling by an open jar of Nescafé and five unwashed mugs. The place had the atmosphere of an obscure charitable foundation which was desperately in need of funds.

'Mr Adiloğlu is expecting you,' the girl said, her smile bright and genuine. She took Carter to a side office. Here the TFSC's press officer in London sat behind a large desk, his back to a portrait of Rauf Denktaş, the Turkish Cypriot leader and Kemal Atatürk, the founder of modern

Turkey. That day's edition of *The Times* was spread open, while a copy of the *Daily Telegraph* lay folded in his in-tray.

'Please, do sit down, old boy,' Adiloğlu said breezily, his accent almost standard English. He stood up and shook Carter's hand as if he was a long lost friend who had come to announce a pools win.

Adiloğlu was a man in his early forties with a pale complexion and dark curly hair, faintly flecked with grey. His pin-striped suit was cut conservatively. He could have been mistaken easily for a city businessman who preferred good food and wine to squash or jogging. 'We would be delighted for you to do a holiday programme on our part of Cyprus,' Adiloğlu said before Carter had time to sit down. 'As you may know, we are eager to develop tourism. So when would you like to go?'

Hell, Carter exclaimed to himself, this was all too easy. There had to be a catch somewhere. After all, he had only outlined his proposition very briefly on the telephone and yet this man sitting opposite was granting his request. 'Of course, Mr Adiloğlu, you do realize that your administration would have to provide the airline tickets and the accommodation were I to visit your area?' Carter was blunt, but careful in his choice of words. He did not want to give the impression that the BBC was giving approval to the north's peculiar status.

'Delighted to oblige. And please, you must bring your family as well. Do you have children?'

'Yes,' Carter answered, even more taken aback by the offer. 'A boy and a girl. The girl's a teenager.'

'Yes, a most difficult time for parents, but they must all come.'

Carter's bewilderment grew. Where were all the difficulties he had been led to expect? He decided to spell out his requirements, more slowly and carefully so that there could be no misunderstandings later. 'I will need to have guarantees in writing, both in English and Turkish. A proper invitation,' he said.

'Yes.'

'And I must be allowed to see whatever I want. Travel anywhere without restrictions. Does that seem reasonable?'

'Yes, of course,' Adiloğlu replied positively. 'I will personally arrange for you to have a car and all the papers you require.' He patted the breast pocket of his shirt. 'Don't suppose you have a cigarette? I appear to have run out.'

Carter pushed his Marlboro pack across the desk and Adiloğlu picked a cigarette.

'Thank you.' Exhaling smoke from deep inside his lungs and looking at the ceiling while he talked, Adiloğlu continued, 'I am a journalist too, with many friends in the BBC at Bush House. I know exactly what sort of things you will need. Be assured, we have no secrets to hide, and we welcome people like yourself to the Turkish Federated State of Cyprus.'

Adiloğlu coughed, stubbed out the cigarette in an ashtray which needed to be emptied, and said, 'Sorry. Your cigarettes are a bit strong, old boy. Yes, as I was saying, we want people to come and see what we are doing and why. As long as they come with an open mind. Not prejudging the situation.'

This was the moment for Carter to lay his cards on the table. 'Mr Adiloğlu, I have just returned from the Greek side of Cyprus, where I produced a programme about tourism. While I was there, I made many friends. Greek Cypriot friends.'

Adiloğlu laughed loudly. 'Of course, yes. I have many Greek friends as well.'

'But I have a brother who works for the CTO. I think you ought to know that,' Carter continued.

'May I call you David?' Adiloğlu asked disarmingly. 'And I will have another one of your cigarettes, if I may?' He helped himself before Carter nodded. Waiting to light it, Adiloğlu added, 'What your brother does, why, and for whom, is surely his business, not ours. But thank you for being so frank with me.' He cleared his throat, inhaled, and changed the subject. 'May I suggest that we arrange your visit to coincide with your children's school holidays? Perhaps August would be convenient, if you don't think it will be too hot for them?'

'That would be great,' Carter replied enthusiastically.

'Good. I will write to you nearer the time.'

Adiloğlu opened his diary and made an entry before rising from behind his desk, an obvious signal that the meeting was at an end. 'A pity, David, that you and I can't have lunch together today, but I have to be at the House of Lords. Do you know Lord Vesey?'

Carter shook his head.

'You must meet him, and our representative in London, His Excellency Major Müftüzade. You know, he served in the British army and has an OBE and a QGM,' said Adiloğlu accompanying Carter to the first-floor landing. 'Lord Vesey understands Cyprus very well.'

As Carter walked out of the building into Cockspur Street, he could not believe how easy it had been to receive permission to enter the Turkish-controlled sector of Cyprus, but he checked his excitement; perhaps it was easier to get in than out.

At Radio London, Freeman and Dawes were equally surprised and immediately agreed that Carter should do a feature for them on the north. 'That is, if there is any tourism in the north,' Dawes remarked cynically. 'From what I hear, the place is a rubbish tip now. Turkish Cypriots, it seems, don't know the first thing about running hotels.'

Freeman added, 'This time we'll be giving you a very detailed briefing of what we'd like you to look at. It's a very controversial subject. Trust you to go looking for trouble. Don't you have enough with your song and dance brigade?'

'Well,' said Carter, striding towards his music office, 'with them on my side, I'll take the Turks any day of the week.'

A few days later Bill Sinclair telephoned and Carter told him that he had received permission from the Turkish Cypriots to visit the north, and that the BBC had approved the project. Sinclair replied that they would need to discuss the matter; an ideal time would be after the CTO reception for travel agents, to which he was inviting Carter.

The reception was an elaborate affair with a buffet of Greek Cypriot foods and plentiful supplies of wines and sherry from the island, all receiving approval from the CTO's travel industry guests. Sinclair was much in demand for a chat here and a whisper there. Carter's brother, Geoffrey, was equally popular.

Watching the crowd of faces, all unknown to him, Carter wondered why Freeman and Dawes had not been invited, as they were Radio London's travel experts. He took his glass of sparkling white *Bellapais* and stood by a corner of the large room. He and his brother avoided contact by mutual consent.

After about three-quarters of an hour, Sinclair came over and said that a film on Cyprus was about to be screened, after which questions would be taken from the audience. 'Your brother helped make this film,' he said. 'But remember, it's only a rough-cut at this stage. I think you'll like it, despite some raw edges. In fact, we're thinking of using parts of your radio programme for the sound-track.'

'Really?' Carter replied. 'You'll have to clear that with the BBC. They hold the copyright.' He did not like being told what people intended doing with his material without first asking permission.

'Well,' said Sinclair, 'if they're difficult, you could narrate the film for us instead. You're a friend of Cyprus, and I'm sure the fee will come in useful. Now don't disappear after the screening, because we've got some talking to do about that business of yours with the Turks.' Before Carter was able to reply, Sinclair had moved on.

The lights dimmed and the guests took their seats after refilling their wine glasses. The travelogue flicked on to a small screen. Twenty minutes later it was over and Sinclair bounded on to the stage, thanked everybody for attending the reception, and then added, 'If you've enjoyed the film, which you should know isn't complete yet, then I think you should put your hands together for the man who helped make it, my BBC colleague, Mr David Carter.'

Carter could not believe his ears. He had had nothing to do with the film and his anger grew. And what was Sinclair saying about being part of the BBC? Now was not the time to shout and make a scene, but, disgusted by what he had heard, he wanted to leave immediately, which was not possible because he was hemmed in by travel agents putting questions to both Sinclair and Geoffrey.

When the two men came off the stage, Carter marched across and demanded an explanation. 'It's all right. No panic,' said Sinclair, trying to pacify Carter. 'I'll explain everything, but not here. Suppose I meet you at, let's see, the BBC Club in half an hour?'

'I'll be there,' Carter replied, still fuming. 'Don't bloody well be late.'

'What was that all about?' a travel agent inquired innocently.

'Nothing to worry about,' Sinclair replied calmly. 'He's very talented, but a little temperamental. That's all.'

Carter waited for Sinclair to arrive at the reception desk of the BBC Club in The Langham building opposite Broadcasting House. Exactly 30 minutes later he was there, smiling. 'Sorry if I upset you,' he said disarmingly. They walked towards the bar, but the duty commissionaire stopped them, tapping Sinclair on the arm. 'Excuse me, sir, but would you mind signing in your guest, please.'

Sinclair crossed to the visitors' book, but before he wrote anything Carter reminded him that it was he who worked for the BBC, not Sinclair, the PR consultant hired by Greek Cypriots to promote their holiday resorts. If there were any visitors to be entered, Carter would do the entering.

'Don't worry,' Sinclair replied, still unconcerned. 'I'm a member. I wasn't sure if you were.'

'How the hell . . . ?' Before Carter completed his sentence, Sinclair had ordered him a large Scotch and offered an explanation. 'I do a bit of this and a bit of that for some Broadcasting House people. So they've arranged my membership of the club as a one of Auntie's freelance contributors. Now, about that business at the CTO. All very harmless, I assure you. You did do a programme about Cyprus and you did like the place. So what's the difference if I show a film which wasn't that different from your radio programme and pay you a compliment by saying you worked on it?'

'Because I didn't work on the film, that's why,' Carter replied sharply. 'Don't ever do that to me again.'

'Fair enough. Now let me tell you a couple of things, but I don't expect you to be pleased by them. Cheers.' Sinclair sipped his gin and tonic and glanced around the room to see if there were any faces he recognized. 'Your trip to northern Cyprus could cause a few problems for you, if ever you wanted to return to the Republic. You do know what I mean, don't you?'

'No. How so?' Carter asked, gripping his glass of whisky more tightly; he had detected a slight threat in Sinclair's voice.

'Well, the recognized government, the only real government, has declared that anybody entering northern Cyprus through ports in the occupied area, the Turkish-controlled part, will be breaking the law and may be prosecuted. What's more, if you stay in hotels which are owned by Greek Cypriots, the same applies. Do you want to put yourself at risk?'

'That's bullshit,' Carter insisted. 'Look, it was George Tsigarides and his friends who almost defied me to try getting to the north. They said

that the Turks wouldn't allow journalists to visit.   Now you come
along and say that if I go, I'll be in trouble with the Greeks. Rubbish.'

Sinclair ordered another round of drinks. 'Nobody minds you going
to northern Cyprus via the Ledra Palace checkpoint,' he said. 'But they
insist you enter the Republic *legally*, at Larnaca. There your passport
will by stamped by the legitimate authorities. That way you won't be
recognizing the illegal Turkish administration.   Remember, it's not
only your reputation at stake. It's the BBC's.'

Carter put down his drink, looked Sinclair straight in the eye, and
said, 'If I were standing outside getting soaked and you told me it was
raining, I still wouldn't believe you. Why don't you just bugger off.'

Sinclair shrugged and smiled. 'Okay. But take these and read them
carefully before you decide to reject my friendly advice.' He pulled
some folded sheets of paper from his jacket pocket. He swallowed the
remains of his drink and passed the papers to Carter. 'Just a final
thought, perhaps the BBC won't like what you're planning either, when
they find out the whole story. After all, Auntie has a correspondent
based in Nicosia and he won't like his pitch being queered.'

The papers were copies of letters sent from the CTO's London office.
One of them, signed by Filios Theodorou, the Director, supported
Sinclair's claims by spelling out how Greek Cypriots saw the legalities,
practicalities and morality of travelling to the self-proclaimed Turkish
Federated State of Cyprus.

The Greek Cypriot CTO claimed the northern part of the island was
'inaccessible to tourism' because the area was 'under Turkish military
occupation' and all hotels there were being operated 'illegally'.
Theodorou maintained that as 'the airport operated by the occupation
authorities east of Nicosia' was 'not recognized by the international
aviation authorities', his Greek Cypriot administration could not 'vouch
that it satisfied minimum safety requirements'.

The letters stressed that the Greek Cypriot authorities had declared
the ports of Famagusta, Kyrenia and Karavostassi, as well as Ercan
airport, 'prohibited points of entry'. With the exception of a single
hotel, the Celebrity, all others were owned by Greek Cypriots or
Britons who had been 'forced to abandon their properties at the time of
the Turkish invasion'.

As a consequence, according to these letters, visitors to the 'occupied
part' would probably stay 'in stolen property', and, if they did, then the
'legitimate owners' intended 'to take all necessary legal actions against
British subjects'.

Following the detailed explanations and threats came an appeal: 'The
moral considerations of supporting an illegal regime are, of course,
obvious and we trust that you will decide not to visit the occupied part
of Cyprus', and finally, 'The military atmosphere prevailing there is not
conducive to carefree holidays'.

After reading the letters and listening to Sinclair, Carter was all the more determined to hear for himself what Turkish Cypriots had to say, but had he been an ordinary holiday-maker he would have immediately cancelled his trip, which was exactly what the writers hoped. As a journalist he believed it was part of his job to find the evidence to confirm or reject the claims of the Greek Cypriot authorities.

But Carter was a realist, too.

He had already approached the British Ministry of Defence for permission to visit the Sovereign Bases where, he said, he wanted to produce a modern version of *Forces Favourites*. If the MoD granted approval, he did not want the Greek Cypriots to challenge him when he arrived there after his northern trip. To clarify his position, he wrote to Antonios Andronicou, the CTO Director-General in Nicosia, asking for a guarantee that there would be no action taken against him for entering Cyprus through 'illegal' ports and for staying in 'stolen property'.

At that time Carter was not aware that all arrivals at and departures from the bases were under the exclusive control of HM Government, not the Greek Cypriot immigration authorities. Their jurisdiction stopped at the perimeter fences of the Sovereign Bases.

While waiting for Andronicou's reply, Carter continued his normal routine as the Music Programmes Organizer at Radio London. As spring became summer his relationship with the management improved remarkably and many of his ideas were approved, including his forthcoming trips to Cyprus, north and south, providing that he travelled and completed the productions in his own time.

Then, during July, Tony Freeman drew Carter's attention to press reports of a judgement by the House of Lords on a legal case involving Greek Cypriot hoteliers and the Turkish Federated State of Cyprus. The newspaper summaries were confusing, but they implied that anybody staying in northern hotels could face prosecution in England.

'So where does that place your trip to the TFSC now?' Freeman asked.

'I haven't a clue,' Carter replied honestly. 'What do you suggest I do, Tony?'

'Don't ask me,' Freeman answered crisply. 'I'd love to have your feature, but it's your funeral. Remember, it's being done in your time. Don't expect the BBC to bail you out if you get into trouble.'

Carter telephoned Mustafa Adiloğlu, the TFSC's press attaché.

'Good to hear from you again, old boy,' Adiloğlu answered in jovial mood. 'Have you heard the good news? The Greeks have lost their case in the House of Lords.'

'I thought it was the other way round.'

'Absolutely not, David. Haven't you seen our official statement?'

'No.'

'I shall have it sent to you immediately.'

Carter was willing to wait for the TFSC's view, but not for his holiday itinerary, written guarantees, and the airline tickets, he told

Adiloğlu.

'Yes, old boy. Some chasing is in order. Those damned chaps in Nicosia are so damned slow at times. I just don't know how they fill their days,' Adiloğlu replied. 'If only they could see how busy we are here. May I suggest that you telephone them yourself. Speak to Mr Vedat Çelik. He's the Minister of Tourism. I'm sure he'd love to chat to you.'

Adiloğlu gave Carter a telephone number in Cyprus.

'But that's a number on the Greek side,' Carter interrupted, recognizing the international dialling code for the Republic.

'Yes,' Adiloğlu agreed, 'but the line continues through Nicosia to our side and the President's office, which the Greeks allow, and from there you can be connected to Mr Çelik.' Before the conversation concluded, he added, 'Before you leave for my country, we must lunch together. Do let me know how everything goes, old boy, and we'll make a date.'

With less than six weeks left to Carter's planned departure, the trip was slipping out of his grasp. He had not heard from Andronicou on the Greek Cypriot side, and Adiloğlu had clearly not had much success in securing from his side what the BBC producer demanded.

That Saturday Carter received the TFSC statement on the House of Lords' ruling. He studied it during lunch in the Wimpy bar in Marylebone High Street, while waiting for one of the station's presenters to join him. They were due to record a programme together later in the afternoon.

What the TFSC said appeared to contradict everything the British press had reported. The Turkish Cypriots maintained the House of Lords had judged that English Courts did not have jurisdiction 'to investigate alleged claims of trespass'. Furthermore, the Greek Cypriots who brought the case must reimburse the Turkish side's legal costs, Adiloğlu claimed.

'The object of this notice is not to enter into discussion as to how Greek Cypriots have been waging economic and political warfare against Turkish Cypriots since 1960,' the TFSC statement said, 'but to put the record straight concerning the Judgement of the House of Lords which has been misinterpreted in some Press reports.'

It concluded forcefully: 'The Turkish Federated State of Cyprus and its London Representative *will defend* any actions brought against them and invites anyone sued or threatened with suit by Greek Cypriot plaintiffs to make immediate contact.'

Carter saw how easy it was to get embroiled personally in the Cyprus problem; nothing was simple. Who was right? Who was wrong? What was legal? What was not? Would Radio London listeners care if he found any answers? In fact, was anybody really bothered about what happened at the far end of the Mediterranean? Probably not, he concluded. Nobody had bothered much about other small places and their internal difficulties until they exploded. Cuba,

Vietnam, Lebanon, and Northern Ireland came to mind. He decided to persevere with his project.

The owner of the Wimpy bar, a huge muscular man, came to where Carter was sitting. 'I see you have been reading something from our London office,' he said, nodding at the TFSC document.

'I didn't know you were a Turkish Cypriot,' Carter exclaimed. He was surprised because they often chatted, but even though the big man regularly contributed generously to all Radio London's various fund-raising programmes, the two had never talked about their backgrounds.

Good, Carter thought, the burly Turkish Cypriot could help again. 'I need to telephone northern Cyprus this afternoon. Will you translate for me?'

'If I can be of service, of course,' the Wimpy bar owner replied without a second's hesitation, folding his dish cloth and placing it neatly by the cash register.

On the short walk to Radio London, the Turkish Cypriot asked whether Carter was going on holiday to northern Cyprus, explaining that he spent his vacations in the south of France, driving there in his Rolls Royce. They passed another restaurant. 'That's managed by a Turkish Cypriot as well,' he said. 'We have been able to make many businesses in England. I think there are more Cypriots in London than even in Cyprus.'

Getting through to northern Cyprus was easy, but reaching Vedat Çelik proved more difficult. The Wimpy bar owner in London and the operator in President Denktaş's office appeared to argue vigorously in Turkish.

Capping the mouthpiece of the telephone with an enormous hand, the Turkish Cypriot told Carter, 'She thinks Mr Çelik is spending his weekend in Famagusta and perhaps does not wish to be disturbed. I have said that he is a government minister and ministers should be on duty seven days a week, and you and I demand to speak to him. I think she is trying to connect us now.'

He resumed talking in Turkish down the telephone, smiling frequently. Carter was grateful that he was not paying for the long-distance call. Eventually the telephone was passed to him. 'Minister Çelik is on the line. I have explained to him your difficulties and said that he must solve them.'

Well, it's different, Carter thought; a Wimpy bar owner telling a government minister what to do. 'Good afternoon, Mr Çelik. I gather you've heard why I'm disturbing your weekend.'

'Yes,' came Çelik's quick reply. 'Good afternoon, Mr Carter.' The voice was heavily accented and echoed on the line between London and northern Cyprus. Carter was certain that the Greek Cypriots were tapping the conversation which crossed their territory. If they were, then he would take advantage of any eavesdropping.

'I hope, Mr Çelik, that your administration intends to honour the promises made to me many months ago by providing the guarantees and facilities I require, because my Greek Cypriot contacts suggest that you won't.'

'But of course we will,' Çelik answered. 'All your arrangements have been completed and we are expecting you and your family as our guests on the scheduled dates. Please instruct Mr Mustafa to give you airline tickets immediately, and whatever papers you require.'

'Minister,' Carter insisted, 'if I may suggest, that's for you to do. But I must point out that unless I have everything by the end of the week, my visit will have to be postponed indefinitely. I can't keep my masters at the BBC waiting in suspense over whether I will be able to make a programme or not.'

'You will have everything. I give my word,' Çelik promised. Carter ended the conversation by thanking him. By the tone of Çelik's voice, he expected Adiloğlu to get his instructions from Nicosia first thing Monday morning. At the same time, if the Greek Cypriots had monitored the telephone call, Andronicou at the CTO would also know what had been agreed. Now all Carter could do was wait.

By the end of the following week Carter received everything he needed: tickets, guarantees and itinerary from the TFSC's London office; and a letter from the CTO in Nicosia.

Andronicou replied, 'I wish to thank you for your letter regarding your visit to the Turkish-occupied Cyprus and to inform you that having discussed your case with the appropriate authorities, I found out that there will be no problem for you to visit the Republic of Cyprus next October provided you will enter Cyprus through an approved port.

'I take this opportunity, however, to draw your attention to the recent decision of the House of Lords which provides, *inter alia*, that the promotion and advertising of hotels which belong to Greek Cypriots in the occupied zone of the island is illegal, and gives rise to a cause of action to the legal owners for trespass on chattels and general movables.

'I will be delighted to see you if you get the chance to cross over or if not on this occasion, when you will be here in October.'

Although the letter appeared to contradict itself, Carter was satisfied that he would not be banned from the Greek Cypriot side after entering northern Cyprus through an 'illegal' port. So much for Sinclair's warning he thought, smiling at the fact that Andronicou had also invited him to lunch in the south at the same time as the laws of the Republic deemed him an 'illegal immigrant' for being in the north.

But was the CTO's Director-General also suggesting Radio London should not mention hotels in northern Cyprus during the course of the programme, effectively censoring it? It seemed a game of bluff, a cheeky one at that, and Carter doubted that anybody would seriously consider taking him and the BBC to court for making a feature on the north's tourism, even if the Greek Cypriots felt that it was promoting and advertising 'the occupied zone'. If an action were brought, the Marylebone High Street radio station would achieve publicity the like of which it had never had, but sometimes deserved.

In the newsroom Carter waved the documents under Freeman's nose. 'All fixed, signed, sealed and approved by the Cypriots on *both* sides.'

Freeman laughed and turned to Dawes. 'Didn't I say Carter was a sharp operator? He'll outlive us both. Right, we'll draft a brief for your visit. You'll have it by tomorrow.'

'Promises, promises,' Carter replied. From his experience he knew Radio London staff needed chasing as much as the Turkish Cypriots.

But the next day, without prompting, the *Holiday Scene* team of two put the brief in Carter's hands. It said:

'The purpose of sending a reporter to Turkish Cyprus is to investigate the situation in the resorts of Famagusta and Kyrenia. These areas were formerly the key holiday resorts on the island, and the Turkish Federated State is now attempting to restore their position in the tourist market. Questions we wish you to investigate are:

'1. What is the situation regarding seized hotels, formerly the property of Greek Cypriots and British businessmen? Two of these hotels were the subject of a recent House of Lords judgement, and it is now suggested that British tourists using goods and chattels in these hotels will be sued in the British courts on return.

'2. What is the position of the Turkish administration over the seized property? Has compensation been paid?

'3. What sort of tourist industry can be re-established based on property occupied during a war?

'4. Are there any British tourists in Northern Cyprus now? And what are their feelings about the holiday in a climate of possible court action in the UK and the moral arguments put forward by the Greek Cypriots in London over the use by tourists of seized hotel property?

'5. Have the seized hotels now been refurbished to dispose of their former furnishings and fittings? According to the Greek Cypriots in London, any tourist from the UK even "walking on the carpet or drawing a curtain" in a hotel room will be sued on their return to Britain.

'6. Have the beaches and tourist developments in Kyrenia and Famagusta now been restored to their former condition?

'We would like these questions fully investigated and tourist officials, hoteliers and tourists interviewed.

'Signed: A. Freeman. F. Dawes
'(Producers, *Holiday Scene*)'

Carter was delighted by the directness of his instructions because they allowed him to take a tougher, more critical line than was usually encouraged in the making of a feature for *Holiday Scene*, but he wondered how the Turkish Cypriots would respond when the time came for them to deliver their promises of open access and to answer his questions. He knew, too, that his task would not be easy as he had no knowledge of the resorts prior to the Turkish invasion and so could not make any comparisons.

From all that Wendy had heard about northern Cyprus, there was little to recommend the place. Carter's wife used a hairdresser whose husband had been a pilot with Cyprus Airways; the tales she told were less than encouraging.

But Wendy agreed to go along with her husband's plans as she had always done, despite her apprehension; she was convinced that they were walking into 'a police state' and that they would probably get arrested if her husband pursued his objectives with any vigour. Like her husband, however, she considered the politics of Cyprus could not be any worse than those of the BBC.

Sitting in the departure lounge at London Heathrow's Terminal 2, waiting for the delayed departure of their Turkish Airlines flight, Carter quipped, 'But at Radio London, they stab each other with rubber knives.' Wendy did not find the remark amusing. The lounge was hot, crowded and sticky. She hated flying and hated airports. She looked around the room and saw that her family members were the only non-Cypriots taking the aircraft to İstanbul, where they would change for a flight to Ercan, the airport east of Nicosia.

But Wendy was puzzled. If northern Cyprus did not exist — officially — how was it that British Airways had handled the family's baggage when they had arrived three hours earlier? Her bewilderment increased when she placed her three-year-old son, Matthew, in the airport's nursery and a member of staff asked their destination. 'Ercan,' Wendy had replied.

'There's no such place,' the nurse insisted.

Carter's wife answered that there most certainly was and, furthermore, the flight indicator board confirmed her statement as did the labels on her bags, put there by British Airways staff. There the matter rested, but it was not very reassuring to know Heathrow workers were as divided amongst themselves as the Cypriots.

Eventually the flight was called and Wendy rose, placing her handbag on her wrist and taking her son by the hand while her husband and their 15-year-old daughter took charge of the other hand-baggage. With boarding-cards at the ready, they prepared to move out sedately, like a party of white hunters at the start of a safari.

But none of the Carters was as experienced as the Turkish Cypriots going home for their summer vacations. They had travelled before on

Turkish Airlines. As if by extra-sensory perception, they had organized themselves long before the flight call, edging their way towards the exit of the departure lounge; racehorses in their starting-gates waiting for the off.

On a signal which only they understood, they charged the doors and galloped across the Tarmac in the broad direction of the Turkish aircraft. Caught completely by surprise, Carter shouted to his wife, now separated from him by about 10 Turkish Cypriot families, 'Come on, Wendy.' He lost sight of her in the crowd and frantically wondered where their daughter had disappeared. He used his elbows to fight his way forward, giving as good as he got. He hoped the momentum of the stampede would force them all on to the aircraft.

Carter reached the steps of the plane, bounded up them, threw his bags across the first row of empty seats he reached. His wife and son joined him a bit later, breathless, battered and bruised. He had protected their places effectively against the verbal assaults of a variety of Turkish Cypriots, all equally dishevelled and concerned about their positions on the flight. Airline stewardesses had stood impassively watching, refusing to intervene. They had seen it all before.

'I never want to go through that again,' Wendy exclaimed, tightening her seat-strap around her son. 'It's never like this when we've been to Majorca.' From three rows further up the belly of the aircraft, Sheryl, their daughter, shouted, 'Next time I'll start training in the January sales in Oxford Street.' Her face showed how much she had enjoyed every push and pull of the last few minutes.

The stewardesses stirred themselves at last and marched along the aisle counting heads. They did it once, twice, and then gave up. A superior member of the team grabbed the microphone of the intercom system, looked severe, and bellowed at the milling crowd in Turkish. Her outburst silenced the babbling passengers, and those who were still standing froze.

The count resumed for a third time. At last the stewardesses found why it had gone wrong before. There were seven passengers too many on the flight. Unceremoniously, they were pushed off the aircraft, arguing, gesticulating with fingers, waving fists and, without a doubt, swearing to bring the wrath of heaven down on the heads of the airline's management. It made no difference that they all had boarding-cards.

Then the doors closed, engines roared into life, and the Turkish Airlines jet streaked down the runway to climb steeply before veering eastwards into the grey afternoon sky.

Carter and his family had learned how to behave for the next leg of their journey to northern Cyprus. When they had to change 'planes at İstanbul they would not be a push-over.

'Turkey rules, OK,' Carter mused.

CHAPTER 7

BLACKOUT AT THE DOME

August 1978

IT was midnight at Ercan airport and hundreds of Turkish Cypriots crowded the roof of the terminal building. They were staring northwards in the pitch blackness, each hoping to be the first to catch a glimpse of the flashing lights of the Boeing 727 of Cyprus Turkish Airlines. The aircraft was carrying their relatives back from London to homes in northern Cyprus, many returning for the first time in more than twenty years. The families had been waiting since sunset, but none was angry or mildly annoyed. They were a patient people.

Standing on the Tarmac outside the small lounge reserved for VIP travellers, Fikri Direkoğlu removed his horn-rimmed glasses and carefully wiped a layer of fine dust off the lenses. By nature he was a private person, by training he was a painter, and by gift of the administration he was the Director of the TFSC's Ministry of Tourism. His face was lined by weather and world-weariness, and tonight he was tired.

With Fikri was Ali Özel, his assistant from Famagusta, who had been forced to hitch-hike to the airport because his car had refused to start. His rotund shape remained despite all his efforts to slim by fasting during the month of *Ramazan*, which still had a week to run. Not by any means a devout Muslim he nevertheless lived his life philosophically, accepting what came round the next bend as being the will of Allah, or just simply luck.

Viewed from a distance in the white glare of the airport lights, the two men could have been mistaken for the Turkish Cypriot equivalent of Laurel and Hardy.

Twisting his black moustache with one hand and holding a bottle of *Bel Cola* in the other, Ali was as relaxed as Fikri was tense. He had tried to allay the worries of his long-time friend, but despite all Ali's persuasive powers, Fikri remained convinced that Carter's trip to northern Cyprus was premature, even inappropriate.

Fikri believed that his government ought to have waited until next year before inviting anybody to review the fledgling tourist industry and then, perhaps, a different BBC representative could have been selected. At the moment nothing was moving smoothly for the administration, least of all the airline schedules. He knew, too, that Carter had been a guest of the CTO, which had large budgets and trained staff to propagandize its case, while he did not. Even worse, Carter's brother worked for the Greek Cypriots.

'How can he be objective?' Fikri asked Ali.

'Be patient and see, Fikri bey,' Ali replied, practising his English in preparation for their guests. He enjoyed the company of journalists and had met many during the siege of Famagusta in 1974. But Fikri did not share Ali's opinion of the press. As far as he was concerned, journalists had done little to explain the difficulties Turkish Cypriots had endured since the formation of the Republic in 1960. He believed that they had accepted without question everything Greek Cypriots told them. Journalists, the United Nations Force in Cyprus and Greek Cypriots were not to be trusted.

'Journalists are only happy when they find bad things,' he muttered in Turkish, although he spoke English fluently, having spent four years studying art in London. But Fikri was a man of impeccable manners and his honour demanded that the Carter family be treated with respect and courtesy.

Fikri had the eyes of an artist; first impressions mattered. He looked at Ali and wished that his friend had dressed more appropriately for the occasion. Ali was wearing his favourite shirt stamped with a portrait of Marilyn Monroe. Baggy grey trousers and sandals, instead of shoes, completed his outfit.

Before Fikri could raise the matter, the Cyprus Turkish Airlines jet touched down on the runway. The roar from the reverse thrust of its engines made further conversation impossible.

On board Wendy Carter woke her son, relieved that their feet would stay firmly on the ground for the next two weeks. She had to admit, however, that the one-hour flight from İstanbul could have been worse. She had found it reassuring and surprising to discover that the crew and cabin staff were a mixture of Canadians and Britons, all of whom stayed at The Dome Hotel where the family had been booked. That gave her confidence, and so did the view from the window of the aircraft; she saw no military activity.

Carter led the way down the aircraft steps, shifting his Uher tape - recorder to the front of his body so that it could be seen easily. He hoped that the officials meeting them would spot the machine and identify him as the man from the BBC.

Barely had his feet touched the ground when he heard Fikri's voice for the first time. 'Welcome Mr Carter. I am Fikri Direkoğlu from the Ministry of Tourism.' He graciously took Wendy's hand and helped her off the steps. 'Madam.' He bowed slightly. 'Welcome. This is my colleague, Mr Ali.'

Ali grinned and tickled Matthew under his chin. 'You, young Matthew, will be my best friend,' he said, remembering the youngster's name from his list. 'And you are Miss Sheryl. May I take your things?'

'No,' said the teenager. 'I can manage, thank you.' Her tone was cool and suspicious. Her snub made Ali's grin grow wider.

The two men flanked the Carter family on the short walk to the terminal building. 'May I have your passports, please?' Fikri asked. 'Mr

Ali will show them to the immigration control. If you do not wish to have them stamped because of your visits to the other side, we will not have them stamped.'

'No,' said Carter with a smile, handing him their passports. 'Go ahead. Do what is usual.' He saw no reason not to observe the local rules and regulations. The Greek Cypriots knew he had come to Cyprus, the Turkish side, and he had noticed the stress Fikri had placed on the words 'the other side'. Having the passports stamped could be considered a friendly gesture by his current hosts.

With a slightly raised eyebrow, Fikri passed the blue and gold documents to Ali without further comment. 'Please, follow me,' he said. 'You must be tired after your long flight and be in need of refreshment. I am sorry but I am unable to offer you any alcohol.' Perhaps reading Carter's thoughts he added, 'It is not because we are Muslim and this is *Ramazan*. It is because the bar has closed.'

They wove their through a long line of Turkish Cypriots waiting to be checked by a team of khaki-uniformed civilian police and immigration officers, some of them women. Inside the building Fikri found the Carter family a place to sit and out of nowhere produced paper cups filled with chilled orange juice.

Still beaming, Ali returned and handed back the passports, duly stamped. Fikri and he exchanged a few sentences in Turkish and laughed. It was the first time that day the Director of the Ministry of Tourism had relaxed. He threw his head back and made a clicking noise with his tongue. Ali said, 'Those immigration officers were asking if you were really from the BBC in London and weren't you frightened about coming to Turkish Cyprus.'

'Very frightened,' Wendy confirmed, making Ali laugh louder. Sheryl whispered, 'Daddy, let's get going. I'm tired.' Ali patted her head. 'We will go as soon as your father has pointed out his cases to me and we have put them in your car.'

'Excuse me,' Sheryl said coldly. 'I don't like my hair being touched.'

'Sorry, dear,' Ali apologized, winking at Carter. 'Mr Carter, let us go and look for the bags so that the ladies may retire.'

Ali and Carter walked on to the runway where airport workers were using large trolleys to off-load the aircraft. They found the family's cases quickly and porters were ordered to take them to the car, bypassing the Customs officials.

'Mr Fikri has arranged some good rooms for you at The Dome Hotel in Kyrenia,' Ali said. 'It is about one hour's journey from here.' He offered Carter a set of keys. 'Do you wish to drive, or shall I take you there tonight?'

'Good grief, I don't want to touch the car on a strange road,' Carter exclaimed, not revealing yet that he never drove anywhere. 'I'd be much happier if you took us.'

'Ah, I thought as much,' Ali replied confidently. 'But actually, what

it is, the Minister, Vedat bey, said that you must have the freedom to do
everything you wished from the minute you arrived, and so this will be
your car all the time. Tomorrow I will show you where to get free
petrol by signing.'

The car was a Renault, almost identical to the one George Tsigarides
had rented in southern Cyprus. As everybody squeezed into the vehicle
for the ride to Kyrenia, Fikri apologized. 'We tried very hard to secure a
larger car for you, but they were all out. Perhaps later in the week, we
could exchange it for you.'

'No, I'm certain that this one will be very good,' Wendy said,
knowing that she was the family's sole driver.

The road to the northern coast wound its way through the
countryside and over the mountains, but in the darkness it was hard to
see anything from the windows of the Renault. Twice they lost their
way, much to Fikri's embarrassment, but, eventually, sometime after
02.00, they reached The Dome Hotel, where they were greeted by a
flurry of activity by a team of night porters. Even before the family had
registered at the reception desk, their luggage had disappeared to their
rooms.

Fikri told them that anything at all they needed had only to be
requested. They were to pay for nothing, not even their drinks at the bar,
which was why, he said, the reception staff needed signatures from
everybody, including young Matthew as he might want a soft drink
from time to time when his parents were busy attending to other
matters. He explained that Ali would stay at the hotel, always on call
to provide any assistance the family required. He suggested Wendy take
a look at the family's rooms to see if they were satisfactory before he
returned to his home in Nicosia.

Wendy replied that she was sure everything would be perfectly
adequate and thanked Fikri for the warm welcome the family had
received.

The Director of the Ministry of Tourism bowed, 'Thank you, Madam.
If there is no more service I can provide, I will bid you goodnight. I
will return tomorrow.'

Barely had those words left his lips when the hotel lights went out.
They were left in absolute blackness, and so was the rest of Kyrenia.
Not a single light could be seen anywhere.

'Do not worry, Madam,' Fikri said, his voice a mixture of irritation
and concern. 'The Greeks have cut off the electricity again.'

Ali was issuing curt instructions in Turkish. They were directed at
any movement which took place in the darkness. He lit a match which
flickered for a few seconds. It provided enough light for hotel staff to
find candles in a desk drawer.

'Damn,' Ali exclaimed as flames from the match reached his fingers
and went out. 'Sorry, Madam.'

From the darkness by the hotel's lift, Sheryl's voice echoed around the lobby. 'Do we all get arrested now?' Fortunately her question went unheeded for the lights came back.

'They do it all the time,' Fikri said.

'They probably knew that you, Mr Carter, were coming to stay at The Dome,' Ali quipped. 'We will go now and celebrate your arrival and the resumption of electricity by having a drink at the harbour.'

'You go, David,' Wendy said. 'I'll go upstairs and unpack.'

Once again Fikri wished the family goodnight, gave Ali more instructions in Turkish and disappeared into the night, while Wendy, Sheryl and Matthew squeezed themselves into the lift which creaked its way to the first floor, leaving Carter and Ali to find an open bar somewhere in the silent resort.

Sheryl was the first to reach her room, struggled with her key in the lock, opened the door, and threw herself on the large bed in the centre. Something cracked and the bed's front legs collapsed. For the remaining hours of the night, Sheryl slept at an angle of 30 degrees.

With his family eager to see what Kyrenia had to offer, Carter rose early in the morning. They had decided to spend their first day relaxing, getting the feel of the place, before organizing any work for the radio programme. It was a decision very much approved by Ali Özel. Man, he believed, had not been designed for a life of sweat and toil.

In his relaxed fashion Ali escorted the Carters around The Dome Hotel, which resembled a set cast off from an old Hollywood musical. Its curving staircases and ornately decorated rooms with high ceilings and potted palms had seen better days. Obvious changes in the decor made its suffering worse. Sliding glass partitions seemed a bit incongruous. Nor did the paintings of Turkish scenes, garish and overdone, rest comfortably on the old walls. At the rear of the hotel, a fresh-water swimming pool was under construction. A sun-terrace overlooked the sea.

Here Carter and his family sat to drink morning coffee. Unfortunately this would not be possible, said the waiters: coffee could be supplied only in the lounge. However, they would be delighted to provide freshly-squeezed orange juice. Apologies, many and profuse, gave way to smiles, wide and generous, when the visitors accepted their offer.

Carter had two problems to solve. First, there was the matter of Sheryl's broken bed. Secondly, he needed to cash some travellers' cheques as he had no local currency.

'You do not require any money,' Ali insisted. 'Tell me what you want to buy and I will get it for you.' But when the Turkish Cypriot escort went to report the broken bed to the hotel's reception staff, Carter made a dash for the Barclays bank opposite The Dome.

Before leaving England, Carter had asked his bank and the BBC cashiers' office what currency he should take with him, but neither group of experts were able to make a recommendation. Each was unsure whether Greek Cypriot pounds were still used or Turkish lira. Playing safe, Carter opted to carry sterling travellers' cheques.

The Kyrenia branch of Barclays bank was quiet and Carter found he had the exclusive attention of its entire staff, two lonely young men. He produced his passport and signed three travellers' cheques, each for £50, and requested an equivalent sum in local currency, whatever that was.

'Turkish lira?' replied one of the counter staff, scrutinizing Carter's signature on the cheques and comparing it to the one in his passport. 'I will give you Cypriot pounds.'

Uncertain whether he had heard correctly, Carter hesitated. 'No, I'd prefer Turkish lira. What's the rate of exchange?'

'No, I cannot give you lira.' The clerk was adamant. 'It is not allowed.'

'I see. But didn't you say that the currency used in Kyrenia is *Turkish lira*?'

'Yes.'

'Then why can't I have some?'

'Because I am not permitted,' the Barclays bank clerk insisted, adding, as if it would explain everything, 'This is Barclays, a British bank, sir.'

Carter shook his head in frustration, but the young Turkish Cypriot was counting Greek Cypriot pounds already and sliding them under the grille. But what was the point of having these colourful pieces of paper if Turkish lira were used in northern Cyprus? He picked up the notes, accepting that discussion had been brought to an end by the clerk behind the counter.

'May I see your manager?' Carter inquired, trying hard not to appear impolite.

'Yes, of course.'

The clerk disappeared into a back room and returned, accompanied by a jovial middle-aged man moulded in the comfortable shape of a Home Counties' suburban branch manager.

'Ah, Mr Carter,' he said, all smiles. 'I am Mr Alpay Sami.' He was holding Carter's passport. 'I am sorry if we seem unhelpful, but this is a British bank and the Turkish Federated State of Cyprus is not recognized by Her Majesty's Government. So I am afraid we must observe the rules of Greek Cyprus and deal only in the legal tender of that State. Cypriot pounds, you see.'

Carter did not see, nor did he understand.

'But what do I do for spending-money here?' he asked.

'I am sure you will have no difficulty changing these pounds,' replied Mr Sami, reassuringly.

'Will you change them?'

'No,' he said. 'That is not allowed, but may I offer you some refreshment instead?'

'No, thank you. Another time perhaps.'

'I see you work for the BBC,' Mr Sami continued. 'I listen to the BBC a lot. For the Victor Sylvester dance music. I like strict tempo very much. Perhaps before you return to London, Mr Carter, may I give you a list of his records for you to get for me?'

'Yes,' Carter replied. He had been unaware that Sylvester's music was still broadcast. 'I'm sure I'll be back again to change travellers' cheques.' He was wondering what sort of world of unreality he had entered. He took his Greek Cypriot pound notes, sandwiched them between the pages of his passport, and backed out of the bank.

Outside, on the island roundabout, less than 50 yards from the bank, Carter saw an armed Turkish soldier directing traffic. Even closer was a military building of some kind which was flying the Turkish flag. Yet here he had found Turkish Cypriots willing only to hand him the currency of a government which considered their existence illegal. It seemed to him that if the north were under the domination of the Turkish mainland authorities, their rule was extraordinarily benevolent.

Crossing the road to return to The Dome Hotel, Carter was beckoned by a Turkish Cypriot sitting on a high stool, taking advantage of the morning sun to top up his tan outside the offices of Atlantic Car Hire.

'Excuse me,' he said. 'English?'

'Yes,' Carter answered.

'Good. Do you change pounds sterling for Cyprus money at Barclays?'

'Yes, I did,' Carter replied, realizing that his movements had been closely observed.

'Very good. Do you wish me to change into lira? I give the best rate of exchange. For sterling pounds as well. Cheques with banker's card, all right too.' The man pulled a mini-calculator from his shirt pocket, ready to compute the deal.

Carter felt uneasy. He looked up and down the street. Was he supposed to change money on the black market, and what would be the penalties if he were caught? The money-changer was waiting for a reply.

'Merhaba, David, hullo,' Ali shouted from The Dome Hotel's porch. With him was Carter's wife, pushing their three-year-old son in his baby buggy. Son and mother were wearing floppy white hats as protection against the hot sun. They could have stepped from the pages of a Kipling book. Above them, two Union flags fluttered from the hotel's flag-poles. Was the TFSC a figment of the imagination?

They reached Carter and stopped. 'Do not change your money here,' Ali ordered, scowling at the man on the stool, who stood up abruptly and began to argue in Turkish. Carter was sure he had made some awful mistake by being caught with a black marketeer.

'No,' Ali continued, still addressing the money-changer, 'if you cannot give Mr Carter a better car, like we ordered from you, then why should he change his money here? Go on, tell me. You know Mr Carter is a guest of the government.'

The man sat back on his stool, resting his head against the wall of the hotel and clicked his tongue against the roof of his mouth. Turkish Cypriots did this whenever words were inadequate to express their thoughts. '*Evet*. I will give Mr Carter 10 extra lira for each pound. Just for you, Mr Ali.'

'That is better,' Ali retorted. 'It is a bargain then. David, give me your Cyprus pounds.' The money-changer pulled a roll of grubby notes from the back pocket of his trousers. The money was unfolded and counted methodically into Ali's outstretched hand. The trade was completed.

Carter had discovered that by obtaining Greek Cypriot pounds from Barclays and swapping them at Atlantic Car Hire, he made a profit. Aided by a Turkish Cypriot official he knew he could do no wrong.

The family followed Ali to where their Renault was parked. He opened the rear door and removed a toy aeroplane which he handed to Matthew. 'A small present for my friend,' he said. 'Right, now what shall we do this fine day?'

'I thought we'd just wander about Kyrenia, walking,' Wendy replied.

'Very good,' Ali agreed. 'Let us proceed.'

'Aren't you going to lock the car?' Carter asked.

'No,' Ali sighed, bewildered by the question. 'Do not fear, we Turkish Cypriots are very honest people,' adding as an afterthought, 'Anyway, the lock is broken!'

Life in northern Cyprus had all the elements of farce, Carter thought. It promised to be far more enjoyable than the precision of official dealings in the south. He looked forward to what the next two weeks held in store.

CHAPTER 8

THE THIEVES' KEBAB

ALTHOUGH the Carters were free to travel where they liked, Ali was never very far away, and so they took advantage and used him to drive them during the days that followed. He was an amusing guide and a mine of historical information. His commentaries were colourful and useful to Carter's programme.

'Bellapais. The Abbey looks due north to Turkey, standing on a natural rock escarpment, the edge of which drops 100 feet vertically to the plain below. The plain, as you can see, stretches for about 10 miles, covered with mulberry trees, oranges and lemons, pines and palm trees,' Ali said, enjoying his role as a broadcaster. 'The abbey was built for a religious brotherhood from Laon in France who called it *Abbaie de la Pais*. By the end of the Venetian rule of Cyprus, the morals of these monks were very poor. They were leading a very licentious life. When the Turks arrived in the sixteenth century all that was stopped and the abbey was handed to the Greek Orthodox clergy to use. Today Bellapais remains one of the most impressive surviving monuments in the Gothic style of the Lusignan period to be found in the Middle East. The Royal Lusignan coat-of-arms is on the lintel of the main door of the refectory.'

They walked inside the church, dusty from lack of use, but apparently undamaged and still intact after the events of 1974. Bibles were piled neatly, but candles in their holders by the altar drooped in the stifling heat.

Back in the fresh air again, Ali continued his commentary: 'And over there, that is "The Tree of Idleness", made famous by Lawrence Durrell in his book about Cyprus called *Bitter Lemons*. I commend it to you.'

A former Greek Cypriot coffee shop, which had been managed by Savvas Kourtellas, was being run now by a Turkish Cypriot, a refugee from a village near Limassol.

During the summer of 1974 Bellapais had been a notorious centre of EOKA-B activity and Brits with pro-Turkish leanings were advised to give the place a wide berth.

With EOKA gone, four summers later there were still no tourists crowding this historical location, unlike those in southern Cyprus where there were always long lines of holiday-makers waiting to pay admission fees.

Nor were there any foreign visitors at the remains of the *Vouni Palace* where Ali regaled the Carters with tales of the fifth-century BC kings of the island, including *King Merion*, a Phoenician who established the site when the cities of Cyprus were rebelling against their Persian occupiers. Built on three terraces, his palace had 137 rooms and a temple to the goddess *Athena*. It was destroyed by fire in 380 BC and ransacked by the people from nearby Soli.

Soli, one of the ancient kingdoms of Cyprus, took its name from *Solon*, an Athenian statesman who came to live on the island around 510 BC when he gave Cypriots a code of law by which to operate government. At the end of the second century AD the Romans built a theatre on the site to accommodate 3,500 people, Ali said, glancing at the auditorium's 17 rows of seats, all empty today.

Wherever the Carters travelled they were warmly welcomed. Local people pressed them to see inside their homes, meet the village headmen, and share meals. They talked about their relatives in London, acting no differently to their Greek Cypriot counterparts in the south, except in one particular way: here elderly Turkish Cypriots were always keen to prove how they had served the British with distinction. They showed faded documents, official records of their military duties with the British army during World War II or their time in the colonial police. Their pride in having served was considerable. These people never spoke about Greek Cypriots, only of their links with the British which they maintained through memory and family. At this Carter did not raise any political issues.

'Famagusta. Or as we call it, Mağosa. The ancient city within the walls has a 4,000-year history. The walls, 50 feet high and 27 feet thick, were built by the Lusignans. They are three miles in circumference and half-a-mile in diameter,' Ali said, once again well into his verbal stride. 'It is said that there used to be 365 churches and chapels within the walls; one for each day of the year.

'You may not know, but much of the construction of the Suez Canal was completed with materials torn from Famagusta's old churches and buildings.

'Here, in the centre of the square, we are flanked by the old Venetian palace and by the Lala Mustafa Paşa Mosque, once the Cathedral of St Nicholas. When the Catholics of the island left after the Turkish conquest of 1571, the only way to preserve it as a holy place was to convert it into a mosque, which is why the minaret was added to the original structure.'

Just as the Turks of the Ottoman Empire adapted the cathedral to suit their needs, so today Turkish Cypriots were taking advantage of the hotels which they had grabbed from their Greek Cypriot owners, Carter suggested, believing now was as good a time as any to raise aspects of the Cyprus problem with Ali.

Ali smiled. 'These properties are held in trust.'

He added: 'We must be practical, but, because I am a Turkish Cypriot, you will say I am very biased. Actually, what you need is not my opinion as somebody from the Tourism Ministry but the views of your own British people who live here, and so I will take you to where the English gather and leave you in their company. You told our minister that you wanted to make an objective report and that you must do. But first, since I see him drinking coffee in the square, you must meet the mayor of Famagusta.'

The mayor was Bora Atun, an English-trained architect in his middle-thirties, whose wife came from Leicester. He was a forceful advocate of the Turkish Cypriot case and unemotionally defended what he called the 'Peace Operation' of the Turkish forces in 1974. He insisted that had the Turks not arrived, at best the Turkish Cypriots would have remained second-class citizens within the Republic or, at worst, would have been wiped out as a people by the Greek Cypriot authorities.

Bora's wife was less concerned about generalities. She chose to speak in graphic terms about the siege conditions which she and their young daughter had endured. 'For 21 days we were without a water supply,' she told Wendy. 'We were bombed all the time by the Greek Cypriot National Guard. If the Turkish army hadn't liberated us, we, the wives, planned to kill ourselves and our children rather than be taken prisoner by the Greeks. I had a pistol and six bullets. Not Britain, not the United States did a thing for us, except to suggest that we leave our husbands, those of us who were foreign nationals. How could we have done that? It would have been a betrayal.'

Her hatred for Greek Cypriots was open and permanent; nor did she have a very high opinion of journalists.

Back in Kyrenia, Carter told Ali that he wanted to find the house which had belonged to George Tsigarides before the war. Without hesitation the burly Turkish Cypriot replied, 'Of course. I will take you, but you will have to show me where you think it is. Did your friend give you details?'

Carter pulled some maps of Kyrenia from his shoulder-bag. They had been given him by the CTO, together with the address of George's home. 'Actually, it will be very difficult,' Ali observed. 'These maps are out of date. We have changed all the street names and we call our villages by their Turkish names. For instance, Kyrenia is *Girne*, Nicosia is *Lefkoşa*, and Famagusta is *Gazi Mağusa*.' Chuckling, he added, 'But very few people know that, yet. What it is you say in England, a rose by any other name is still a rose?'

But even four years after the Turkish Cypriot authorities had taken control of northern Cyprus not all signs of previous Greek Cypriot ownership had disappeared. As they strolled through the back streets towards the harbour front, Carter saw that the only Greek language signs obliterated were those within easy reach, and they had been crudely covered in black spray-paint.

The name *Catsellis* was still embossed in the plaster of a building on the corner of what had been Hellas and Catsellis Streets. Here, at number one, the K. Brothers had operated, selling souvenirs, books and newspapers. Theirs, like other Greek Cypriot businesses, such as The Cyprus Art Shop opposite The Dome and Kikas, 'the shop of quality' in the main street, were no more, their premises used today by Turkish Cypriots, many of whom were refugees. They had been given these properties by the TFSC administration as compensation for their losses in the south.

Nevertheless Kyrenia was still a bustling town, far more so than Carter had been led to believe. Its Turkish Cypriot inhabitants gave the impression that they were happy and healthy, and their children were as bright and noisy as youngsters everywhere. The shops were open and well stocked. There were more brands of American cigarettes and Scotch malt whisky than Carter had ever seen at home, and they were being sold at prices far below those charged at the duty-free shop at London's Heathrow. The largest of these shops was now the Tan supermarket, which had belonged to the Neocles family.

Wendy's eyes caught sight of the piles of Pyrex dishes, Spanish blankets and giant jars of Nescafé. 'Ah,' said Ali, who had taken charge of Matthew and the baby buggy, 'those are for the tourists.' But she had not seen any tourists and pressed the man from the ministry for an explanation.

'Yes,' Ali insisted, 'there are tourists. Lots. Why it is you may not have noticed them is because these people are mainly from Turkey. You see there is a coffee shortage over there, which is why they come here to purchase it. Also they like very much the Pyrex dishes and Spanish blankets. It gets very cold in parts of Turkey.' How Turkish Cypriots came to have stocks of coffee when their mainland supporters did not was something Ali did not explain and Carter did not ask.

At the harbour, tables and chairs were being placed by the water's edge and laid for dinner by the restaurateurs. When they spotted the Carters, each wanted the family's custom and ran eagerly after them, some tugging at Wendy's arms.

Halil was the winner of the contest. With a polished brown face and thinning black hair greased flat across his head, he resembled an energetic munchkin from Oz, making do with the harbour walkway in place of 'the yellow brick road'.

Halil had rolled out of his kebab restaurant, dashed to the best-positioned table, dusted the seats, lit a candle, and presented Wendy with a rose, all done in one continuous, flowing movement.

'You have kebab A to Z,' Halil grinned, easing Carter's wife into the nearest chair. 'Have a seat, and if you don't like my food, I don't charge you. You are my guest. Cheers.' His enthusiasm was outstripping his ability to speak the English language, but nothing was going to thwart his powers of persuasion. Had the family been Swahili or Mongolian, it would have made little difference to the jolly Turkish Cypriot's sales methods.

'I will give you *köfte, şeftali, şiş,* lamb chops, chicken, fruit. And chips. All the best,' he bubbled. Even as his words flowed, Halil's young assistants, lads in their teens, were placing the first dishes on the table. They made the hustlers outside Soho strip clubs appear positively lethargic. In his programme-diary, Carter wrote, 'Are they really enthusiastic, these Turks, or are they simply desperate?'

During dinner the Carter family and Ali were joined unexpectedly by Fikri Direkoğlu and his wife Sevilay, a tall, elegant woman who was a staff newsreader for Bayrak Radio, the Turkish Cypriot station based in northern Nicosia. They had gone to The Dome Hotel hoping to meet the Carters but, told that they were out, decided to visit the harbour.

The harbour was the customary place for tourists and residents to congregate in the evening. By nightfall all the restaurants did brisk business. Children, parents, grandparents, in-laws, cousins, uncles, aunts, everybody came together in one gigantic street party and extended-family reunion.

'Tomorrow, David, you have been invited to visit The Celebrity,' Fikri said. According to the Greek Cypriot side, this was one of only two hotels owned legitimately by Turkish Cypriots. 'Will you be wishing to interview the owner, Mr Aziz? He comes from London.'

Carter promised to take his tape-recorder with him.

Ali mentioned that Carter also wanted to visit George Tsigarides's house and, as it appeared to be somewhere west of Kyrenia along the road to The Celebrity, he suggested they should look for it on their journey.

'Who is this Tsigarides?' Fikri queried suspiciously, removing his glasses to wipe the lenses with a paper napkin. Before Carter could reply, Ali switched to Turkish, calming any doubts which Fikri may have had. 'Perhaps I knew him before 1974,' mused the more solemn of the two Turkish Cypriot officials, before changing the subject. He wanted to know how many recordings had been made so far and whether The Dome was to the family's liking.

All was well on both fronts, Carter assured Fikri. 'Good,' the ministry man nodded as Halil served the next dish. 'Mr Halil has brought us one of his specialities.' It consisted of large chunks of mutton roasted on the bone. 'We have 127 different kebabs in Turkish cuisine,' Ali explained. 'This one is called the *Thieves' Kebab*.'

Halil stayed by the table waiting to judge his guests' reactions to this speciality of the house. Even Sheryl, who hated experimenting with food, was obliged to prick the lumps of meat with her fork. Only Matthew could ignore the dish as he had fallen asleep.

With synchronized timing, the family lifted forks spiked with lamb to their mouths and chewed slowly and purposefully. Together they wiped grease from their lips. Wendy spoke first. 'Yes,' she said flatly, 'very good. Very fattening.' She swallowed again. Carter knew she was enjoying it as much as him. They would try to avoid the dish in future.

'What did you say the name of the dish was again?' Wendy asked, 'I must make a note for the next time we're out.'

'It's called the *Thieves' Kebab*,' Sevilay repeated. 'My mother will make it for you when you come to visit us in Nicosia.'

'Is it called the *Thieves' Kebab* because Turks steal things?' Sheryl's question silenced the group. For further impact, she added, 'Like you've stolen The Dome Hotel?'

Carter winced. Wendy told Sheryl not to be rude. Sevilay fired Turkish words at her husband. And Ali roared with laughter, running his broad hands through the teenager's black hair.

'Get orf,' Sheryl exclaimed, furious with him for not having taken her more seriously. 'Anyway, how would you like to have your house stolen?'

'Mr Halil did,' said Fikri quietly. 'He lost his home and his business in Limassol, where your father has Greek friends. But do not be upset. Stay a few more days with us and you will learn a lot.'

'Don't think you're going to brainwash me,' Sheryl replied forcefully.

'No, but even if you do not change your opinions, you will still have more knowledge with which to debate.' There was nothing patronizing in Fikri's voice; he himself was the father of a teenage son and daughter. 'Sheryl, I think you must meet our President to tell him how you feel. It is good that you should express your thoughts so openly and without fear.'

'All right, I will,' Sheryl stated, adding, 'And I don't like being called Sheryl. I want to be addressed as Melanie.' She was always changing her name for reasons best known to herself.

'Right, Melanie,' said Ali, his eyes twinkling in the candle light.

'Good,' replied Melanie. 'Now I want to go home, I mean to The Dome Hotel.'

'Yes,' her father agreed, 'if you don't mind sleeping in a broken Greek bed.'

'No, no,' Ali interrupted, still smiling. 'It is not a Greek bed. Remember, David, we have told your British Lords how we have changed all the fittings and furnishings. Melanie will be resting in a broken Turkish bed.'

Noticing that Carter's plate was still filled with pieces of *Thieves' Kebab*, Sevilay said, 'David, you must not go yet. You have not finished your meal.'

'Couldn't eat another mouthful,' Carter replied ambiguously, trying to catch Halil's eye. 'May I have the bill, please?'

'When you arrived, I say to you, if you don't like, you don't pay. Anyway, you are my guest.' Halil refused payment for the meal, adding several glasses of brandy to his generosity. 'Cheers. All the best.'

Halil turned to Fikri and spoke in Turkish. 'He wants to know when your programme will be broadcast on the BBC,' Fikri translated. 'You see, Mr Halil has a son living in Maida Vale and he wishes him to listen.'

'If he gives me his son's address before I leave Cyprus, I will write to him myself with the details,' Carter replied. 'And I'll send a cassette recording of the programme so that Mr Halil can listen here.'

'In that case,' said Halil, 'I will write for you the recipe of our *Thieves' Kebab* so that you can enjoy it in London as well.'

True to their word, the next day Fikri and Ali drove the Carter family to George Tsigarides's house. They found it standing completely undamaged on the edge of what was now called *The Landing Beach*. It was occupied by a Turkish Cypriot family who had left their property in the south. Having promised to bring back pictures for George, Carter fired off a roll of colour stills and a cartridge of cine-film. He made certain to photograph the area from all angles, in close-up and long-shots.

(George Tsigarides saw the stills and cine-film some months later when he visited the Carters in Welwyn Garden City with his mother. Both refused to believe what they were shown. 'I am sure these pictures are not right,' he said. 'The views do not show enough detail. I think you could not have noticed all the damage.')

Before they arrived at George's house, the Carters had been taken to the Turkish war memorial, some 500 yards away. Shaped from stone blocks to represent a symbolic canon pointing towards the Kyrenia or *Beşparmak* mountains, it was a powerful but unattractive monument.

Turkish soldiers were buried in the nearby cemetery, their graves laid in neat rows, flanked by the rusting hulks of tanks and other armoured vehicles captured from the Greek Cypriot National Guard and the Greek army in 1974.

Holding posies of flowers and wrapped in black robes, a quiet group of elderly women sat in the shade of lemon trees by the road. 'They are relatives of the dead soldiers,' Ali whispered. 'They come here regularly to pay respect.' Carter was reminded of the Greek Cypriot mothers and wives whom he had seen in Metaxas Square mourning their missing sons and husbands. Were the women of Kyrenia any different?

When the Carters arrived at The Celebrity Hotel, John Aziz, the owner, was holding court in the centre of a group of Turkish Cypriot friends and relatives, many talking English with cockney accents. They were sitting on a terrace facing the sea. Aziz wore a tartan kilt with a sporran. Valerie, his English wife, sat next to him. She was an attractive brunette. She stood up and took Matthew by the hand.

Moving with the bearing of a ballet dancer, she walked the toddler to where her sons, Gordon and Attila, were playing on the shingle beach below. 'I've got them down for Harrow,' Valerie told Wendy casually. 'Gordon starts next term.'

Before John Aziz's hospitality went to everybody's head, Carter switched on his Uher and started his interview with the extrovert hotel owner. 'In Turkish cuisine, there's a dish called the *Thieves' Kebab*,' Carter began, 'and there are those who say that it's aptly named for a people who steal and occupy properties belonging to others.'

Just as the BBC interviewer hoped, Aziz responded passionately. 'I
completely disagree,' he fumed, hammering the table with his fist.
Those around him were silenced by the outburst. 'The Celebrity Hotel
is registered in Britain. It has been built entirely by my own finances.
As for the other hotels in northern Cyprus, I must say, "What has
happened to the Turkish Cypriot properties left in the south?"'

During the next hour Carter ran spool after spool of tape while
Aziz told him how, as a child, he had left his village near Lapta and
arrived in London as a teenager. His first job was washing dishes, then
he waited at tables and later was appointed a restaurant manager.
Eventually he became the owner of several nightclubs in London's West
End.

From his savings he bought the land on which The Celebrity now
stood, but not without overcoming many difficulties. He claimed the
Greek Cypriot authorities had imposed unfair restrictions on him and
other Turkish Cypriots who wanted to be businessmen.

'First they would say, "Yes, John, you can build your hotel, but we
must see the plans." Fine. I would submit my plans and then they
would say, "Sorry, John, the area has been designated a military zone.
You can't build here." Then a Greek would come and say he would buy
my land. Suddenly for him the place would not be a military area. Then
they would say, "All right, John, build your hotel, but you must have
Greek partners." But they never wanted to put up any money. They only
wanted to take the profits. So it went on, my friend. But I succeeded.
All done legally, but it has taken me a very long time.'

But John Aziz's victory had been short-lived. Within weeks of the
hotel's completion, the coup took place followed by the war. Tourism
came to a halt in the areas under Turkish control. As few British
tourists were braving the difficulties involved in travelling to northern
Cyprus, it was costing Aziz a lot of money to keep his hotel open, yet
virtually empty.

Aziz was outspoken and critical of the attitudes of *both* his
governments. 'I am a British Turk and I think it is all wrong that we are
not allowed to have direct flights to Cyprus. I am angry, too, that we in
the north don't make the justice of our case more clearly known.' But he
had a plan to change attitudes. 'I will bring British Members of
Parliament to northern Cyprus at my own expense,' he stated
categorically, thumping the table again. 'I will show them what is
happening. They will see for themselves. We need more people like you
to come here and tell the world. I am glad you are here for the BBC, but
you should have insisted on staying at my hotel, as my guest. *We* have
the experience.'

It was hard to stop Aziz talking into the microphone or deflecting
him from the belief that one day northern Cyprus, under exclusive
Turkish Cypriot control, would be as successful as the Greek south. He
was unashamedly proud of playing his part in the development of

tourism. His investment, heavy as it was, would earn him and his people large profits in the future, he insisted.

Aziz admitted that he was a gambler in every sense, and he explained that he had persuaded the administration to grant him a gaming franchise at The Celebrity and at The Dome in Kyrenia. But, for the time being, Aziz's only guests were his family and friends. Today they were the winners.

In the evening Carter went to The Dome's casino to see how it worked. Although the signs at the entrance pointed out that local people were prohibited from entering, he saw that rules were being operated with all the thoroughness he had come to associate with Turkish Cypriots. He recognized two policemen in plain clothes. They recognized him too, smiled and insisted they were there on duty; their collection of chips was greater than their conviction or any number of likely arrests for breaches of the law.

What surprised Carter more was the number of English girls employed as croupiers, taking their direction from a man not unknown to the British police. 'Yes, it is who you think,' said one of the girls. 'But he's playing it straight out here.' Who next, thought Carter, Lord Lucan perhaps? Enough said. Carter turned a blind eye and walked out of the casino still wearing his shirt and carrying his tape-recorder.

Upstairs, in the hotel bar, Carter bumped into an elderly Englishman whom he had noticed several times during the past few days. If the man were a tourist, now was the moment to record his reactions to northern Cyprus.

'No, I'm not a tourist as such,' the man replied. 'I'm a barrister, here on business. A guest of Mr Denktaş, in fact. He, by the way, is a barrister as well.'

He explained that he had assisted the Turkish Cypriots with their defence against the charges brought in London by the Greek Cypriot hotel-owners. One of them was Mr Catsellis, The Dome's original proprietor. Perfect, thought Carter. This was just the person to unravel the legal aspects which had to be covered by his holiday programme.

The barrister agreed to be interviewed, but insisted on two conditions.

First, his words must be broadcast uncut or not at all, and secondly he wanted to know exactly how Carter intended to introduce his contribution, which had to be anonymous. Unhesitatingly Carter accepted the first, but had to think aloud about the second.

'Suppose I say something like gambling is allowed in northern Cyprus, but do holiday-makers want to gamble with their holidays in view of the House of Lords' ruling, which both Greek and Turks have hailed as a victory?' Carter was ad-libbing, something he did often during his live broadcasts. 'Then I could add that The Dome Hotel, where I found you, is one of the places caught in the legal tangle. Because you're a leading barrister, I put the question to you. Then I'll cut to your answer. How does that sound?'

'Fine,' said the barrister. 'Switch on. Are we recording?' He cleared his throat and tried to take hold of the microphone which Carter held tight.

'First, I am not concerned by threats of prosecution on my return to the United Kingdom. Press reports give the appearance that in some way or other the House of Lords has changed the law. In fact, it has done nothing of the sort,' he claimed, his words chosen with care. 'Secondly, certain newspapers referred to *prosecution*. It has astonished me that any newspaper purporting to be reputable could possibly use the word *prosecute* in relation to what are essentially civil proceedings. *Prosecute* implies the commission of a criminal offence, and the further implication, therefore, is that if a holiday-maker returns to England from a stay in north Cyprus, he or she is liable to be arrested and charged with the commission of a criminal offence, and this is absolute nonsense.'

'But what if he walked on the carpets of The Dome Hotel?' Carter asked, remembering that he had been warned about using 'goods and chattels' belonging to Greek Cypriots.

The barrister answered, 'It is important to remember that if walking on a carpet in The Dome, or wherever, constitutes a *civil* offence, then this is a civil offence committed in *Cyprus*. The newspapers concerned seemed entirely to overlook the fact that the allegation made in this case was not of any wrong being committed in Cyprus, but of a wrong being committed in *England*. Therein lies the difference. Walking on carpets may or may not constitute trespass here, but I doubt it.'

If Carter had understood correctly, the barrister was telling him that the Greek Cypriots would have to charge holiday-makers in courts on their side, and, in every practical sense, that was not a likely possibility.

Now that Carter had legal opinion for his programme, his next task was to discover something about the state of the 'goods and chattels' of The Dome Hotel. He needed to talk to somebody who had lived in Cyprus before the events of 1974. To stop any allegation that his interviewees had been selected by the Turkish Cypriot administration, he must avoid seeking assistance from either Fikri Direkoğlu or Ali Özel.

A good place to begin his search would be St Andrew's, the tiny Anglican church marked on his CTO map of Kyrenia.

CHAPTER 9

ON THE GRAPEVINE

NEXT day Carter slipped out of The Dome Hotel, leaving his wife and family sunbathing by the rock-pool. He walked by himself, heading for Kyrenia castle and the church. When he was almost there, a brusque voice hailed him in English. 'I say, are you the chap from the BBC? My name's Trevor Taylor.'

Taylor was strongly built, a man with a glowing sun-tan. His crisp white shirt and khaki drill shorts were perfectly creased. His bald head shone in the hot sun. He could have been a Foreign Legion officer on leave from a desert campaign.

'I heard one of you chaps was in town,' he shouted, dodging the slow-moving traffic as he dashed to Carter's side of the street. 'Thought I might be able to give you some help.' He explained that he had been the editor of *Cyprus News*, the local English-language weekly-paper, had lived in the district for some time prior to 1974 and knew most of the expatriates or 'ancient Brits' as they were known. He said that for gossip there was no better place than The Grapevine.

'The place is a bit colonial. Used to be called Peter Lines' Bar,' Taylor remarked. 'Quite dreadful really, but it has its uses. The GODS staged a satirical musical there last Christmas.'

'The GODS?' Carter queried.

'Yes. The Girne Operatic and Dramatic Society. The Grapevine is down there, on the left-hand side, past the petrol station.' He pointed in the direction of the Nicosia road. 'You can't miss it. They do Sunday lunches, English-style. Warm beer, that sort of thing. Swap paperbacks. Play bridge. You ought to visit when you don't really have anything better to do. And what about Betty and Phyllis? Have you met them? They're called "The Cave Ladies".'

'No, I haven't,' said Carter. 'Not yet.'

'Well, you really should. They've been here donkey's years, and speaking of donkeys, I must dash because mine's in foal. Tell you what, I'll come round to The Dome this evening and we'll have a long chat. Pity, though, that you're staying there. It really is such a dull place. Always has been. Shall we say seven-thirty?'

The Grapevine was less than welcoming. In its dark interior there were fewer than a dozen Britons, mostly of pensionable age.

Carter ordered a pint of Efes lager, collected the drink, turned and wished everybody a good day, hoping for a positive reaction. His greeting was returned with half-hearted acknowledgements, thin smiles and a grunt or two before they resumed their muted conversations.

Then, after a few minutes, a woman came across to the bar to re-order drinks. 'Fill these up, Graham dear,' she said, then turned to Carter. 'I see from your machine that you work for Radio London.'

'Yes,' Carter replied brightly. 'Yes, indeed.'

'I suppose you'll be reporting the usual sort of rubbish?'

The woman picked up her glasses, filled to the brim with a lot of gin and a little tonic. 'You know what I mean. How everything is terrible here, how the Turks are doing awful damage to the country. That sort of thing. We've had quite a few reporters out here and we've seen what they've written. We're not as isolated as you may think.'

'I'm sure you're not,' Carter said calmly, nevertheless surprised by the woman's hostility. She was joined by three friends and he found himself backed up against the bar; a frontier marshal in a strange western town. 'Why don't you write to their editors and complain?'

'They wouldn't publish our opinions,' the solitary male in the group replied. 'They're all in the pockets of the Greeks.'

'Well,' said Carter, 'I've got my tape-recorder here. Mine is only a travel programme, not a full-blown documentary, but I'd still welcome your views on tourism today in northern Cyprus.'

'Quite ridiculous,' exclaimed the aggressive woman. 'We couldn't possibly allow our voices to be broadcast by the BBC.'

'Why not?'

'It's obvious. The Greeks would know immediately that we had talked.'

'What have they got to do with it?' Carter asked. 'They can't touch you here.'

'No, you're quite right,' the man agreed, 'but they could stop us from travelling south.'

'Okay,' said Carter, 'but why should you want to visit the south when you live here?'

'Because, young man, we are British. Settled here before partition and it's our right. Some of us demonstrated our rights during the war. We sailed our boats up and down the coast, flying the Red Ensign, to show the Turkish navy we weren't afraid.'

'That's true,' said the man, supporting the woman's claims, adding, 'and some of us still shop down south.'

'And it really is far pleasanter flying British Airways from Larnaca than having to mess about at Ercan, stopping off in Turkey before getting home.'

'Yes, dear, and there's never any certainty about getting a seat on the Turkish 'planes.'

Later Carter told Ali about his encounter in The Grapevine.

'What it is, actually,' the TFSC official explained in his most meaningful voice, 'they are old people. They like their bacon and ham for breakfast, and we do not have those any more, being Muslim. So they go for their shopping to the Greek side. We understand, and that is why we allow them to register their cars with the Greeks and let them put on Greek licence plates, even here. It is really no trouble for us. Anyway, why should they be involved in our differences and difficulties?'

Ali was either exceptionally tolerant or vaguely indifferent. Carter was not sure which, nor how typical his views were.

At 19.30, promptly, Taylor arrived at The Dome. He took an immediate liking to Wendy, Sheryl and Matthew, although his confirmed bachelor status made him awkward in their company. Nevertheless he invited everybody to his house in Ozanköy, an invitation which was taken up later.

'First of all,' he said, not a man to waste words or time, 'let's get cracking with the interview.' It was clear that The Dome bar staff knew Taylor well, for they brought him a drink without Carter having to order. Glancing disdainfully around the lounge, he added, 'Well, it always was an old-fashioned hotel, but it's been changed quite considerably since the Turkish Cypriots took over. Not structurally, except for the addition of a casino. You see, it had to be done up at the end of the war because the place was used to hold prisoners and other displaced people. They spent a month or more doing it up after the war's end. Since then there have been many other changes in the arrangements in the bar, *et cetera*. I'd say that anybody looking at the hotel then and now would only recognize the shape. There is a complete change of furnishings inside.'

But what did he think of the moral issues of tourists using these properties, Carter asked?

'I think anybody should use the property until there is a settlement,' Taylor replied quickly. 'It's up to both sides to get round a table, not just the Turkish Cypriots. It's quite ridiculous to see properties deteriorating badly. That's true of Varosha, which has been offered back to the Greeks, but it will cost a lot to put right. Now is it a good thing that the running places in Kyrenia and other parts of the north should be allowed to go to wrack and ruin as the property has done in Varosha? If Turkish Cypriots are forced to neglect properties by not using them, then, without the income from tourism, they can't be expected to maintain them in good condition. You can't have your cake and eat it. So, to make compensation a practical and realistic proposition, these properties must be kept going.'

With Taylor's answers and the statement from the British barrister, Carter had now covered three of the areas of Tony Freeman's brief: the legal, the moral and the 'goods and chattels' issue. With his own impressions already written, all that remained were the interviews with tourists, but where were they?

The two men from the Ministry of Tourism debated Carter's problem and suggested the family move to the Salamis Bay hotel near Famagusta. Here, they were sure there would be several British holiday-makers, and the family's stay on the east coast would allow Carter to make comparisons between the two main resorts.

At the Salamis Bay, Carter did find tourists for his Radio London tapes; not many, but enough. He asked them all the same set of questions: had they been aware of the Cyprus problem prior to their arrival? Were they troubled by the large numbers of Turkish soldiers, something which the Greeks maintained spoiled the island's holiday atmosphere? And, were they getting value for money? Finally he asked if they had heard that they could be breaking the laws of the Republic of Cyprus by staying in the north.

Hearing the last question the tourists became confused, insisting that they were British and law-abiding. They spluttered, fumed and demanded to know why a BBC producer should be spreading such falsehoods. They knew, they said, they could not be law-breakers as they had bought their holidays in the United Kingdom from legitimate agencies. And that, as far as they were concerned, was that.

Fikri, although understanding what Carter was trying to do, was visibly unhappy about the final question. He suggested it should be dropped to avoid problems. Carter refused and continued to record.

One couple to whom Carter spoke did not realize Cyprus was partitioned between Turkish and Greek Cypriot communities. They told him that they knew now why the staff at the hotel's reception had failed to book a taxi for them to visit friends in Larnaca in the south, and why waiters in the restaurant walked away in sullen mood when they had simply wanted to compliment the chefs on the excellence of their *Greek* cuisine.

Carter was pleased with most of his recordings, especially his interview with Councillor Mike Williams, of Stroud in Gloucestershire. Williams had given clear-cut answers. 'If you are put off by trouble having taken place somewhere in the world, then you'll never travel anywhere these days,' he said, firmly denying the presence of the Turkish army had affected his holiday. 'We went to Greece when the Colonels were in power and their soldiers were walking the streets all the time, and we saw as many soldiers when we spent a holiday in Gibraltar. No, they haven't put me off at all.'

Williams was convinced that no useful purpose would be served by avoiding northern Cyprus. 'People went to Spain when Franco was in power,' he pointed out, 'and they go to Romania and Yugoslavia now, which are Communist states. I can't see why we should be advised to avoid Turkish Cyprus.'

Some days before the Carters' trip to northern Cyprus came to an end, Fikri told the family that they had been invited to a formal reception which was to be hosted by President Rauf Denktaş in Nicosia. The President also wanted them to attend an informal picnic in the Kyrenia mountains at which several TFSC ministers would be present with their relatives.

Carter accepted the invitation, which included Sheryl, and Fikri's mother-in-law agreed to baby-sit Matthew.

Fikri and Sevilay used their car to drive the Carters to the Turkish Cypriot leader's official residence, following a long line of military staff-cars and large black limousines which drew up outside the entrance. Mr Denktaş stood with his wife in the doorway, greeting each new arrival with warm hand-shakes and wide smiles.

Because Carter and his wife had never attended a diplomatic reception, neither was certain what constituted correct etiquette. They decided to play the scene without rehearsal and worry later.

'Mr President, this is Mr David, the BBC producer, and this is Madam Carter,' Fikri said, ever helpful. 'They are accompanied by their daughter, Miss Sheryl.'

Wendy's hand moved forward and Mrs Denktaş took it. Carter pushed his arm around his wife and found his fingers squeezed by Mr Denktaş. Caught in the middle was the shy man from the Ministry of Tourism. Sheryl stood aside from the scramble. Coming fast from behind were more guests, each wearing formal decorations and ironed dignity. Bump, push and squeeze followed as the group tried to unwind themselves whilst still retaining their appearance of cool aloofness.

The President gave a lusty chuckle and his wife added the flicker of a smile. Sheryl looked up to heaven. 'Oh daddy, you are causing problems,' she exclaimed in a whisper that could have been heard by the drivers outside.

The reason for the reception and dinner was the departure of the commanding Turkish general whose tour of duty had come to an end. Staff from the British High Commission, officers from the United Nations Force, Turkish Cypriot officials and representatives from several embassies, none of whom officially recognized their host's Turkish Federated State of Cyprus, were among the guests. For reasons which became apparent later, not everybody would stay for dinner.

On the far side of the room Carter saw his barrister friend mingling in the crowd and, with Wendy, edged his way towards him. They were joined suddenly by a member of the British High Commission. 'Forgive me,' he said, 'but aren't you the chap who's something to do with the BBC?'

Carter nodded. 'Did you by any chance travel here via Ercan?' the man asked.

Carter nodded again. 'Bad form,' the Briton commented. 'You really should have come through the Republic. You are, of course, aware that you're an illegal?'

'Is there a British government ruling against me travelling anywhere I want?' Carter asked coldly.

'No,' replied the official, sipping whisky from a large tumbler. 'Are you an American?'

Because of his slight accent Carter was often mistaken for a US citizen and normally would have answered with a detailed explanation, but the man had annoyed him by suggesting he was not a free agent to do as he wished and so he ignored the question.

'As somebody from the BBC, you, like all of us, should do the right and proper thing, old chap.'

'Exactly. And I am.'

The British official drained more Turkish Cypriot government hospitality from his glass while continuing to express disapproval of his hosts. HM Government's representative was short in stature and low on good manners.

'You obviously don't know much about the situation out here,' the man continued condescendingly. 'We must have a chat soon and I'll give you a proper briefing. Put you straight on a few points.'

'Really?' Carter said, noticing that the official wore brown shoes with a black suit. 'You know, I have done a little homework. For instance, I've read the 1975 House of Commons Select Committee Report on Cyprus. Don't you think, sir, that it roundly condemns the government for mishandling the situation in '74?'

'Where did you get hold of that report?'

The barrister interrupted. 'I gave it to him,' he said, smiling broadly.

'It's a document readily available at Her Majesty's Stationery Office in Holborn,' Carter added, 'or didn't you know?'

'Well, I just hope you don't cause us any difficulties,' the High Commission man replied petulantly. 'Really, the BBC ought to know better.' He turned on his heel and walked away.

Close by, a UN officer from Ireland was explaining incorrectly, in a deep brogue, the Turkish Cypriot dishes and dips that were laid on long tables. The officer's audience was an elderly couple who could have been his parents. Carter watched as the Irish swallowed large mouthfuls of alcohol as if they would never taste another. Long before the evening ended, the officer would be unable to tell north from south or, for that matter, left from right.

The crowd in the room began to thin. Diplomats and UN officers were leaving quietly in groups as if cued by some coded signal which only they understood, but the Irish officer remained.

Moments later the Turkish Cypriot officials began toasting the Turkish general who was being reassigned. Like all tributes on occasions like these, the speeches were fulsome and flowery. Where a small shower of petals would have been perfectly adequate, the Turkish Cypriots preferred to throw large bouquets.

To each toast the Irish officer raised his glass and emptied its contents, ready for a refill, until another UN officer re-entered the room, made his way to his colleague and whispered, 'Come on, we don't stay when they toast the Turkish army.'

'Oh,' the Irishman exclaimed loudly, 'do we not?' He swallowed the last drops of spirit in his glass and was removed from the reception.

Carter wished the day would come when Turkish and Greek Cypriot soldiers wore UN blue berets and served in Ireland; just to balance matters.

At dinner Carter and his wife were placed opposite the President and Mrs Denktaş, while Sheryl was seated to the left of the Turkish Cypriot leader.

When the meal was nearly over, Sheryl, who had found the whole affair a little boring, looked at her father and boldly declared that it was time to go home. 'Daddy,' she said, 'you've drunk too much and I'm sure we've been eating off Greek plates.'

There was no time for Carter to splutter a response, because Mr Denktaş was already leaning in Sheryl's direction and whispering words which were inaudible to the other guests. Nobody knew what was being said, but everybody could see that for the next few minutes the English teenager and the President of northern Cyprus were locked in an animated dialogue of great importance to each of them. Sometimes there were smiles; mostly there were frowns.

After dinner Wendy went to Mrs Denktaş to apologize for Sheryl's behaviour, but Sevilay intercepted Carter's wife before she could speak.

'Mrs Denktaş wishes to say that you have a charming daughter,' Sevilay declared. 'Yes,' she continued, as Mrs Denktaş smiled regally, 'she says that His Excellency, the President, has been most impressed by her high intelligence and honesty. He wishes you to know that their conversation has been most refreshing and that it has been, how do you say, "very frank". So many people only talk what they think he wants to hear. For this reason Sheryl is invited to visit again at any time as a guest of the Government so that she may learn more about Turkish Cypriots.'

Sheryl preened. Wendy sighed with relief. Carter remembered the man from the High Commission and the Irish officer from the United Nations.

The next day the Carter family was driven to a picnic area near St Hilarion castle, where ministers and their relatives were relaxing and mixing easily with other Turkish Cypriots. Ali tried to identify each of the people present, but Carter lost track of their names and Ali lost track of their titles within the administration. 'We are most democratic,' he quipped. 'We give everybody a turn.' Sevilay, dark glasses resting on her dark brown hair, sat composed in the shade watching Fikri chop wood for the barbecue fires.

While eating his kebabs, Carter tried to spot security guards. There was none that he could see, civilian or military, although most of the administration of northern Cyprus was here, out in the open. The scene contrasted sharply with what he had witnessed in the south. There, when the President left his office for lunch, his car hurtled down the main thoroughfares, accompanied by armed police on motorcycles, preceded by police cars to clear traffic from their path.

Unlike his Greek opposite number, President Denktaş had arrived in
an ordinary domestic saloon which had seen better days and probably
would not have passed its MoT examination in the United Kingdom.
He had stepped out from behind the steering wheel to receive bear-hugs
from friends and supporters, before being waylaid by an old village
woman who blocked his path to the picnic site. She shouted vigorously
in Turkish and waved her hands at the President. It was obvious his
manner of running of the government had displeased her.

Mr Denktaş listened patiently, put his arm round her shoulder and
led her to the shade of some pines, where his friends were seated. For
several minutes they chatted together before the old lady returned to
her own family.

'What was that all about?' Carter asked.

'David, she is a woman from a village where the water-pump has
stopped,' Fikri replied. 'She has been telling the President that if he is
the leader of our country, then he must do something immediately to
get matters put right. Mr Denktaş has promised to do his best.'

Carter remembered moments like these as Ali drove the family to
Ercan airport on the morning of their departure from northern Cyprus.
It was a quiet journey and Wendy was sad at leaving. Even Ali was
subdued.

At the crowded airport Ali carried the family's bags to the check-in
counter and made sure that Carter's case of tapes went safely on board
the parked 727 which was to carry them to London.

'You are lucky today,' said Ali. 'I think there will only be a short
technical touch-down at İzmir for about 20 minutes. They will change
the flight number and you will continue without disruption. Come,
let us go to the guest lounge.'

Here Ali arranged the final hospitality of their stay, presenting
young Matthew with a large Lego kit as a personal present. 'We will
put you on board first,' he said, 'so that you can pick your seats.'

'Is Fikri going to say bye-bye?' Sheryl asked.

'Have you not heard? He had an accident last night in his car,' Ali
answered.

The Carters were shocked. 'Serious?' Wendy inquired. Ali replied
that Fikri had broken an arm and bruised his face, but otherwise was
well. 'Please wish him a quick recovery,' Wendy added.

'You may wish him yourself, with a kiss,' came Fikri's voice from
the doorway. He stood there with his left arm in a sling, his face
marked by strips of plaster. 'This is for you, Madam,' he said, handing
Wendy a bouquet of roses with his right hand.

Wendy threw her arms round the lean official and kissed him on
both cheeks. 'Thank you for a marvellous time. All of you.'

The flight was called. The family walked to the Tarmac, escorted
by a Turkish air hostess. At the top of the stairs to the 'plane, they
turned to look back. Ali was still wearing his shirt with Marilyn

Monroe's face.

'David,' Fikri shouted, 'you will come back again.'

During the five-hour flight Carter scribbled a draft script for his programme. He wondered how George Tsigarides, his Greek Cypriot friend, would react to this holiday report on northern Cyprus. He chose his words carefully, trying hard to avoid needless offence, but, at the same time, equally determined not to play down his affection for the Turkish Cypriots.

'The north has a great deal to offer in friendliness, hospitality and scenic beauty,' he wrote. 'The difference lies in the character of the people. Judge the events of 1974 in the context of all that went before, and try to visit both sides of Cyprus. The island may be partitioned geographically, but there is a common unity in the welcome the two communities give strangers. For this is the island of Cyprus, still.'

When refined and polished, these thoughts would provide the closing lines for Carter's programme. He had travelled hopefully to the Greek and Turkish parts of the island and come away satisfied. His third journey to Cyprus was due to begin within a few months and this time he would see what the Sovereign Bases had to offer.

Cyprus had cast a spell and Carter was caught. He glanced at his aggressive 15-year-old daughter. Sheryl was fast asleep, clutching a Turkish-English dictionary. *Barış. Peace.*

CHAPTER 10

THREATS AND PROMISES

RADIO London was almost deserted. Apart from some activity in studio 1B, indicated by the glowing red transmission light above the door, nothing else was happening. It was always the same at 09.30. Nothing had changed during Carter's two-week stay in northern Cyprus. He would have been surprised if it had.

As he walked through the quiet newsroom towards his office, he saw a scrawled message on the side of the photocopying-machine warning that it was not working, again. If that were so, then it was fair to assume that the coffee dispenser was out of order too.

Green BBC canteen plates rested on the last desk he passed. Each plate was smeared with the dried remains of yesterday's lunch. On the floor were bundles of unopened mail tied loosely with string. For a moment he paused to consider whether to sort these letters and packages, then decided to leave the chore to others.

Carter found his office open, although he had the only key to the security lock. It was not the first time that the curious and the greedy had entered while he was away, nor would it be the last; respect for the privacy of the individual was not a trait common to the station's staff. For this reason he often took work home to complete; that would be where the Cyprus tapes would be edited.

'Had a good holiday?' Tony Freeman asked. The news editor had slipped into the office behind Carter, who turned sharply, dislodging a pile of LPs that he had arranged in a neat stack on the floor before his departure. 'Yes, better than I expected.'

'Any good ones in that lot?' Freeman inquired, glancing at the records.

'I don't know. I haven't sorted them yet.'

'Well, if you see any jazz funk albums, I wouldn't mind a couple, if you can spare them,' Freeman said. 'By the way, did the Turks answer all our questions?'

'I think so. They were surprisingly helpful.'

'Good.' Freeman's reply was positive. 'When can Frank and I have the finished programme?'

'Within a couple of weeks, I guess,' Carter answered. 'Unless something unexpected turns up.' He nodded at the papers and packages lying on his desk.

'That's fine,' Freeman said. 'Talking about the unexpected, your mates at the CTO want to see you urgently, and somebody called Sinclair has been telephoning. He wants to have a word as well.'

'About what?' The thought of having to deal with Sinclair again held no appeal for Carter.

'Don't know,' Freeman shrugged. 'One of the secretaries took the calls, and you know what they're like,' he added dismissively.

'Anything else happen while I was away?' Carter changed the subject as Freeman flicked his fingers through the records on the floor.

'No, nothing special that I can think of,' Freeman replied, his concentration fixed on the LPs lying around him. 'They're talking about wanting to cut our budgets again. But they do that all the time, don't they? Hey, this looks a good one.' He held a compilation album of Diana Ross hits. 'May I have it?'

'Yeah, okay.'

Freeman turned towards the door, clutching his record. 'Oh yes, I knew there was something else. While you were with the Turks, did you do anything to stir up the travel agencies which deal with holidays to northern Cyprus?'

'No, I don't think so,' Carter smiled, puzzled. 'I don't even know the agencies doing business with them.'

'Well,' Freeman continued, 'it seems that at least one of them has been annoyed by you. They've been complaining to Frank about some question you put to their clients. Give the buggers a call and sort it out. You'll find their number in your in-tray.'

Carter shuffled his papers.

'I don't know how you ever manage to find anything under all that debris,' Freeman observed. 'You know, you should keep your office locked with all these records around. You never know when people might want to knock off a few for the barrows down Petticoat Lane.'

'So what's new, Tony?' Carter responded sarcastically.

During the next half-hour Carter was busy on the telephone. After arranging meetings with the CTO and Sinclair, he dialled the Turkish Cypriot travel agency which had complained to Frank Dawes about his behaviour in northern Cyprus. The manager turned out to be an English woman.

She said her complaint centred on Carter's question about whether tourists to the north were aware that they were breaking Greek Cypriot laws by entering the island at Ercan airport. Despite his efforts to pacify her, she remained adamant that he had caused distress to her clients and demanded to know how he intended to put matters right. She suggested that he stress in his report that her holidays were absolutely legal and of high quality. Unless he did, she would raise the matter again, she said, and it would be 'at the highest level'.

Carter lost patience. 'Look Madam,' he snapped, 'I did not go to northern Cyprus to review your company's holiday packages. I have no idea how you operate and I have absolutely no intention of drawing particular attention to your company's products and services. But I will describe what I saw in northern Cyprus, the good and the bad. No more, no less. If you hear the programme and you don't like it for a particular reason, then complain to your heart's content and I'm sure the matter will be investigated. Right?'

'And what's your name?' she demanded.

'Carter,' he replied coldly. 'Isn't it a bit silly to complain about something you're not sure about or even who is responsible for the alleged cause? Goodbye.' He slammed the telephone into its cradle.

Carter was still smouldering when he was ushered into the CTO director's office in Regent Street. Several Greek Cypriots were present. They invited him to share coffee with them. Within minutes they were pressing for his opinions of life in northern Cyprus and wanting details of how Turkish Cypriots were managing the hotels in Kyrenia and Famagusta, which, they pointed out sternly, still belonged to Greeks. They also wanted to know what his *Holiday Scene* report would contain.

Carter replied that it was still too early to say exactly what shape the programme would take, but it would be balanced and comprehensive. He recommended that they listen to Radio London and hear for themselves.

'Did you see how they have ruined Kyrenia?' one of the Greek Cypriots asked.

'I don't know what it was like before 1974, and so I can't say it's been ruined,' Carter replied.

'But then, can your report be objective?'

'It will be as objective as the programme I did on your side, which, if I recall, the CTO praised highly.'

Carter's words appeared not to please the people in the room, and one complained: 'Although holidays in the occupied area are illegal, you still intend to encourage your listeners to go there?'

'I'm neither encouraging or discouraging,' Carter replied testily. 'I simply went there to report a situation, and one of the points with which I will deal is the question of legality. And with due respect to yourselves, there is no need for me to be here to be cross-examined.'

There was silence for several moments and Carter felt uncomfortable. The time had come for him to leave. It had been a bad morning for him. Filios Theodorou, the London director of the CTO, came to the door. 'Will you be returning to Cyprus in the future?' he asked.

'Yes,' Carter said, 'probably in mid-November.'

'Travelling to the legal part?'

'I'm going to the Sovereign Bases and the UN Force headquarters in Nicosia to record a programme of Christmas messages from British servicemen.'

'Be careful,' Theodorou suggested. 'You may have some difficulties in being allowed to enter the Republic now that your passport carries the illegal stamps of the occupied area.' His voice was friendly and there was no suggestion of a threat in his warning.

'I don't think I'll have a problem,' Carter replied. 'I have a letter from your boss in Nicosia which not only assures me there won't be any difficulties, but he also invites me to join him for lunch.'

Theodorou smiled. 'As long as you remain a friend of Cyprus, you will find your stay pleasant, I'm sure.'

'Thank you,' Carter said, but Theodorou had already returned to his office, leaving his guest to reflect on the events of the morning. He had offended both sides equally, which was some consolation.

Bill Sinclair was waiting for the BBC producer at The Rising Sun opposite Radio London in Marylebone High Street. It was here, a year earlier, that he and Carter had met for the first time.

When Carter entered the public house, Sinclair immediately ordered him a large whisky. It was the brand Carter enjoyed when others paid and he was impressed that Sinclair had remembered.

'I know you've been seeing Filios at the CTO,' Sinclair said almost immediately. 'What was his reaction to your little jaunt to the north?'

'I really don't know,' Carter replied honestly. 'I found them all a bit confusing.' He was sure Sinclair was probing and knew more.

'But you still like Cyprus?'

'Yes, of course.'

'Then I have a suggestion,' Sinclair said. 'Cheers.' He raised his glass and Carter waited to hear his proposition. 'How would you and your family like to visit Cyprus on a regular basis each summer? All expenses paid.'

'And the catch?'

'None really,' Sinclair replied quickly, but unconvincingly. 'Have another drink.'

Carter covered his glass with his hand and shook his head. If he waited long enough Sinclair would have to add some words of explanation.

'Let's sit down,' Sinclair said, glancing round the bar which was beginning to fill with lunch-time regulars. They found an empty table by the door, sat down and Carter's patience was rewarded. 'Just don't broadcast your report on northern Cyprus and the Turks.'

'You're kidding?'

'No,' Sinclair whispered. 'There's no point in making trouble, is there?'

'For Christ's sake, Bill, how could my little piece for Radio London cause trouble?' Carter exclaimed. He felt Sinclair was attributing to him influence and power he had never had.

'Well, maybe the Greek Cypriots who live in London these days would feel Radio London and you were praising their enemies. They have lost a lot to the Turks, you know.'

'But who says I'm going to praise the Turks or Turkish Cypriots?' Carter demanded.

'Either way, it doesn't matter,' Sinclair replied, his voice soft and reassuring. 'It would be much more helpful if the Turks weren't mentioned at all. You could say you had lost the tapes. Nobody would ever know.'

Carter had never before been offered a bribe, not even from record companies, and did not know how to react. He wanted to express indignation, but stayed calm, hoping to discover the reasons behind the offer.

'You'll have to tell me why I should lose the tapes,' Carter insisted. 'I've made a number of friends in the north.'

'And I hope some friends in the south as well,' Sinclair added, reaching for a blue leather briefcase embossed with the logo of Cyprus Airways. He opened it and withdrew a folder containing a set of black-and-white photographs.

'Have a look at these,' he said. 'You'll find them very interesting, *Dave.*'

The photographs showed Carter and his family in northern Cyprus. There were shots of them leaving The Dome Hotel in Kyrenia, standing by the Turkish war memorial with Ali Özel and Fikri Direkoğlu, and even some taken at the picnic at St Hilarion castle, with several Turkish Cypriot officials in the background.

'Who took these?' Carter asked. He tried to recall who had been present at all these different places and had carried a camera. Nobody came to mind.

'It doesn't matter who took them,' Sinclair replied calmly, pleased that he had won the first round. 'I only showed them because I wanted you to know that everybody who goes to the north is observed. Don't underestimate Greek Cypriot intelligence. Even in the Turkish-occupied areas they have their people.'

'The last time we met, you were playing the part of a BBC producer. Now it's James Bond.' Carter tried to hide his concern behind sarcasm.

Sinclair began round two. 'There are a lot of hotheads about and if they ever thought you weren't a friend of Cyprus . . . ' His words tailed away. He believed Carter would see sense.

Carter finished his whisky, stood up and said, 'My programme goes ahead. Even if I have to stand on top of the bloody transmitter and shout the script, I will now.' He left without waiting for Sinclair's reply.

During the next two weeks Carter cut and mixed the sounds on his tapes, wrote and recorded his commentary, and handed the completed programme on northern Cyprus to Tony Freeman. He did not mention his conversations with Sinclair or at the CTO, taking the view that there was no point adding to the news editor's worries and running the risk of having his material dropped; not that he doubted Freeman's integrity. He also believed that Sinclair had probably acted on his own initiative for his own reasons.

Nevertheless, paranoia, real or otherwise, gripped Carter and so he made copies of the programme, one of which he hid in his office and the other he took home. Tapes had gone astray before at Radio London or were damaged prior to transmission. He was not prepared to take any chances on this occasion, especially as Freeman and Dawes had both indicated their satisfaction with the content and agreed to broadcast the report without a single cut.

The day after the programme was broadcast Freeman took Carter to one side of the newsroom and spoke to him about listeners' reactions. 'There were more than 280 telephone calls logged while *Holiday Scene* was on the air. That's some reaction,' he exclaimed. 'The trouble is that they were all from listeners *objecting* to your programme. There wasn't a single caller on your side.'

'My side?' Carter queried. 'I don't have a side.'

'Don't be so sensitive. You know what I mean.'

'What are you going to do about them?'

'Nothing,' Freeman replied. 'It was obviously an organized protest led by Greek Cypriots and their supporters. I'm not worried as long as you can defend everything you reported, and I'm sure you can.'

Later that Monday morning Freeman caught Carter again. This time he looked concerned. There had been a more serious protest. It had come from the Greek Cypriot High Commission in London. As a result, Radio London's station manager had agreed a meeting with a commission representative at which the producers of *Holiday Scene* would be present.

Carter felt he should be there as well, but Freeman, a shrewd editor, turned down the request, aware that Carter's temper-threshold was low. He promised, however, that the programme would be defended on the grounds it was factual and fair. He would point out, too, that its content had not deviated from the station's editorial policy, which was decided corporately and not by individual producers.

There the matter rested and was eventually forgotten by the station's staff. Nobody told Carter what had taken place in the station manager's office. Whatever had been said, it had not affected the BBC's decision to allow him to return to Cyprus again.

As the date of his departure approached, Carter wondered whether he would discover a third point of view on the Cyprus problem from the people he met at the Sovereign Bases and at the UN Force headquarters in Nicosia. He was also concerned by what Filios Theodorou had said about Greek Cypriot immigration officials and their attitude towards the stamps of the TFSC in his passport. But he need not have worried. For when he arrived at the RAF base at Akrotiri in a VC-10 of Transport Command, everybody, military and civilian, was processed by Britons. They belonged to the British Frontier Force, a leftover from the days immediately after World War II, and they decided who entered and departed from the Sovereign Bases in Cyprus.

All they wanted to know from Carter was the purpose of his visit and how long he planned to stay on the island. When Carter replied that he was sponsored by the Ministry of Defence and would be working closely with the British Forces Broadcasting Service in Cyprus, they smiled and waved him forward. The TFSC immigration stamps were worth no more than a passing glance of curiosity.

For the next 11 days Carter was kept busy at both Episkopi and Dhekelia recording messages from servicemen for their families back in the UK. His constant companion was Alan Grace, a cheery optimist who had worked in Cyprus for many years as a BFBS producer. His contacts were extensive amongst the Greek Cypriot community.

Grace tried to avoid political discussions and kept his views on Cyprus to himself. Because of the complexities of the problem, BFBS staff were prohibited from mentioning the UN Force's British contingent, he said. If Carter wanted material on the UN role, he would have to get it himself, although he could provide names and telephone numbers of helpful UN personnel. He also agreed to drive his BBC colleague to the UN base headquarters in Nicosia.

Here Carter met Major Cedric Mercer, the Military Public Information Officer of the force. They got along very well, partly because Mercer believed in keeping the media informed; partly because he felt it was the UN's obligation to deal impartially with the affairs of Cypriots on both sides of the cease-fire line; and partly because Carter had served as an officer in the Royal Signals, which was Mercer's own branch of the service.

Mercer briefed Carter thoroughly on how and why the UN went about its business in the island. From what the BBC producer was told, it was clear there was much more material to gather before conclusions should be drawn about who had done what to whom in Cyprus.

When Carter suggested he make a documentary on the UN's role, Mercer responded enthusiastically and promised to investigate whether his organization would co-operate, but he warned there could be difficulties because because all countries contributing to UNFICYP would have to agree, as well as the two opposing sides, the Greek and Turkish Cypriots.

Mercer said he would give Carter a decision in the New Year.

At Radio London, Carter convinced his station manager that the making of a documentary about Britain's participation in UNFICYP would be worthwhile and he was given permission to go ahead with the project, providing the BBC did not have to pay the costs of his travel and accommodation.

If the project were completed, it would be the first time that radio or television had taken a close look at the UN 'peace operation'.

Carter did not anticipate any objections from the British government, but thought the Turkish and Greek Cypriot administrations might raise problems. Surprisingly they did not. Instead they promised their full co-operation and, on both sides of the cease-fire line, they kept their word. In London, however, civil servants in Whitehall were reluctant to give their approval, not wanting Carter to focus his attentions on UNFICYP in general and the British contingent in particular. Instead they suggested he make a documentary about the Sovereign Bases, 'emphasizing their value to British defence'.

In Cyprus, Major Cedric Mercer, the UNFICYP MPIO, ran into opposition as well. His civilian opposite number, a Palestinian who travelled on an Iraqi passport, insisted it would be 'dangerous' to give unrestricted access to a journalist, even one from the BBC, as the UN had to maintain a delicate balance between the Greeks and Turks; an outsider could inadvertently cause an upset.

Mercer, however, won the day. He flew to London and convinced the Ministry of Defence not only to support the documentary but to provide Carter with free travel and accommodation. In this matter Mercer had been backed by Derrick Knight, one of the ministry's press officers, who considered that the British contingent had become 'the forgotten army'.

Between UNFICYP, the Ministry of Defence and Carter, it was agreed that the documentary could be produced subject to two conditions. First, Carter must be accompanied at all times by a Whitehall official. Nominated for the role of 'minder' was a retired major, Sherry Sherbrooke. Secondly, any tapes containing military information must be cleared by UNFICYP personnel before they were broadcast. As a former officer himself, Carter understood the importance of not breaching security. He had no desire to argue about the freedom of the press and the rights of journalists to report without controls.

Agreement having been reached, a schedule of work was drawn up and a date of departure given. He was to visit Cyprus for ten days in July. As an official UNFICYP visitor, he would be allowed to travel to northern areas to meet his contacts in the Turkish Cypriot administration and receive briefings by the Greek Cypriot authorities. Because of his status he would be subject to all UN rules and regulations, and, if he committed a crime, could be tried by courts martial and sentenced under military law.

Before Major Mercer returned to Cyprus he gave Carter a list of books to read and supplied background material on the force. If Carter failed to do a good job, it was unlikely that other journalists would allowed to visit UNFICYP in the future, Mercer said, and, in his opinion, that would be a bad thing. He was a man who believed strongly in an open dialogue between the media and the military. His service in Ulster had strengthened his views, not that his superiors always agreed with them.

Carter's motivation was different. He wanted to prove to his Radio London colleagues that he was more than a producer of pop music. He wanted to become an expert at something, anything. Had Bill Sinclair, two years earlier, invited him to visit another part of the world for *Holiday Scene*, then the chances were that Carter now would have been studying the history of that place, not Cyprus.

It was only because Sinclair and others had tried to persuade Carter, sometimes by dubious means, not to probe the problems of the island that he had developed his single-mindedness to dig deeper. The more he read, the more obsessed he became; greater were the contradictions in the arguments put by both sides; less impressive the role of the UN; and larger the responsibility of Britain for having sown the seeds of discord in the first place.

The Cyprus conflict on the ground was over, but the war of words continued across a thin blue line in the middle.

CHAPTER 11

HOLY ORDERS FOR WAR

CARTER, to understand the reasons for the establishment of UNFICYP, had to study the former Crown Colony's recent history. He started with the fifties and the island's road to independence, and the formation of the 1960 Republic of Cyprus. It proved to be a decade of violence instigated by Greek Cypriot nationalists without consideration of the wishes of the Turkish Cypriot population. The three years after independence were little better.

At the start, the Greek Cypriot independence movement was largely peaceful, but Greek Cypriot student demonstrations soon gave way to terrorism spearheaded by the National Organization of Cypriot Fighters or *Ethnikí Orgánosis Kiprion Agonistón*, EOKA for short. It was a vicious movement of extremists who demanded *Enosis*, union with Greece.

EOKA's military leader was Colonel George Grivas, a graduate of the Pancyprian Gymnasium in Nicosia. He gave himself the nom de guerre Dighenis after the 10th century Byzantine hero *Dighenis Akritas*. He had the total backing of The Archbishop Serapheim of Athens and all Greece, who provided the terrorists with their first arms supplies.

Grivas collected the weapons from Ioannina in north-west Greece and the island of Rhodes, smuggled them to Cyprus in 1954 and waited to strike against British troops and civil administrators. The arms were hidden in monasteries throughout Cyprus, protected by monks and priests.

Ironically, Grivas had been rescued at the end of World War II by 'Tommies' after Greek Communists in the Thesion district of Athens threatened to kill him for being a Nazi collaborator. His hatred of Turks was widely known. They had defeated him in the Greek Asia Minor campaign of 1922-1923.

In Cyprus, Grivas waited for a signal from Archbishop Makarios to start the war against the colonial administration. It came on 31 March, 1955, with a blessing from the Ethnarch. Makarios himself watched the start from his balcony at the Archiepiscopal. It began with a Greek Cypriot riot, followed by bombings of the Cyprus Broadcasting Corporation and several government buildings, using material provided by the deputy headmaster of the Pancyprian Gymnasium. There was only one death, a bomber who electrocuted himself by incorrectly wiring his explosives.

In the months ahead, Grivas stepped up his terrorism campaign. By leaving the Pallas cinema early, the Governor narrowly missed death when a bomb exploded where he had been sitting. In July, the capital's tax office was hit. In September, the British Institute Library was destroyed, with many valuable works going up in smoke.

Funding for the EOKA movement came from many sources, but a key contributor was Constantine Pericles Manglis, the owner of the KEO distillery in Limassol, who used Makarios as a conduit. Greek Cypriot clergy regularly administered the loyalty or death oaths made by those recruited to EOKA.

The UK government believed a tough stance had to be taken and, in October, appointed Field Marshal Sir John Harding as the island's new Governor. He was also the Commander-in-Chief of British Forces in Cyprus. He maintained that probably no more than three per cent of the Greek Cypriot population supported EOKA.

Perhaps so, but the other 97 per cent were being terrorized themselves. Even EOKA supporters were not safe from Grivas. Andreas Lazarou was one of them, but nevertheless was assassinated in so-called 'Murder Mile' in Nicosia -- for having been a British agent in Egypt during World War II.

The Governor had no choice but to declare a State of Emergency, which lasted for the next four years.

By the end of the year, 12 Britons had been killed as well as several Greek Cypriot policeman, including PC Michael Poullis.

The colonial administration began to rely more and more on the Turkish Cypriot members of the police force to keep law and order, but it was common knowledge Britain would not govern forever and was looking for a dignified way to leave.

On 29 August, Britain chaired a tripartite conference which lasted 10 days. Its purpose was to try getting a consensus over the island's route to independence. Nothing was agreed.

To counter EOKA, the exclusively Greek Cypriot organization, the *Türk Mukavemet Teşkilatı* or TMT was formed, aided by Turkey. Its aim was to defend the Turkish Cypriots' interests and, if necessary, battle for *Taksim*, the partition of Cyprus between Turks and Greeks.

For EOKA, 1956 opened with several failures. Ronald Hutchins, given his first Royal Navy command as a captain in charge of patrolling the eastern Mediterranean, used a destroyer to intercept and seize the *Saint George*, a caique carrying arms for Grivas.

Very soon afterwards the island's Director of Police Operations captured Socrates Loizides, a key EOKA operative and several other important players — together with secret plans. The administration believed EOKA's terrorist operations would now cease, but mainland Greeks and Cretans strengthened the nationalists' resolve.

Hoping that there could be a peaceful resolution, the British government held direct talks with Makarios, but as they were taking place 13 bombs were exploding in Nicosia.

With Makarios failing to co-operate, the British snatched the Archbishop as he was setting off from Nicosia airport to visit Athens on 9 March 1956. He was placed on a Hastings aircraft with military guards and flown out of the island. *The Times* reported: 'He took his arrest quietly and chatted with his companions.'

Field-Marshal Sir John Harding told the press: 'I have ordered the deportation under Emergency Powers Regulations and he has left the island under escort for a destination which will be announced later (the Seychelles).

'I entered into discussions with the Archbishop on the political and constitutional future of the island in the hope he might be induced to denounce violence . . . Over the past five months, further evidence has accumulated that he has been personally implicated in the activities of EOKA, but nevertheless these discussions have been pursued to the furthest possible limit of conciliation and concession so as to open the door to co-operation and orderly constitutional progress . . . This hope has now been disappointed by the Archbishop's refusal to abandon the weapons of violence and intimidation in the pursuit of political aims . . . I have reluctantly concluded, therefore, that his influence must be removed from the island in the interest of peace, order and good government.'

Group Captain Norman de W. Boult supervised the Archbishop's exile. A single-eyed Anglo-Irishman, the British officer held one of Greece's highest honours — the Royal Hellenic Air Force Cross for training Greek pilots during World War II.

Rather than terrorism decreasing with the Archbishop's exile, it escalated. On 1 April, 1956, EOKA launched a campaign of killing British civilians. There were 246 attacks during the next three weeks.

At the same time, Athens Radio accused Britain of mistreating EOKA prisoners held in Kyrenia castle and a facility near Kokkino-Trimithia, north of the capital.

Lawrence Durrell, the novelist considered to rank alongside Proust and Borges, was the person responsible for having to counter the allegations. It was his task to put the British case against 'the united howls of Enosists, British pressmen and fact-finding MPs'. He was the administration's Head of Information, commuting daily to Nicosia from his Bellapais home bought from Turkish Cypriot businessman Sabri Tahir. It was in Bellapais that he wrote *Bitter Lemons*.

Durrell, although prepared to try anything 'short of selling my bottom to a clergyman', found his job 'a hedgehog of a problem'. After a long spell in Greece, Durrell had arrived in Cyprus in 1953, living in the Villa Christina in Kyrenia before moving to Bellapais. He described Cyprus as 'a rather lovely, spare, bland sexy island, totally unlike Greece, with a weird charm of its own', but he was adamant that Greek Cypriots were not Greeks. They were 'just parrots' of the mainlanders.

In June 1956, EOKA attempted to kill Durrell. Having had enough of the place, he quit the island in August.

With the Suez crisis in October, Cyprus became a vital staging post for British forces when attacks were launched against Egypt, with French and Israeli collaboration.

Arms smuggling increased because Royal Navy warships, under the command of Captain Fitzroy Talbot on board HMS *Saintes*, were dispatched as part of Operation Musketeer, the Anglo-French operation, to the waters off Egypt.

On shore, the colonial administration tightened security as best they could, showing terrorists little mercy. On 28 October, they hanged Michael Karaolis for the murder of PC Poulis the previous year. Riots broke out and in Athens seven people were killed by Greek police enforcing order. Karaolis had been a tax inspector suspected of EOKA involvement. Evidence against him was given by a Turkish Cypriot, who was forced to flee to Turkey in fear of his life.

Seven EOKA members were hanged by the end of 1956. There had been 214 murders, half of them Greek Cypriots.

Life continued much the same throughout 1957, but in 1958 the UK increased the pressure on EOKA and EOKA returned the favour.

A flotilla of mine-sweepers, each with a crew of 50, was deployed to patrol the Cyprus coast to reduce Grivas's supply of arms. HMS *Ashton* was one of the vessels. It was commanded by John Cadell, later knighted and promoted to Vice-Admiral for his service with the 104th Squadron.

The Belgian wife of Ben Wilson, a young British officer with the Royal Horse Guards later to become the 4th Lord Nunburnholme, had to be smuggled out of the island. EOKA had tried to kill her with a bomb placed under her car. She had been targeted because her husband's patrol had captured 15,000 rounds of ammunition held by the terrorists. A fellow soldier on that patrol died from a bullet in his back. Information about arms caches and the movements of EOKA were coming from British forces disguised and hidden alone in the Troodos, a role for which Carter had been trained but not used. Following an incident at Christmas time that year, all officers were ordered to attach lanyards to their side-arms to prevent them being snatched.

By 1959, with violence increasing, Cyprus had become the centre of international attention. Britain recognized that the island could not be kept a colony any longer. Greece had brought Cyprus to the United Nations at every available opportunity. Now the Soviet Union was ready to support Enosis, while the United States and the UK were for dividing Cyprus between Greek and Turkish sectors.

In February 1959 representatives from Turkey and Greece, together with those of the two communities in Cyprus, met in London with the British government to hammer out an independence agreement which would satisfy the feuding factions. It had been preceded by the same parties — with the exception of the UK — meeting and agreeing matters amongst themselves in Zurich.

Although representatives of all the various concerned parties met in various places in and outside the island. Colonel Angus Irwin MC, the Commanding Officer of 1st Battalion of the Highland Brigade in Cyprus, was not prepared to ease the pressure on the terrorists. His men hit hard and many EOKA members wished they were elsewhere.

Eventually the British government agreed to transfer power to an independent Republic of Cyprus on 16 August 1960, while retaining sovereignty and jurisdiction of two military bases and certain other facilities. The Republic's Constitution recognized the existence of two ethnic communities within the central government, legislature, judiciary, civil service and the army, with various checks and balances built into the system to prevent one side or the other becoming dominant.

There would be a Greek Cypriot president and a Turkish Cypriot vice-president, each separately elected for five-year terms by their respective communities. There would be universal suffrage with 35 Greek and 15 Turkish Cypriot members of the House of Representatives. They would be elected by voters belonging to separate electoral rolls.

Equally important was the Treaty of Guarantee signed by the UK, Greece and Turkey. These three countries promised to defend the integrity of the new Republic as laid out in the London Agreement. Greece and Turkey would have the right to station small contingents on the island to ensure Greek and Turkish Cypriots did not attack each other.

Because the Greek Cypriots had been denied *Enosis*, the Turkish Cypriots dropped their demands for *Taksim*. As 16 August neared, there were high hopes for a peaceful Cyprus managed by Greek and Turkish Cypriots working in partnership. Even so both communities remained suspicious of each other, not helped by Archbishop Makarios, the first President of the Cyprus Republic, who, until his death in 1977, insisted he had only agreed the Constitution to secure rapid independence from the British and that his intention was always to make changes, something the Turkish Cypriots, led by the Vice-President, Dr Fazıl Küçük, were equally determined to resist.

Küçük believed his people were protected by the Treaty of Guarantee signed by Britain, Greece and Turkey, because it allowed the signatories, individually or collectively, to *intervene* in Cyprus if the independence and integrity of the Republic were threatened from any quarter.

The Turkish Cypriots nevertheless considered the 1960 Constitution had only given them basic legal rights and limited protection within a strongly nationalistic Greek society. For their part, many Greek Cypriots continued to argue that their independence was incomplete as they were prevented from pursuing *Enosis*.

To secure their aim of union with Greece, they would have to change the Constitution and neutralize the Turkish Cypriot community's resistance by any means possible.

Even if the two communities remained divided by social customs, religious beliefs and political aspirations, there was a peace of sorts in Cyprus between 1960 and 1963, although both EOKA and the TMT remained in place. They were equally harsh on those of their own who advocated co-operation. The Greek and Turkish military contingents on the island did nothing to stop EOKA or the TMT. Greece and Turkey were, in fact, smuggling arms and advisers to their supporters in Cyprus.

The TMT stepped up its military training in Turkish Cypriot areas and drafted contingency plans to seal their enclaves if they came under attack by EOKA. The TMT plans included cutting main roads along which the Greek Cypriots would send reinforcements. No less determined was EOKA. Its leaders, too, were plotting to destroy Turkish Cypriot communities by military ways and means. Some senior members of the Republic's government were implicated in what became known later as the *Akritas Plan*, designed as 'The Final Solution' to rid Cyprus of 'the Turkish *barbarians*'.

Many Cypriots, fearful of both sides, left the island to live abroad. London was a favourite destination.

Traditionally the Turkish Cypriots had lived in well-defined areas throughout Cyprus and managed their own local affairs. This tendency gave some Greek Cypriot extremists cause to argue *Taksim* was taking place by default and must be stopped.

By 1963 several former members of EOKA held key positions in the Republic's government. These were their rewards for fighting the British and killing those Turks who had opposed them. They vigorously refuted any sections of the 1960 Constitution that granted Turkish Cypriots rights of self-government within their areas. The Turkish Cypriots complained understandably that EOKA gunmen should have no place in the administration of the island

The Turkish Cypriot leadership protested about the way the Constitution was being implemented and took matters to the Supreme Constitutional Court for a definitive judgement.

In April 1963, the Court ruled in favour of the Turks, but the Greek Cypriots in the government refused to accept the judgement. As a direct consequence, the neutral President of the Court, Ernst Forsthoff, a Professor of Public Law at Heidelberg, resigned in anger.

Just as alarming for ordinary Turkish Cypriots was the increasing power and violent anti-Turkish rhetoric of Polykarpos Yorgadjis, the Minister of the Interior who operated from offices in Byron Avenue, Nicosia. He had the means to turn words into deeds because he had charge of the Republic's internal security forces. With them he was able to stifle any opposition from the Turkish Cypriots to whom he said bluntly, 'There is no place in Cyprus for *anyone* who is not Greek.'

Yorgadjis had proved his point during the fifties. His EOKA fighters, the island's most fanatical, had terrorized and silenced critics of *Enosis*, whether they were Turkish, British or even Greek.

The son of a farmer, Yorgadjis was a man of limited education who had quit the Cyprus Chamber of Commerce, where he worked as a messenger, in 1955 to join EOKA. He was arrested three times by the British forces in the colony, but was released because of lack of evidence.

For his underground activities, Yorgadjis became a hero to young Greek Cypriots who believed he had secured their independence. His popularity amongst this electorate was one reason why Archbishop Makarios appointed him Minister of the Interior.

Minister Yorgadjis had the full support of the President, who declared on 4 September 1963, 'Unless this small Turkish community, forming part of the Turkish race which has been the terrible enemy of Hellenism, is expelled, the duty of the heroes of EOKA can never be considered as terminated.'

Against this background the Turkish Cypriots stepped up their military training in their enclaves and drew up contingency plans to seal off their areas should they come under attack from EOKA activists.

Then, towards the end of 1963, Makarios announced he proposed to change the Constitution in 13 different ways.

Essentially he wanted to remove the Turkish Cypriots' right of veto.

His proposals brought an end to the debate on whether the Greek Cypriots had implemented the terms of the original Constitution or whether the Turkish Cypriots had been intransigent in negotiating changes. The truth was that neither side's political leaders had completely honoured the terms of the Constitution, either in fact or spirit.

Now, by his declaration, Makarios brought the fundamental differences between the two communities directly into the open, dropping any pretence about his political aims.

The moderates who hoped in 1960 for a united Cyprus could no longer sit on the fence, their ideals intact. They had to take sides.

The armed factions of both sides prepared for the long-expected battle. In their opinion, it would settle the future of Cyprus once and for all. Particularly in Nicosia the atmosphere became heavy with mistrust and fear. Only a spark was needed to ignite a violent explosion.

That spark occurred on 21 December 1963, just after 02.00.

From the material available on the incident, Carter tried to construct an account of what may have happened, using facts neither side disputed.

Two cars carrying Turkish Cypriots from Kyrenia were heading to the Turkish quarter of Nicosia early that Saturday morning when they were stopped by a group of armed Greek Cypriots who claimed they were policemen. They said they were conducting a routine, official search for illegal weapons.

The Turkish Cypriot males, although suspicious, agreed to be searched, but refused to allow the women with them to be touched.

A loud argument ensued. It woke the street's inhabitants. In nearby houses lights came on and windows were thrown open. Seeing what was happening, a large number of Turkish Cypriots, still dressed in their pyjamas, dashed outside and tried to prevent the women from being bodily searched.

Then, without warning, several cars raced down the street, screeched to a stop by the angry crowd, and disgorged uniformed policemen who opened fire in all directions with Sterling sub-machine guns. They collected their Greek Cypriot colleagues, leapt back into their cars and raced off into the darkness, continuing to shoot from the windows of their vehicles. By now Turkish Cypriots were firing back.

Two passengers from the car stopped by the Greek Cypriots lay on the ground riddled with bullets. One was 25-year-old Zeki Halil Karabulut, a father of three young children, and the other 32-year-old Cemaliye Emir, a divorcee with a 12-year-old daughter.

The man had died instantly, but the woman lived long enough to say she had recognized one of the gunners. She said he was a man called Yanni from *Olympiakos*, the Greek Cypriot soccer club. Others said the attackers were EOKA terrorists disguised as special constables.

These claims were believed immediately by the Turkish Cypriot community, which viewed this incident as the precursor to an island-wide assault by the Greeks against the Turks. It gave the TMT, the 'Freedom Fighters', a reason to come out openly and convert their plans into actions.

An official Greek Cypriot explanation of the incident followed. It maintained that the two Turkish Cypriots died resisting arrest, after they had been found to be carrying weapons illegally. Furthermore, it added that two Greek Cypriots, one a policeman, had been killed in the street riot which ensued.

The Turkish Cypriots dismissed this claim, but Greek Cypriots did not.

Before daylight the 'Freedom Fighters' were on the streets of the Turkish Cypriot section of Nicosia and so were the EOKA activists who had crossed from their side of the capital. Many of the latter were dressed in police uniforms and said they had been appointed 'special constables'.

Both EOKA and the TMT began shooting at each other. The offices of Rauf Denktaş came under attack. At that time he was the President of the Turkish Communal Chamber.

Throughout Cyprus, Turkish Cypriot communities began to erect barricades.

Soon afterwards Dr Küçük, the Turkish Vice-President of the Republic, and Archbishop Makarios met in the Presidential Palace, where British Governors of Cyprus had held court in colonial days.

Present at the meeting were the Interior Minister Yorgadjis, Justice

Minister Mrs Souliotou, and three other Cabinet members: Dr Niazi Manyera, the Minister of Health; Fazıl Plümer, the Minister of Agriculture; and Osman Örek, the Minister of Defence. The latter, quite surprisingly, was a Turkish Cypriot.

The moderates on both sides recognized that if a blood-bath were to be averted, swift action was needed to cool the situation. Together they attempted to hammer out a policy to bring the increasing violence to an end. At one stage the diplomatic representatives of the United States and Britain were invited to join the debate. But whatever was agreed between them, nobody outside was taking notice. In an attempt to make hot-heads listen, Makarios and Küçük toured troublesome areas, both calling on their supporters to stop any actions which could provoke retaliation.

Large crowds of angry Turkish Cypriots, eventually estimated at 10,000, gathered in northern Nicosia to attend the funerals of the couple killed in the early-morning shootings. The men were cursing and threatening Greek Cypriots while the women wailed and cried for retribution.

The civil authorities were losing control rapidly.

From his office in Shakespeare Avenue, Dr Küçük continued to call for all Cypriots to stay calm and urged them not to get involved in the clashes taking place, but the Cyprus Broadcasting Corporation refused to broadcast Küçük's appeal. Only Archbishop Makarios, the Greek Cypriot President, and his supporters were given air-time.

Rather than calm the situation Makarios, compounded the tension by declaring again that he intended unilaterally to change the Republic's Constitution. For good measure he added that as far as he was concerned, the Treaty of Guarantee was also null and void. Both statements stunned the Turkish Cypriot community.

Before nightfall on 21 December 1963, under the pretext that the Turkish Cypriots had staged a rebellion against the Republic, Minister of the Interior Yorgadjis sent Greek Cypriot police to restore law and order in the Turkish quarter of Nicosia. He also told them to remove all Turkish Cypriot policemen from their posts throughout the island. He was backed by the Republic's Chief of Police, Charalambous Hassapis.

Theirs were futile commands as Turkish Cypriots only policed Turkish Cypriot areas, where that day none was prepared to listen any longer to what the Minister of the Interior said, and where all were determined to resist by any means.

Ill-equipped to repulse any organized, large-scale attacks on their scattered villages, they accepted that they were in mortal danger.

Their fears grew when Nicos Sampson, one of the three main EOKA leaders, used the CBC to call upon his supporters to collect weapons from police stations and ordered them to attack Turkish Cypriots, wherever they were.

Sampson's former EOKA partners immediately intensified their attacks against Turkish Cypriot enclaves, particularly those in Nicosia and its suburbs. At the conclusion of the battle for Omorphita, Sampson was hailed as 'the conqueror' by his Greek Cypriot followers and condemned by the Turkish Cypriots as 'the butcher'.

Sampson enjoyed killing and had honed his skills between 1954 and 1956 when he used his reporter's job at *The Times of Cyprus*, an English-language newspaper, as cover for his EOKA activity. In fact he was the head of an assassination squad in Nicosia.

Later, after the British had left Cyprus, Sampson claimed that during those twilight years of colonial rule, he personally had killed 27 people, all shot in the back of their heads; many of them butchered in Ledra Street, which became known as 'Murder Mile'.

It took the British Special Branch a long time to work out how Sampson was always the first photo-journalist at the scene of these killings, taking pictures for his newspaper. Arrested eventually by the colonial authorities, he served a short prison sentence in Britain.

By the time independence was declared, Sampson was back in Cyprus, regarded a hero by many. Unlike Yorgadjis, he chose not to enter the government. Instead he became the owner of a virulent anti-Turkish, right-wing newspaper called *Makhi* or, in English, *Combat*.

By Christmas Day 1963, Sampson's EOKA units were joined by 950 soldiers of the Greek army stationed in Cyprus and commanded by Colonel Djuvelakis. With their artillery, mortars and heavy machine-guns, they inflicted considerable damage on Turkish Cypriot fortifications. The Cyprus Broadcasting Corporation reported, 'Security forces have launched a mopping-up operation in Nicosia, following heavy attacks on unarmed Greeks by Turks in the area of Omorphita.'

Following the Greek lead, the 650 soldiers of the Turkish contingent, also based in Cyprus under the Treaty of Guarantee, joined the action and took up strategic positions on the main road from Nicosia to Kyrenia. Trying to inspire the Turkish Cypriot resistance, Rauf Denktaş dashed between various positions throughout Nicosia in his scarlet Mini, always wearing a red baseball cap.

Despite the efforts of the TMT and the Turkish army contingent, it seemed northern Nicosia would nevertheless fall to the Greek Cypriots.

At this point Turkey intervened openly in the conflict for the first time by sending three jet fighters screaming over the capital in a series of low-level flights.

This unilateral action was followed by a joint appeal for a cease-fire from the island's guarantor powers, including Turkey. They suggested the formation of 'a Peace Force' made up of units from their three countries.

Makarios accepted the British, Greek and Turkish offer, but simultaneously called for a meeting of the UN Security Council, where he accused Turkey of aggression and interference in the internal affairs of an independent state.

Because Britain had not been involved in the fighting, the so-called 'Peace Force' was eventually formed exclusively by troops stationed at the Sovereign Bases. They were placed under the command of Major-General Peter Young. They included Lt-Colonel Frank Keating's 2 Para, a regiment of tough, no-nonsense fighting men.

Meanwhile, according to UN reports, 30,000 Turkish Cypriots had been forced to flee from 103 villages in just four days of fighting.

By New Year's Day 1964, General Young had drawn a 'Green Line' between the two sides in Nicosia only and positioned his soldiers to 'police' a cease-fire. Members of the RAF Regiment were the first on patrol. Verbal persuasion was their chief weapon; the men had no authority to use arms, other than in self-defence. Nor did their writ run outside the capital, where fighting continued.

The Ledra Palace was declared a 'neutral' zone and, at the request of the hotel's Swiss manager, General Young placed two British armoured cars outside to protect the place.

At Makarios's insistence, British forces in Cyprus were rapidly reinforced by the UK's 3rd Infantry Division under the command of General Sir John Archer who re-established a security framework on the island. Because UN Secretary-General U Thant chose to station an official observer, the seeds were sown for the creation of UNFICYP. The UN's official representative was Lieutenant-General Prem Singh Gyani from India.

While British soldiers did their best to hold the feuding sides apart, the Western allies tried hard to find a diplomatic solution which would satisfy Greek and Turkish aspirations. Because Turkey and Greece belonged to NATO, the organization was in danger of fragmenting unless there was a settlement soon.

To maintain unity, Britain recommended a 10,000-strong Nato 'Peace Force' with the United States providing 2,000 soldiers for island service. Makarios immediately rejected the plan. He wanted Cyprus to remain a non-aligned state.

Spasmodic fighting continued throughout the island despite the sterling efforts and good intentions of the British troops. Prevented from taking offensive action, the British felt increasingly frustrated by their mission. On one side the Greek Cypriots mocked their impotence and accused them of being partisan, while on the other, the Turkish Cypriots thought their limited protection insufficient and wished they were defended by men of the Turkish army.

In February 1964, the British, fed up with the thankless position in which they found themselves, handed 'the Cyprus problem' to the United Nations to solve.

Early in March, UNFICYP was founded with Lieutenant-General Gyani appointed its first Commander, reporting directly to the UN

Secretary-General. General Sir John Archer was appointed the force's first Chief Operations Officer.

Of the options considered by Archbishop Makarios, by now allied to the Soviet Union, this was the most politically acceptable solution of all, because it prevented direct NATO involvement in the dispute.

For the next ten years life would be hard for the Turkish Cypriots despite the UN presence.

CHAPTER 12

UMPIRES RUN OUT

WHEN the first Finnish soldiers of the United Nations Force arrived at Nicosia International airport on 26 March 1964, they unloaded bicycles from their aircraft, formed up in battalion rank, and, led by their commanding officer, pedalled down George Grivas Dhigenis Avenue in the direction of the capital of Cyprus to join the Britons who were there already, wearing blue berets.

People who lined the route on that sunny spring day said that the sight of 700 soldiers in white helmets cycling purposefully to take up positions on the feuding island was 'most impressive'.

The Finns were followed by units from Australia, Austria, Canada, Denmark and Ireland, to create an army of 7,000 soldiers: UNFICYP. Security Council Resolution 186, passed on 4 March 1964, stated that the mission of the peace force was:

> 'To prevent a recurrence of fighting by assisting pragmatically in the maintenance of the cease-fire;
> 'To contribute to the maintenance and restoration of law and order, with particular reference to the security and well-being of the communities, as requested and agreed by them; and
> 'To contribute to the restoration of normal conditions.'

The Security Council was so confident the UN force would succeed quickly that its mandate only ran six months.

More than two decades later, the force remained in Cyprus, with Britain continuing to make the largest contribution in terms of manpower and logistics. By the early eighties the cost to British taxpayers was estimated at more than £20 million annually.

UNFICYP was prepared to recognize the independence of Cyprus with Makarios alone as the Republic's President, and tacitly regarded the Turkish Cypriot community as needing protection only from 'hot-heads', nothing more.

Makarios considered UNFICYP his own military tool to prevent any violent responses from the Turkish Cypriots to his modifications of the Constitution and other laws he chose to reform. UNFICYP, he was sure, would stifle any opposition simply to keep the peace.

Makarios and his supporters believed that as long as UNFICYP fulfilled its very limited 'peace-keeping' mandate, Turkey would never again dare to exercise its rights under the Treaty of Guarantee. From now on 'the insurgents' — namely the Turkish Cypriots — could be controlled by a Cyprus government consisting exclusively of Greek

Cypriots and backed by the United Nations.

Unfortunately for Makarios, all those assumptions were to prove incorrect during the next decade.

For the time being, however, UNFICYP deployed its troops island-wide. They were posted wherever the UN considered there was a threatened minority, which continued to mean the Turkish Cypriots. But yet again, this force could not act unilaterally, nor was it allowed to take preventive military action. Only if their own lives were endangered could the 'peace soldiers' use their weapons.

There were now two classes of British soldier in Cyprus: those retained at the Sovereign Bases, directly under British command, and the others who wore the UN Blue Beret and took their orders from the Secretary-General in New York.

But whose 'law and order' was UNFICYP to maintain and restore?

Turkish Cypriots were managing their own enclaves, and what could UNFICYP do if the Greek Cypriot administration passed laws which Turkish Cypriots deemed unconstitutional and refused to obey? After all, Turkish Cypriots were never going to 'request' or 'agree' anything which they disapproved. As far as they were concerned, the original Republic of Cyprus was no longer; it had ceased to exist immediately they had been ousted from all government posts and Makarios had decided to change the Constitution without their agreement as co-founders.

Equally difficult for UNFICYP was how to implement that part of the Security Council mandate which insisted the force promote 'a return to normal conditions' and 'contribute to the security' of the communities in conflict.

As a force for change UNFICYP was impotent. At best, it could only maintain the status quo.

Blaming the major powers for all the ills of this tiny island had been a favourite Cypriot pastime, but now UNFICYP became the prime target for abuse.

When fighting broke out, UNFICYP troops would put their heads down, wait for the shooting to stop, and then get up and count the casualties. They became known as 'umpires', 'summertime soldiers' and 'paid tourists'.

For its apparent failures during the next 10 years, the force would face a barrage of criticism from many directions. Nevertheless, between 1964 and 1974, there were only two *major* outbreaks of violence.

One of these incidents began on 6 August 1964, when 1,500 Greek Cypriots of the National Guard launched an organized assault on Kokkina, a Turkish enclave on the northern coast. Under the command of General George Grivas, EOKA's founder, they swept aside the UNFICYP soldiers in the area, despite protests from Colonel Jonas Waern, the senior officer of the Swedish contingent. With a gun pushed against him by a Greek Cypriot, Waern ordered his men to withdraw, which they did, under mortar fire.

From the sea, Greek patrol boats fired canons and from the land 25-pound artillery shells rained down on the 500 Turkish Cypriot defenders.

This action prompted Turkey's *second* open intervention in the affairs of Cyprus.

Once again Turkish warplanes flew over the island. The first flight consisted of four F-100s. Their pilots fired rockets out to sea as a demonstration of aerial power. The Greek Cypriots appeared unimpressed. Their attacks continued.

Two days later the Turkish air force returned, but on this occasion they strafed and bombed the National Guard, inflicting a significant number of casualties. Foreign observers said the air strikes were delivered with extreme precision.

Makarios was furious. He threatened his forces would attack *every* Turkish Cypriot enclave without mercy unless Turkey stopped its intervention. The next day the jets were back, destroying Greek Cypriot reinforcements, gun sites, and armoured cars in a widespread area of the north-west. General Grivas and Minister of the Interior Yorgadjis left their men and escaped by helicopter to Nicosia.

The UN Security Council demanded a cease-fire and this was agreed.

Kokkina was held by the Turkish Cypriots, who continued using it to smuggle arms and men into the island.

Following this disaster for the National Guard, its Greek mainland commander, General Karayannis, resigned and returned home. He condemned Grivas for mishandling the situation and Makarios for approving it in the first place.

On 10 September 1964, UN Secretary-General U Thant published a report condemning both sides.

Thant blamed the Greek Cypriots of the Republic government for starting the battle and for preventing UNFICYP in its efforts to secure a cease-fire. He continued by saying, 'I feel compelled also to express the view that the aerial attacks on Cyprus communities by Turkish aircraft in early August, whatever their supposed tactical significance, were most unfortunate and have made the solution of the Cyprus problem far more difficult.'

The next major incident took place on 15 November 1967, when several UNFICYP soldiers were disarmed by the Greek National Guard who then proceeded to pulverize Turkish Cypriots living in Kophinou and Ayios Theodoros, near Larnaca.

Two thousand National Guardsmen and Greek mainland soldiers were involved in the operation, again commanded by General Grivas. Appalling atrocities occurred. Civilians were machine-gunned after they had surrendered to the National Guard and others were covered in kerosene, set alight and burnt to death.

Turkey's response was swift and sure. The Ankara government told

the UN and Athens that there must be an immediate cease-fire in
Cyprus; Greek Cypriot forces must withdraw from villages they had
captured; Turkish Cypriot hostages must be released and returned to
their homes safely; and the Makarios government must guarantee the
future security of the island's Turkish Cypriots.

Unless this happened, Turkey, 'if necessary', would go to war. The
crisis, Turkey said, would 'go beyond the borders of the island'.

Turkey ordered its air force to stand by for action and put its land
forces on alert. Along Turkey's borders, the Greeks did the same.

Within hours the National Guard acceded to the demands of Turkey
and began withdrawing.

On 19 November Grivas was returned to Greece and the new Greek
regime, a right-wing military group led by Colonel George
Papadopoulos, recalled 12,000 mainland soldiers from Cyprus. They
told Makarios that their primary interest was maintaining good
relations with the United States and NATO. They were definitely not
going to war with Turkey simply to allow President Makarios to
realize his political ambitions of *Enosis*, especially as he had aligned
himself with Communist nations and relied on arms from behind the
Iron Curtain.

The Colonels and Makarios never trusted each other again.

Some political observers claimed that the Turkish and Greek
governments of the time had much more in common than was imagined
outside the corridors of power in their two capitals. Both were anti-
Communist; both relied heavily on American military and economic
aid; and both wanted Cyprus.

Had it not been for the presence of the leftist-leaning Archbishop,
perhaps a rapprochement could have been achieved; one by which the
island was divided into two zones: Greek and Turkish, thereby
satisfying at the same time their supporters' demands for *Enosis* and
Taksim.

Turkey's *third* intervention had nevertheless achieved a great deal.
Aside from causing the withdrawal of the Greek mainland forces from
Cyprus, it forced Makarios to begin a meaningful dialogue with the
Turkish Cypriot leadership.

To start the process, Rauf Denktaş was allowed to return to his own
country, having been banned earlier as an undesirable. He began talks
immediately with Glafcos Clerides, like himself a London-trained
barrister, and another man eager to achieve high political office in
Cyprus. They were old sparring partners, understood each other very
well and carried the support of their respective communities.

A 'Provisional Turkish Cypriot Administration' was agreed. It
included Dr Küçük, the internationally-recognized Vice-President of the
Republic. Beyond that however, nothing else was settled and the
intercommunal talks were suspended. Although neither *Enosis* nor
Taksim had taken place officially, clearly both communities were going

their separate ways.

While Turkish Cypriots still felt desperately insecure, they were administering themselves to all intents and purposes, and there was nothing the Greek Cypriot authorities in Nicosia could do to change the situation. Rather than try, they set about developing their standard of living. The Greek Cypriot economy began to boom.

The extremists knew they would have to bide their time to achieve *Enosis*.

Sir David Hunt was the UK High Commissioner between 1965 and 1967. A fluent Greek speaker, he got along very well with Makarios. Too well, some said. A year later, he married a Greek Cypriot and, after his retirement, became President of the Society for the Promotion of Hellenic Studies, co-writing *Caterina Cornaro, Queen of Cyprus* with his wife, Ino Myriamthousis.

Some balance returned to the High Commission when John Phillips was appointed as deputy high commissioner. His family had served the Raj for several generations. He himself had been born in India, where he became student of Islam. He was very aware of the needs of Turkish Cypriots.

Whether the ensuing no-war, no-peace in Cyprus sprang from Turkey's three interventions or had been caused by UNFICYP's presence was open to debate; Carter intended to raise the question with the Force Commander and record his answers.

On the other hand, the calm could have been due entirely to other factors, not least exhaustion. For the Turkish Cypriots had been subjected to a ruthless economic blockade by the centralized Greek Cypriot administration and almost half were unemployed. Ordinary Greek Cypriots had suffered as well from the futile civil war.

Considerable amounts of foreign financial aid started to enter the Republic for reconstruction and development programmes, but few of these benefited Turkish Cypriots as they were still not able to operate within the internationally-recognized Greek Cypriot government that controlled the distribution of funds.

Greek Cypriot government policy was to try starving the Turkish Cypriots into submission or voluntary exile by economic means, since military force had failed.

Throughout this period the Greek Cypriot press urged Turkish Cypriots to leave, even suggesting that the government should speed their emigration by paying the costs of transportation. If Turkish Cypriots could be forced or persuaded to quit the island, then the door would be opened again for union with Greece.

On 16 May 1974, Makarios told the German newspaper, *Frankfurter Rundschau*, 'If I had a free choice between *Enosis* and independence, I would support *Enosis*.'

But, behind the scenes, relations between Makarios and the Athens authorities were going seriously wrong. Through *Enosis*, the Greek

Cypriot President had seen himself becoming a major force in Greek politics, and ultimately even President of this new Greece.

The Greek government wanted a different outcome.

While it supported *Enosis*, it wanted Cyprus to be governed by one of its own nominees, not an independently-minded left-winger like Makarios. Furthermore it was never going to allow a Greek Cypriot — a 'small islander' — to rule the mainland.

Matters came to a head when Makarios ordered the expulsion of all Greek officers from Cyprus. He vigorously denounced the Colonels in Athens, accusing them of trying to subvert the Greek Cypriot National Guard, and declared he had rejected all thoughts of *immediate Enosis*.

The Greek Colonels were not pleased. They decided to overthrow Makarios and install a right-winger who would do as he was told. They chose Nicos Sampson as the next President of Cyprus.

On 15 July 1974, Makarios was ousted in a Greek-planned coup d'état. Sampson replaced the Archbishop and this posed a major dilemma for UNFICYP. What was its position now? How should it respond to the changed circumstances?

Before the UN could find answers, Turkey intervened unilaterally for the *fourth* time.

On 20 July 1974, its forces landed on Cyprus. The partition of the island in a social and geographical sense had begun. UNFICYP was unable to prevent it.

Ironically, only the day before, Makarios, who had escaped from Cyprus, addressed the UN Security Council with these words: 'The Security Council should call upon the military regime of Greece to withdraw from Cyprus the Greek officers serving in the National Guard, and put an end to the *Greek invasion* of Cyprus.'

In the end it was the Turkish military who achieved that objective, rather than Makarios or UNFICYP.

Much later, in 1979, Major-General J. J. Quinn, the robust Irish Force Commander, gave Carter an explanation. 'We were never intended for fending off a major attack from either side,' he said. 'However, our very presence in Cyprus resulted in peace being established at a very early stage. Remember, had it not been for UNFICYP, I doubt you would have had a truce so early on.'

Eight UN soldiers died during the war, 60 were seriously injured and many other lives were risked by trying to save Greek and Turkish Cypriots.

By the time Carter was due to fly to Cyprus again in 1979 he had concluded it would not be an easy task to compress all the different facets of the Cyprus problem and the UN's involvement into a single 60-minute programme. He decided instead to focus on Britain's contribution to UNFICYP and take the Cyprus situation as it was. He would record a typical 24-hour period in the life of the force. He wanted to keep his commentary to a minimum, allowing UN soldiers to tell their own stories.

This method meant Carter would have to carry his recorder everywhere. To avoid wasting tape and having to spend many hours editing on his return, he needed Major Mercer to pick good locations and articulate interviewees. From experience he knew that servicemen were not ideal speakers and their officers were often stilted and stuffy when confronted by a microphone.

The Ministry of Defence had told Carter he would be flown by VC-10 from RAF Brize Norton in Oxfordshire to Akrotiri, part of the Western Sovereign Base Area, but when he and his fellow passengers reported for their scheduled departure at 04.30 on a Thursday in July, they were informed that their VC-10 flight had been cancelled.

In its place there would be a chartered civilian aircraft brought from Gatwick.

Some three hours later the aircraft arrived. It was a DC-10 in the livery of a Laker *Skytrain*, which astonished everybody because DC-10s around the world were supposed to have been grounded while safety checks were conducted, following a series of mishaps.

If the Ministry of Defence considered the DC-10 safe for British military personnel, why had the government's aviation experts taken the aircraft out of civilian service? Carter was tempted to leak the story, but discretion prevailed.

Neither fear nor bad publicity worried Carter's Ministry of Defence 'minder'. Instead Major Sherry Sherbrooke looked forward to being served with 'a few snorts of the hard stuff' by Laker's glamorous air stewardesses on the four-and-a-half-hour journey to the island of *Aphrodite*. His expectations were dashed, however, when the officer in charge of the flight insisted that the crew and passengers observe military rules and travel 'dry'.

But Sherbrooke was prepared for all eventualities. From his sturdy leather briefcase he produced a silver flask filled with brandy, called for two paper cups and openly poured Carter and himself a double somewhere high above the Alps.

'Cheers,' he exclaimed, toasting Carter and wishing him success in his documentary-making efforts in Cyprus.

'I'll be about if you need any help,' Sherbrooke growled, 'but don't expect me to follow you everywhere. I'm not that sort of chap. Just give me a hammock in the sunshine, a good book and a cold drink and I'll be happy as a sandboy.'

Large crowds had gathered at the RAF airport in Akrotiri to see the arrival of the giant DC-10. Never before had such a large aircraft landed there. The station comfortably handled RAF Phantoms, VC-10s and even American U2s, the notorious 'spy 'planes', but this was something very different.

With hardly a bump when its wheels touched the runway the DC-10 landed perfectly. Then it taxied carefully to a parking bay, its wing-tips

almost shaving the roof of the Customs shed. The people outside and
the passengers on board cheered. The last time this had happened in
Carter's presence was when his Turkish Airlines jet had arrived at
İstanbul. Was the applause relief at landing safely or recognition of the
crew's skills?

This British UN contingent had travelled in style and comfort. It
was a far cry from the day when the first Finnish soldiers arrived with
their bicycles.

Carter and Sherbrooke were met by Major Mercer, who wasted no
time in collecting their bags, placing them in his UN car and driving
them over the Troodos mountains to UNFICYP headquarters at the
disused Nicosia International airport.

Here, before a late lunch, he outlined a programme of activity and
immediately began setting up Carter's interviews for the next day.

Between telephone calls Mercer talked enthusiastically about his
work and the UN's current tasks in Cyprus. Laying maps on a large
table, he pointed to where the force had its troops stationed in the
Buffer Zone or 'BZ', which had been created between cease-fire lines
agreed by the Greek Cypriot National Guard and the Turkish army.

'The Buffer Zone meanders its way along a 70-mile front starting in
the north on the coast near Kokkina point, crossing the Troodos
mountains to reach Astromeritis,' he said crisply. 'From there it
continues through some of the island's finest arable land and citrus-
producing areas until it reaches the eastern edge of Nicosia.

'Then it zigzags and divides the capital, emerging near Omorphita.
From there it cuts through the countryside until it stops on the
perimeter of the Eastern Sovereign Base Area — ESBA — at Dhekelia.
On the far side, near Dherinia, it resumes again until it reaches the coast,
just south of Famagusta and Varosha.'

Mercer pointed to each place with a pencil and tapped his map for
emphasis. He continued, 'In parts of the BZ, Turkish and Greek Cypriot
National Guard forces are separated by several miles, while in other
parts, in Nicosia for example, the distance may be, quite literally, only
the width of a narrow street.

'Along the line there are more than 100 UNFICYP observation
posts — OPs — manned round the clock, with a linking patrol track
used night and day by UN vehicles only.

'You'll be interested in knowing that Britain continues to make the
largest contribution to the force. Of the total strength, a quarter is
British. This includes a battalion of soldiers for service in the BZ, a
squadron of Ferret Scout Cars and a helicopter flight. In addition, there
are several other support facilities which are provided to UNFICYP by
the Sovereign Bases. It makes UNFICYP the most cost-effective
mission ever mounted.'

Carter smiled and kept his tape-recorder switched on.

There was no need for him to make notes. Mercer was doing all his work, his speech providing a commentary for the programme. By cutting the tape into segments Carter would be able to use Mercer's statements to link other words and sounds he planned to record at various locations along the cease-fire line.

While Carter changed tapes and Mercer talked 'off the record', Sherbrooke dozed.

The situation since 1974 had made the UNFICYP mission more clear cut, said Mercer; its tasks were less contradictory and its successes more satisfying. The force no longer had to rely on a battalion of bicyclists armed with good intentions and moral authority. Now it had many years of experience at maintaining a peaceful status quo.

If UNFICYP were doing its job so well by ensuring stability, with the co-operation of the Turkish army and the Greek Cypriot National Guard, was there not a danger of politicians forgetting the problem and thereby never solving it, Carter speculated?

It was Mercer's chance to smile. He glanced at the tape-recorder to see whether it was on. Satisfied it was not, he said, 'That's a question you must put to Mr Yakub. He's the civilian "Spokesman" for the UN in Cyprus. I'm sure he'll be delighted to answer *political* questions. I'll do my best for the military, but it's really up to you, David, to raise the *right* questions. We'll be getting you out and about, starting tomorrow, early. I say again, ask the right questions and you'll get honest answers from the chaps.'

Sherry Sherbrooke woke with a startled look. 'What's that?' he asked. 'Did somebody say it was time for a G and T?'

CHAPTER 13

FIRE AND WATER

UNFICYP HQ
Blue Beret Camp
In the United Nations Protected Area
Nicosia
08.05 hours

AT Blue Beret Camp, on the edge of Nicosia International airport, the working day has just begun for the key members of the UNFICYP headquarters staff. The conference room in which they have assembled forms part of a single-storey building shaded by eucalyptus trees. Its design has been used wherever the soldiers of the Crown have put their boots down, whether in Catterick or Calcutta, Rochester or Rawalpindi. Branded with the stamp of anonymity and maintained in an atmosphere of disinfectant cleanliness, the camp's rows of buildings stand on a unique square mile of territory, the only ground which the 'Peace Soldiers' will fight to defend. It's a canton in the very centre of Cyprus where the inhabitants are answerable only to the UN Secretary-General and live by laws passed on the banks of the Hudson River in New York.

Those present this morning include the current Force Commander, Major-General Gunther Greindl, an Austrian career officer with an advanced degree in civil engineering. He has a long track track record of UN service, including a previous tour of duty in Cyprus.

General Greindl is accompanied by Colonel H. W. K. Pye, a fourth-generation officer who is the Deputy Chief of Staff and Commander of the British contingent, known as BRITCON. Pye's background is impressive. He's served in several trouble-spots and in Berlin where he commanded the Independent Armoured Squadron.

In terms of personality I think Greindl and Pye are poles apart. While Pye, who often wears a tracksuit, welcomes his guests with dry wit and dry gin, Greindl remains formal and straight-backed, never a hair out of place.

Also in attendance are the Military Public Information Officer and the 'Spokesman' for the UN Secretary-General's Special Representative in Cyprus. Present, too, are several other officers who perform specialist roles. Their uniforms are cut in different styles and are coloured in varying shades of khaki and olive-green, depending on their nationalities, but all are pressed with razor-sharp creases, and every officer carries a blue beret, the only common item of garb. The mood in the conference room is relaxed.

A lectern and a large screen for the projection of slides and film dominate the stage. To one side there are large maps of Cyprus on which chinagraph pencils have been used to draw lines to mark the Buffer Zone. A series of small squares and triangles, some with dots and others with stripes, identify the size and status of every UNFICYP site on the island.

A British sergeant, his shirt-sleeves rolled up, makes a few adjustments to the flags marking the latest deployments of Turkish and Greek military units.

I've been told that it was in this room in 1974 that the two sides signed agreements establishing the cease-fire line and Buffer Zone.

A Canadian major takes charge of the lectern, resting a clipboard within his eye-line. He grips a wooden pointer firmly with both hands and reminds us that the information we're about to hear is classified. His remarks are directed particularly at me. I must remember to clear all my tapes with UNFICYP before I return to London.

In a voice slightly tinged with a north American accent, the major says that his report will summarize the events of the past 24 hours and the activities of the UN force. Like a class of sixth-formers a week away from our A-level examinations, we sit and take notes. 'There have been no violations of the cease-fire by firing,' the Canadian declares solemnly. Suddenly he notices my tape-recorder and, believing I have it switched on, begins to project his voice more loudly. I'll persuade him later to repeat his report for the benefit of my Uher.

'There was one Turkish violation yesterday at Maple - .' He breaks off in mid-sentence and points at a spot in Sector Four, the responsibility of the Canadian contingent, CANCON. It's in the centre of Nicosia, where the Buffer Zone winds its way through narrow streets, where buildings on either side are sometimes less than fifteen feet apart. The major has decided not to speak aloud the names or numbers of actual locations, because he wants to minimize the risk of inadvertently revealing in my broadcast the dispositions of the opposing forces. UNFICYP impartiality must not be jeopardized.

I remember what Major-General J. J. Quinn, the previous Force Commander, said: 'Our aim is to maintain stability which we have established, and naturally, we will fall foul of one side or the other at different stages. But the greatest insult that you could pay me would be to say that I was not impartial.'

The morning report continues: 'A single Turkish soldier was observed at 09.23 moving forwards by 15 metres from the CFL — the cease-fire line — into the BZ — the Buffer Zone. After three minutes the Turkish soldier returned to his own lines. There was no response from the Greek Cypriot National Guard.

'At 10.34 CANCON lodged a UN protest at Company level with the local Turkish battalion. At 17.00 hours the Turks replied, having conducted their own investigations. They said the soldier had been newly posted and had not been properly briefed. The UN protest was accepted. The matter is now closed.

'There was one Greek National Guard violation yesterday. At 07.35 a Sector Two vehicle from BRITCON noted seven National Guard soldiers digging on an escarpment here . . . preparing rifle trenches on or forward of the CFL.

'At 12.30 the BRITCON Company Commander lodged a UN protest with the local National Guard battalion. At 15.00 hours the National Guard replied that the trenches were well behind the cease-fire line and that the UN protest was rejected. The UN protest was re-submitted personally by the UN Company Commander at 18.00, and it was rejected again. But the National Guard has agreed to a joint on-site inspection and this is scheduled for 11.00 hours tomorrow.'

The major speaks for 20 minutes. His report catalogues a series of minute incidents, each observed, logged, reported and followed up swiftly by UNFICYP, giving neither side the opportunity to escalate situations.

'It's been a quiet 24-hour period. I say again, there were no violations of the cease-fire by firing.'

Tape 2

DANCON
Sector One
Limnitis Camp
Morphou Bay
In Turkish-controlled northern Cyprus
09.10 hours

The sound of its rotor blades thrashing the wind reaches us long before we see the Whirlwind helicopter flying in low and fast over the rocky ridge towards Limnitis Camp, part of the Danish contingent's operational area in Sector One. Blowing gritty dust in all directions, it hovers for a few moments above the flattened square like a predatory locust. There's a high-pitched whine as Flight-Lieutenant Martin Kay cuts his engines and the helicopter drops the last few inches to settle on the sun-baked ground. Three Danish soldiers, all tanned a deep brown, dash forward to greet the pilot and his crewman, Flight-Sergeant Richards.

Already the temperature has reached 90 degrees, and the two members of 84 Squadron, RAF, are finding their lightweight, grey flying suits have become their personal sauna baths. Removing their helmets, they wipe sweat from their foreheads. Lieutenant B. Lett, the Administrative Officer for C Company, offers them bottles of chilled Coca Cola.

Although the two RAF men will chat to me for a few minutes, Kay and Richards point out they can't spare long; they have a very busy schedule this morning, employed on Task CHARLIE, a thrice-weekly re-supply mission to seven UNFICYP Observation Posts stuck in this mountainous region, the responsibility of DANCON.

All military activity west of a perpendicular line drawn from Astromeritis to the northern coast, is observed and reported by the Danes. Viking Camp, the Danish headquarters at Xeros, exists in Turkish Cypriot-administered territory. The Danes have a broad expanse of Morphou Bay ahead of them and the solid mass of the Troodos mountains rising steeply behind. Apart from having the most difficult geographical sector of any UNFICYP contingent, they have the additional worry of watching a secondary Buffer Zone around the Turkish military enclave of Kokkina, held by Turkish Cypriots since 1964. Although this spot poses tremendously difficult re-supply problems for the Turks, as everything must be moved in or out by sea, they hold it for emotional reasons rather than for any military value. They have named it Erenköy.

'Because the terrain is so tough and the travel restrictions on the ground so many, aerial re-supply of the Danish OPs is much more convenient than using trucks,' Flight-Lieutenant Kay explains. Today his Whirlwind is carrying 1,500 pounds of fresh rations, 2,000 pounds of drinking water for those sites which have no access to pipelines or wells, and a drum containing 500 pounds of fuel for an electricity generator.

'We couldn't do anything without the British helicopters,' Lieutenant Lett adds, paying his compliments to the RAF. 'Our OPs are placed on the tops of mountains in very rocky areas. It can be very lonely up there.'

Once the supplies have been off-loaded, five Danish soldiers will fly out in the helicopter to start a week's leave in Limassol. But not everybody wants to get away.

'I recall one instance when a Danish CO was on his traditional tour of all OPs by helicopter on Christmas Eve and he found himself meeting soldiers for whom he had signed leave-chits, but who chose to stay,' Flight-Sergeant Richards tells me.

Lieutenant Lett adds: 'I can confirm that story. Many of the soldiers create homes away from home in their self-built OPs. There is much solitude here in the Troodos, and the men are very industrious in their off-duty hours. They are always building new things, improving facilities. For example, they made this place. Some men even breed chickens and goats.'

We're sitting by a rock-garden packed with cacti and species of ground orchids. There's a small pond in which goldfish are lazing. Screens of bamboo matting protect us from the sun. We have a grand panoramic view of the mountains; slabs of black, white and red stone splattered with thorn bushes and a few Aleppo pines. Some of the bright streaks of colour in the rocks are mineral oxides. Since the second century BC the area has been mined for copper.

More recently the Cyprus Mining Corporation of Skouriotissa attacked the ground and by its efforts improved the economy of Cyprus, but scarred the landscape forever. Not undeservedly, the corporation became better known as 'Our Lady of the Slag Heaps'.

The corporation's activities began in 1911 when an American mining engineer, C. Godfrey Gunther, found a Latin manuscript in a New York library. It told of mining activity in ancient Cyprus near Soli, where today lie the remains of a large Roman amphitheatre, its seats in stepped rows carved out of the hillside facing the sea. As a result of his discovery, Gunther became a millionaire.

Almost directly opposite Viking Camp at Xeros, the jetty used by Gunther's company to ship processed copper abroad rusts and rots. It's as desolate as *Vouni Palace*, the other great historical site on the coastal road leading to Limnitis Camp.

During my visit to northern Cyprus last summer, Ali Özel introduced me to several Turkish soldiers in their front-line positions. Their task was to observe the UN and Greek Cypriot observers in their positions.

The mining activity at Skouriotissa has sometimes endangered the Danes. OP DELTA 15 was erected on an old slag heap, but suddenly a fissure developed and the Force Engineer realized quickly that the hut and watch-tower of the OP could disappear down a deep precipice after a rainfall. While DANCON's CO, Lieutenant-Colonel Madsen, had no difficulty finding a better site, his problem was how to re-establish observers in a new position without a break in their round-the-clock duties.

Using workshop facilities at Viking Camp, the colonel's pioneer platoon built a new watch-tower faster than ever before. Meanwhile, a bulldozer of 62 Support Squadron, Royal Engineers, dug a track, almost all the way to the new location, where supplies were rushed by truck and then picked up by Allouette helicopters and flown to the top of the mountain by pilots of the British Army Air Corps.

Finally, the new watch-tower was suspended under a Wessex helicopter from 85 Squadron and lowered in place; followed soon afterwards by a mobile 'privy'.

DELTA 35, the new OP, was ready for business before DELTA 15 was shut down. It had been a close-run race against danger because a single thunderstorm would have caused disaster.

Tape 3

Continuing impressions at DANCON's Limnitis location

Lieutenant Lett is an enthusiastic talker who responds well to my questions and doesn't fear a microphone. However, what he says has little to do with UNFICYP but a lot to do with the area's history, geography and geology, of which he knows a great deal.

'Of course the Greek mining and mineral processing came to an end in Xeros when the Turks arrived in 1974,' the Danish officer explains. He's interrupted by Flight-Sergeant Richards. 'Gosh, is that the time?'

The crew of the Whirlwind helicopter must continue with Task CHARLIE. 'We'll fly by twice so that you can get a good recording of our engine,' Richards shouts from the cockpit as his craft springs off the ground with Kay driving it into the sky at a steep sideways angle.

I resume recording but my Uher can't cope with the strength of the sound and I fear there'll be a lot of distorted noises on the tape. The helicopter flies off.

The Danes have been part of UNFICYP since its establishment in 1964 and some members of DANCON are on their second tour of duty. Cyprus holds a special attraction which extends beyond the high salaries they earn while serving here.

Lieutenant Lett is quite open about the financial rewards he and his men receive for 'keeping the peace'. According to him, one member of the contingent has been with UNFICYP since its inception. 'This soldier sends his money home every month to be invested,' he says. 'When he retires I expect he will be able to buy Denmark.'

'Did you know,' Lett asks, pointing in the direction of the sea, 'that over there, *Dighenis* — the hero of olden times, not the EOKA leader - — threw giant boulders at the Saracens who were attacking Cyprus? They say that those are the same rocks you see sticking out of the water today.'

On a nearby mountain peak the Turkish flag flies above a military position overlooking Limnitis Camp.

'Yes, we have been in danger,' says Lieutenant Lett, reading my thoughts. 'In 1974, two OPs were hit by bullets and shrapnel from mortars. I don't know from who. One Dane, shot in the back. Dead.'

I switch off my tape-recorder.

Tape 4

BRITCON
Sector Two
St David's Camp
Five miles west of Nicosia in Greek-controlled southern Cyprus
09.45 hours

Five miles west down the main route from Nicosia to Peristerona village, a minor road diverts to the right and comes to a halt at a military check-point. Beyond the barrier there's a shabby collection of brick and wood huts roofed with sheets of corrugated iron and asbestos. A pole, stuck in a concrete block, flies the flags of Britain and the United Nations. The block is surrounded by a line of evenly-sized and spaced whitewashed stones. The regimental insignia of the unit forming the current British contingent is painted on a board nailed to a wooden stake.

Anglican services take place every Sunday in the small church next to the guardroom where discipline parades are held every day. Prayer and punishment coexist here as they have throughout Cyprus for the past five centuries.

This is St David's Camp, BRITCON's battalion headquarters and the home of the senior personnel of Eastern Company on duty along the cease-fire line in Sector Two. For the men based in the OPs of the Buffer Zone, there's no nearer place for relaxation and a drink in the NAAFI or the Sergeants' Mess.

The Officers' Mess is a quiet haven in which to catch up on the world outside Cyprus by reading week-old editions of *The Times* and *Daily Telegraph*. Visitors like myself are encouraged to hand over our more up-to-date reading material. The highlight of the evening is the screening of an old movie after dinner. It's usually something quite blood curdling. Last night we saw Steve McQueen in *The Bounty Hunter*. By the fourth reel, snores smothered the sound-track.

While some junior officers find the routine at St David's rather dull, they are fortunate in not having been like their predecessors at the camp. When the British ruled in the fifties, they used St David's to imprison EOKA terrorists. After independence the Greek National Guard upheld the tradition by holding their opponents here.

Captain Hawgood gives me the impression he is a no-nonsense officer and confirms this by what he tells.

'You can't afford to take a soft attitude with either side. Some British regiments in the line have tried to be lenient,' he says, 'but they found that the number of incidents increased. You have to be firm and tough in your approach or they will take advantage.'

Hawgood is proud of having reduced the number of incidents in Sector Two and says the policy of the British contingent is to resolve difficulties at Sector-level and not report problems upwards to UNFICYP headquarters for solutions. While he refuses to be drawn on the overall rights and wrongs of the situation, or even whether he believes there's any value to the UNFICYP mission, he's frank about BRITCON's relations with the Turks.

Captain Hawgood: 'We have much less trouble with the Turkish side. The Turks, by the way, don't officially recognize the cease-fire line. They observe it, but have never put anything down on paper to admit that there is such a line. At the moment, the ratio of incidents is three to one against the Greek National Guard.'

I suggest this may be due to the fact there are Greek Cypriots living in the two villages, Dhenia and Mamari, *inside* the BZ, and that they are accountable to UN civil policemen for their behaviour, *not* the authorities of their Republic.

Hawgood replies: 'Both Dhenia and Mamari have young men who belong to the Greek Cypriot National Guard which, by itself, is no great problem. But these men are not supposed to bring their weapons to the villages or wear uniforms when they are there, because the BZ is *demilitarized*. However, they either fail to remember or don't bother when they return home at weekends.

'Our patrols discover them sitting in the village cafés wearing uniforms and carrying arms. We have to insist that they remove themselves immediately or face the consequences.'

If the Greek Cypriot National Guardsmen were to refuse they would be arrested immediately by UNFICYP, even though they were in their own villages.

Were the Turkish army to spot these individuals in the Buffer Zone, armed and wearing uniforms, at the very least there would be serious protests from the north.

I leave Captain Hawgood's office and walk the veranda outside the officers' living quarters and see a faded mural. It reminds me that British soldiers have had to play the part of policemen many times before in Cyprus.

Although the painting on the wall is very faint, I can make out the frying-pan shape of the island and the outline of its nearest European neighbours. Beneath a drawing of a dove in flight, there's a man reaching out desperately from the heart of Europe to grasp the extended fingers of a young, smiling woman who stands on Cyprus. The man is wearing the remnants of a prison uniform, marked with the Star of David. At the bottom of the drawing there are some Hebrew letters, none completely decipherable.

On this island rich in rumour, legend and make-believe, the painting is yet another mystery. Generations of soldiers have tried to cover it with countless layers of whitewash, but the original colours still seep through. I've been told that this is the work of a young Jewish girl, a survivor of the holocaust.

In 1947, having escaped from internment in post-war Europe, she was making her way to 'the promised land' of Israel, so far unborn. She had boarded a leaking tramp-steamer whose hold carried a cargo of refugees, all optimistic that they could avoid the blockade of British warships in the eastern Mediterranean and reach their destination, Haifa in Palestine. But the vessel was intercepted off the coast of Cyprus and ordered to sail to Limassol under escort. Here the Jewish refugees were unloaded and British 'Tommies' placed them in covered trucks. They were carried to their next destination, a camp where they would be concentrated while their fate was decided.

I wonder what thoughts went through that girl's mind when she reached St David's Camp. With barbed wire and a perimeter fence patrolled by armed soldiers, it was a place not dissimilar to others she had known. The British guards, no less than the guarded, must have found their situation depressing.

Some say the young artist was a teenager, expressing her adolescent concern for the last remaining member of her family. Was he a brother or cousin lost somewhere in Europe?

Her canvas was a prison wall in Cyprus which the tourist brochures call the 'Island of Love'.

She probably never knew that in AD 115 there had been a Jewish rebellion at Salamis and, as a consequence, a quarter of a million inhabitants died and the Roman Senate passed a decree expelling all Jews from Cyprus.

Many of the refugees held at St David's eventually reached Palestine and rebuilt their lives, but nobody can tell me if the young artist was amongst them. There's no record of her name. All we know about her is contained within the outlines of her bold design and simple brush strokes which military conformity and neatness tries hard to hide.

All the thousands of Jews held in detention camps in Cyprus were released in batches soon after 14 May, 1948, when the state of Israel was declared and British forces withdrew from the Palestine mandate areas. They came under attack from Spitfires flown by the Egyptian air force, but later the Spitfires were shot .down by RAF Tempests based in Cyprus.

Don't we go round in circles?

Tape 5

BRITCON
Support Company Headquarters
Jubilee Camp
United Nations Protected Area
Nicosia International airport
10.40 hours

Some of the toughest fighting during the Turkish army's intervention in 1974 took place here at Nicosia International airport and, because of the determined stand by the Greek army, the Turks failed to capture their prime objective. Had they succeeded, it's probable that the north would now face far fewer economic difficulties. The Turkish Cypriots would have direct access to the outside world from a recognized airport which the Greeks could not describe as unsafe and not meeting international standards.

Today, however, the two main runways are fighting a battle against an army of weeds, and losing. On the far side from where UN helicopters land and take off, a fixed-wing aircraft lies smashed by the perimeter fence. It belonged to Cyprus Airways. Like this aircraft, offices and passenger lounges bear the scars of war, but not all the bullet holes were caused by Turks. Many are the result of the coup when Greek fought Greek Cypriot.

The Customs sheds are locked, still containing goods in transit, including a consignment of tobacco, stale and valueless. Nothing is allowed to be removed. To make certain everything remains exactly as it was in July 1974, Greek and Turkish teams conduct regular inspections accompanied by UNFICYP officers.

This morning Jubilee Camp is one of the hottest spots in Cyprus. A thermometer registers a temperature of 100 degrees. Tempers are stretched in the oven-like atmosphere of the hangars used by the Support Company personnel to maintain their 10-ton Bedford trucks, Land-Rovers and sewage tankers.

In a very small cubicle incapable of protecting us from the searing heat or the noise of engines under test, a British army captain of the Royal Corps of Transport and Major Rolf Green of the Austrian army want to tell me about the high fire risk and the shortage of water — factors which are giving them cause for concern.

RCT captain: 'Our water here at Jubilee was unexpectedly cut at 06.20. I know that we're at the start of the season when supplies will be restricted, but we should have been given some warning. As it was, we didn't expect the cuts and our soldiers weren't able to wash or shave this morning.'

'At least you have cold drinks here,' Major Green interjects. 'The real difficulties will be experienced by the men in the OPs, which don't have piped water.'

Major Rolf Green is UNFICYP's Economics Officer. He suggests that the force makes its most valuable contribution by working in the sphere of public utilities. 'Water,' he says, 'was a serious problem before 1974, and the situation is even more difficult and confused today as pipe-lines cross the Buffer Zone in several places, supplying both sides. For example, both Greek and Turkish parts of Nicosia get their water from the Morphou dam, which is in the Turkish area, while Famagusta, under Turkish control, is supplied by the Greeks.

'And *all* the electricity of Cyprus comes from power-stations in the south. There's one generating station near Dhekelia and the other at Moni, east of Limassol, to supply the island-wide grid.

'If for one reason or another, usually because a line breaks or a pump fails, supplies of electricity or water are cut, the people in the villages get very anxious. We have to find out what's gone wrong on the relevant side, and then pass on this information quickly to the other side, so that nobody does anything to cause trouble. I liaise a lot and find that my relationships on both sides are good.'

Fires in the Buffer Zone are another great problem for UNFICYP as the force has no fire-fighting equipment of its own at the OPs. In Sector

Two there's at least one outbreak of fire a week. When these occur, Greek Cypriot firemen are rushed from Nicosia, but before they can go into action, the Turkish authorities must be informed. The Turks have never refused permission, if only because the wind could change direction and spread the fire into their zone. It's not uncommon for Greek Cypriots to be joined by their Turkish Cypriot counterparts on these occasions.

CHAPTER 14

DIVIDED BY 60 MINUTES

Jubilee camp. Recordings continue

BEFORE we set off for AUSCON, I ask my driver, a Lance-Corporal in the Royal Corps of Transport, who the civilians are that I've seen working here at the old Nicosia International airport. He replies, 'They're Cypriots, very good workers. We couldn't do without them. They're from both sides. The Greeks come in from the main gate in the south of the camp, and the Turks arrive by bus from the north. At the end of each shift, they leave the same way. They get along very well. I've been here for just under a year and during that time, I've never heard of any trouble.'

Somewhere on the road to Famagusta
In Turkish-controlled northern Cyprus
11.45 hours

Because I'm an official UNFICYP visitor I hold a temporary identification document, a simple blue card, slightly larger than a pack of cigarettes, printed in English, Greek and Turkish. It bears no photograph. With it, I'm allowed to cross into northern Cyprus in our UN vehicle at various points in the Buffer Zone, without having to produce my civilian passport for examination.

This morning we drove down Ch. Mouskos to the Ledra Palace check-point, where Greek Cypriot policemen control all civilian movements. Had they seen my passport with its entry and exit stamps of the TFSC, there could have been problems.

At Ledra I held my UN identification card to the windscreen of our car and the Greek and Turkish guards waved us through the maze of barricades without hesitation. We then skirted the walled city and went along north Nicosia's busy streets. Now we're driving fast down the main road to Famagusta to keep my appointment with AUSCON in Sector Six.

We could have travelled to AUSCON by using roads in the south, but because of time factors, we've chosen the less busy route allowed by the Turkish authorities. It skirts Ercan airport. Ironically, I'm banned by them from visiting the place because the whole area is 'off-limits' to UNFICYP personnel and today I'm officially a member of the force.

We're travelling at a steady 50mph, keeping within the speed limit, just. Unless our car breaks down, we're not permitted to stop. My driver tells me the Turks are logging the time we pass each of their positions and notifying the ones ahead. I'm impressed by the way Turkish soldiers snap to attention and salute our vehicle. It's quite different in the south. If the Greek soldiers bother to acknowledge our UN existence, it's only with a desultory nod.

'The Turkish army is very disciplined,' my driver says. 'They're a bit like us. Professionals. Them Greeks, they're a bit shambolic, but I still wouldn't want to mix it with them.'

Wherever we go our two-way radio is kept on, ready for us to make contact with UNFICYP headquarters should we run into any difficulties. Our call-sign is UN 153, Uniform November One Five Three, the same as the registration plates on our black Ford.

When we reach the outskirts of Famagusta, I suggest a short diversion from the route authorized by the Turks, of which, quite rightly the Lance-Corporal driver disapproves. 'I want to go to the mayor's house,' I tell him. 'I don't think Mr Atun will file any complaints against us.'

'Okay, sir,' the driver replies, 'but if there's any trouble, I'll leave it to you to explain to my boss.'

For the record his boss is the MPIO, Major Cedric Mercer.

Outside the Turkish Cypriot Mayor's house
In Famagusta, Turkish-controlled northern Cyprus
12.50 hours

'Good grief! I didn't know you were in Cyprus. How delightful to see you, old boy. Is the family with you?' That's how Bora Atun, the Turkish Cypriot Mayor of Famagusta, greeted me a few minutes ago on the veranda of his house, another relic of colonial days. The British-trained architect was visibly surprised to see me and the UN car. I had interrupted his shower and he came to the front door wrapped only in a damp towel.

'Come inside,' said Bora. 'Let me offer you a drink.' I replied that we couldn't accept his invitation as we had already broken Turkish rules imposed on UN personnel and felt nervous.

'Come on,' Bora roared. 'Bring your driver as well. I'll telephone AUSCON and tell them you have been delayed. I know them very well.'

'Don't do that,' I replied. 'We'll be in trouble. After all, it's your lot, your administration that restricts UN movement in the north.'

Bora did not contradict me, but gave an apology of sorts. 'It's not my fault, David. It's the military and matters of security. I know what we can do instead; we will eat lunch together at the Salamis Bay Hotel. The UN is allowed there without problems. AUSCON is on the way and I will travel in your car. Mine is off the road, waiting for a spare part.'

'No,' I replied. 'Not possible. Turkish Cypriots aren't allowed to ride in UN vehicles. You'll have to order yourself a taxi and follow us. If we get stopped by the Turkish army, I'll blame you, saying we didn't want to cause a diplomatic incident by turning down your invitation.'

Bora smiled and returned indoors to dress.

A few minutes later we received a call on the car radio from UNFICYP HQ asking us to verify our position. With the engine running in the background, my driver replied ambiguously: 'We're leaving Famagusta for AUSCON on the road to Salamis.' He turned to me and added, 'You won't put that in your radio programme?'

Now we're on our way again.

Tape 7

AUSCON
OP ALPHA 28 in Sector Six
UN Buffer Zone, near Famagusta
13.30 hours

Lieutenant Peter Meyer of the Austrian contingent has walked me to the edge of a low cliff and we look out to sea. A small hut and a tall sentry box painted in UNFICYP colours stand on an island some 100 yards ahead. The waters of Famagusta Bay this afternoon are calm and deep blue, with only a light sprinkling of white caps on the surface. When storms whip the sea, angry waves can submerge the tiny rock path which connects OP ALPHA 28 and its five soldiers to the shoreline.

On our left, I see the browns and greens of the Karpas mountains which appear faintly in the heat haze. Meyer points to the deserted apartments and hotel blocks of Varosha, the former Greek Cypriot holiday resort. Guarded by the Turkish army, this is the so-called 'forbidden city'.

'Syria is only 60 miles away to our front,' Meyer tells me. 'Do you know, its national flag has a star to represent Cyprus? Everybody wants to claim this island.'

Here at ALPHA 28 we've reached the land limit of the UNFICYP Buffer Zone, but now an imaginary line begins, extending through the sea. It's called the MSL or Maritime Security Line.

'As in the case of the other OPs we may only observe, warn and report, but our duties include watching for ships at sea,' Meyer explains. 'No ship is supposed to cross the MSL. Military craft very rarely break the rules, but upwards of a dozen civilian vessels intrude into the zone during some 24-hour periods. They are mainly fishing-boats, because these waters have more fish than elsewhere. The fish are not stupid; they know it is safer here with UNFICYP.

'Look, this is my log-book in which I must record exactly what we see. At 09.25, for example, there was an incursion by a Turkish fishing-boat which crossed the Line, proceeding from the NE to SW, 300 metres off the shore. We fired two red warning flares and he turned back.'

What does Meyer think of his UNFICYP service?

'It's a beautiful life here,' he answers. 'We can swim and we can cook for ourselves, often grilling the fish which we catch.'

So you're a bit like salaried tourists?

'No, no, this is not right. It is is very hard to stand in the hot sun of Cyprus in a sentry-box only six metres square,' Meyer insists. 'We are on duty 12 to 14 hours a day for three weeks. It is like being in a hospital. We have a fine dinner, but we have no contact with people.'

The last time I visited Cyprus, Bora Atun told me a story which I hope Meyer can confirm.

Apparently a British businessman arrived at Ayia Napa on the Greek Cypriot side for a three-week holiday, bringing his secretary, a very attractive female, with him as a partner. Back in London he had told his wife that the secretary was necessary because he had a lot of business to conduct.

Soon after their arrival, the couple rented a motor-cruiser to sail round *Cape Greco* lighthouse and then northwards up the coast in search of a secluded lagoon where they could concentrate. On the way they became so involved with their professional activities that unknowingly they sailed over the Maritime Security Line, failing to see the warning flares fired by the Austrians at ALPHA 28.

Now they were in Turkish Cypriot waters off Varosha. A Turkish navy patrol-boat spotted them and tried to make contact. When radio calls went unanswered, the Turks fired a warning shot across the bows of the motor-cruiser. The sound of the canon broke the businessman and his secretary's concentration and brought them on deck in a hurry.

Shocked to see armed Turkish sailors heading towards them on the starboard side, the couple realized they were in trouble and turned their vessel about and tried to race for the safety of southern waters. Lacking sailing experience and in a panic, the businessman ran his craft on to rocks. The chase was over and instead of a sea-battle, the Turks found themselves mounting a rescue.

Once the Britons were collected from the sea, the Turks sailed with them for Famagusta port, where the couple were questioned. Having satisfied themselves that the two people were not Greek Cypriot saboteurs, the northern authorities agreed to hand them to UNFICYP for a safe return to their holiday hotel in Ayia Napa. But while they waited for the UN to arrive, the Turkish Cypriots decided to demonstrate local hospitality. However, they had a problem to overcome.

According to Bora, the businessman was only wearing swimming-trunks when he'd been arrested and his secretary was without the top of her bikini. To bring an end to their embarrassment, the local military commander's wife was asked to provide clothes. For the man she raided her husband's wardrobe for a suit and for the girl she supplied one of her own dresses.

Twenty-four hours later, after a big dinner, several drinks and a hastily-organized press conference at the which the couple praised the Turks highly for their courtesy and generosity, the two Britons were back in the south.

At the end of Bora's tale, which I suppose could have been an elaborate Turkish joke, one of his friends added: 'I do believe it is very unwise for a boss to give a secretary dictation without clothes in a military zone. Turkish soldiers may understand the situation, but will a wife?'

Lieutenant Peter Meyer says he can neither confirm or deny this incident, but I notice he has raised his binoculars and is looking very closely at a sailing-ship on the horizon.

Tape 8

SWEDCON HQ,
Sector Five
Larnaca in Greek-controlled southern Cyprus
16.00 hours

My driver and I have reached the headquarters of the Swedish contingent, SWEDCON, on the outskirts of Larnaca. We have two reasons for being here. First it's a place to pick up some light refreshments as we've eaten nothing since the morning; secondly, I want to meet Sergeant Dennis Labdon, nick-named 'Mr Land-Rover'.

We had hoped to eat lunch at the Salamis Bay Hotel as guests of the Turkish Cypriot Mayor of Famagusta, but we misread our watches. Time, as well as religion, language, culture and politics, divides north from south. Usually, time-changes occur when travelling east or west, but it's different in Cyprus. Here, in the south, on the Greek Cypriot side, it's four o'clock in the afternoon, but in the north, it's five in the evening, simply because nobody can even agree a common time for the two areas. That one hour's difference caused us to miss Bora.

To reach Larnaca we drove through the British Sovereign Base of Dhekelia with its tidy rows of semi-detached houses, neat gardens, polished NAAFI supermarkets and golf course, arriving at the coastal road which is on Republic of Cyprus territory.

A mile or so outside ESBA the Greek Cypriot police have a road-block through which we passed without a hitch, but most other vehicles, especially large trucks, were stopped and searched. I'm told that smuggling thrives, involving the peoples of both sides.

Greek and Turkish Cypriots work in the Sovereign Base, the latter group entering at a British army check-point outside Famagusta. Many of these Turkish Cypriots were employed by the British as policemen prior to the events of 1974 and continue to work side by side with Greek Cypriot civilians. There's also a 'mixed' village at Pyla, where, it's alleged, the smuggling deals are made. The trade is centred on the northerners selling lamb and beef for Republic of Cyprus pounds which have a high rate of exchange against the Turkish lira. It's rumoured that Scotch whisky, plentiful in the shops of Famagusta, moves south in return for English gin taken in the opposite direction. Because gin is produced by the Turks, imported brands carry a heavy tax. Scotch does not. These spirits are exchanged on a one-for-one bottle basis, because whisky in the south is very expensive.

As the Greek Cypriot police check-point is on the only road out of the Sovereign Base, it suggests that, to ensure a profit, there must be some private arrangement between the poachers and the gamekeepers. None of this concerns UNFICYP and the Swedes of Sector Five.

On our approach to Larnaca I noticed several holiday hotels in various stages of development, and the silver tanks of the adjacent oil refinery. This refinery satisfies all the needs of the south and fulfils some of the fuel requirements of the north, as oil and gas still move across the cease-fire line in vast tankers at the Ledra Palace check-point.

Larnaca, in ancient times, was called *Kition*. It was a prominent trading port and a centre of learning. With the loss of Famagusta to the Turkish Cypriots, Larnaca is regaining some of its old value as a commercial and tourist town. *Zeno*, the *Stoic* philosopher, was born here, and *Lazarus* came to live in the town after his resurrection. His tomb is in a local Greek Orthodox church, but his mortal remains are to be found in Marseilles. More transitory by nature are the flame-coloured flamingos whose migratory base is the great salt lake which they use on their seasonal flights between Europe and Asia.

These days tourists fly to Larnaca airport, which was set up rapidly after the loss of Nicosia International in 1974. The increasing number from Europe amply compensates for the loss of pilgrims from the east who used to flock to the *Hala Sultan Tekke*. Situated three miles west of the salt lake and bounded by lush vegetation, its golden dome and minarets shimmer in the evening sun. Buried here is *Umm Haram*, claimed to be Mohammed's foster-aunt. She died during the first Arab attack on Cyprus in AD 647. Theologians may argue about her relationship to The Prophet, but nobody disputes that the Tekke is the third most important place of Muslim pilgrimage after the *Kaaba* at Mecca and the *Shrine* at Medina. Today the Tekke is little more than a museum.

In 1965 the Greek Cypriot National Guard occupied it and ordered out the *Hodja*, Hadj İbrahim Sidki Yavaş, a venerable priest who spoke five languages, none of which did him any good in persuading his Christian neighbours to permit him to continue his services.

Nowadays visitors wander at will between 08.00 and 17.00 after paying an entrance fee which goes to the coffers of the Republic's

At the EMI studios in Manchester Square, London, for The Beatles' first recording session, David Carter asks the young Merseysiders if they think their music will have lasting appeal!

David Carter at work presenting his daily BBC show, Lunch a la Carter, in the '70s

David Carter records some Cyprus tapes with Colonel H. W. K. Pye at Blue Beret Camp in the UN Protected Area in Nicosia. Colonel Pye was Deputy Chief of Staff and Commander of the British Contingent in 1979

Arif Gürbüz, of the Famagusta water board, Bora Atun, the former mayor of the city, and Wendy Carter, David's actress wife

After a meeting at the Turkish Ministry of Defence, David Carter looks across
Ankara, Turkey's capital

Rauf Denktaş enthrals the ladies with stories of his favourite hobby — photography

'The Cave Ladies' — Major Betty Hunter Cowan, TD, bends David Carter's ear about the Cyprus question, while Major Phyllis Heymann, MBE, has heard it all before

Those who lost their lives at the hands of Greek Cypriots in 1974 are not forgotten at the memorial to three devastated villages outside Famagusta

Carter disregarded UN protests at his picture-taking in Varosha

EOKA continued to declare Cyprus was Greek in lettering on a broken shack in Varosha

Almost untouched by the ravages of time, the Varosha bungalow of Dr Marangos, OBE, who treated Greek and Turk alike when he lived here. Out of respect, special attention is paid to his home

While foreign-owned properties in Varosha were treated with respect by the Turkish army in 1974, these Greek National Guard barracks were set alight and left to rot

As Turkish officers look on, a civilian employee unlocks the doors of the British-owned Golden Sands Hotel in Varosha to let Carter in

THIS PLAQUE COMMEMORATES THE OPENING
OF THE GOLDEN SANDS HOTEL
BY HIS BEATITUDE ARCHBISHOP MAKARIOS III
PRESIDENT OF THE REPUBLIC OF CYPRUS
8ᵗʰ MAY 1974

Carter's first glimpse of The Golden Sands' interior, a plaque which only a few tourists got to see before the Turkish army locked and bolted the hotel in August 1974

Thick dust covers the furnishings of the hotel's lounge area, where speed boats have been stored haphazardly

A Turkish officer shows Carter the limits of the area at The Sandy Beach Hotel in Varosha that Turkish military families can use during their holidays

Department of Antiquities. Neither my driver nor I have had the time or inclination to join the tourists at the Tekke.

In the very untouristic environment of the SWEDCON motor-pool, I want Sergeant Dennis Labdon to outline his UNFICYP role. This he does quickly, using clipped phrases. 'Because British Bedford trucks and Land-Rovers are used by all UNFICYP contingents, except the Canadians, a British technician must be seconded to each to handle the vehicles' maintenance.' He's always nick-named 'Mr Land-Rover'. 'That's me. I was a bit apprehensive when I first joined the Swedes, but I'm accepted now. Their ranking structure is all over the place. Very confusing. I never know when I'm supposed to salute or not. You see, 90 per cent of the men here are civilians in uniform, volunteers who have signed on for six months' UN service in Cyprus. They wear badges to show both their civilian and military ranks. There's this one guy, for instance, who was an immigration officer in Sweden, but he works in the canteen now.

'They get paid whatever they received in civilian life, plus UN pay. It's like a working holiday for them. They are the most affluent of all us UN soldiers.'

A postscript to the Labdon interview:

Labdon admits that it's very hard not to be resentful of the Swedes' salary structure. Many of them, he says, save enough money in six months to buy an expensive car, which is why they call Cyprus 'The Volvo Posting'. The least I could do was pay for everybody's cold drinks and chocolate bars after the interview.

So much for Sergeant Labdon, a solitary Brit soldier amongst the Swedes, sweating over the engine of one of his five Bedford 10-tonners and worrying about 34 Land-Rovers. For sure, he won't have the additional burden of memorizing a Volvo maintenance manual on *his* return to the UK in three months' time.

Tape 9

BRITCON
Sector Two, OP BRAVO 22
150 yards south of Avlona village, in the Buffer Zone
18.30 hours

An hour ago the British soldiers at BRAVO 22 finished eating their evening meal and now some of them are watching a video version of The Dirty Dozen, a World War II blood-and-guts adventure starring Lee Marvin. Their make-shift living-room is hot, stuffy and filled with cigarette smoke which does nothing to hide the smell of sweat. The remaining off-duty members of the platoon are outside, shooting a football at the gap between two olive trees. The long shadows of the supports of an enormous water tank cross the rough ground. There's a tin hut on top of the tank. This is the actual OP. From a distance of about 150 yards, a group of children and a Turkish soldier are watching the action. All of them are in the Turkish-controlled village of Avlona.

Corporal Peter Friday of the 2nd Battalion The Queen's Regiment is the NCO in charge at BRAVO 22. He's taken me to the barricade separating us from the village. It consists of a three-inch-diameter pole resting on two blue-and-white oil drums on either side of the road. There's nothing really to prevent us from walking round and joining the children, but we must stay where we are and simply wave. They return our greetings with friendly laughter and then attempt to impersonate soldiers on parade by marching up and down, stomachs out, chests in. They shout, 'Hello, British soldiers', probably the only English words they know.

I've balanced my Uher on the barrier to interview Corporal Friday.

'If those Turkish kids slip over the line, and sometimes they do, we can't play with them or give them sweets and chocolates because, first of all that would encourage them even more, and secondly, we'll be accused of not being impartial if a Greek soldier sees us from his side of the line and complains.

'Then there's this old lady, a Greek Cypriot who used to live in Avlona. She keeps coming into the Buffer Zone, where she's not allowed, and stands where we are now, crying and pointing out that house over there. She says it was hers in 1974. Of course, we have to escort her back to the Greek side. She's always asking us to tell her when she'll be able to return to her home. None of us knows what to reply. Some soldiers find it very hard.'

If UNFICYP soldiers must be visible examples of absolute impartiality, satisfying the subjective views of both sides, was Corporal Friday allowed to solve the problem of the break in Avlona's water supply this morning?

'At first we weren't aware that the village had a water problem, because it gets its supplies from the UN tanks here at BRAVO 22 and, in return, we get our electricity from Avlona. As we had plenty of water we didn't realize there had been a break in the pipes to the other side, until this lad of about 14 came up to the barrier and started shouting at us. He spoke quite good English, the only person who does in Avlona. He said that they had been without water for three days. We asked him to find out if we would be allowed into the village to check the situation for ourselves. He ran back to the Turkish soldiers who nodded and waved us over.

'It was very interesting because we found that the Turkish soldiers are very much part of village life. Everybody calls them "Turkish brother soldier". We got on very well. The headman, the *mukhtar*, shook us by the hand and so did everybody else. They made us sit down and have coffee, and when we returned to our position, the soldiers saluted. Back at the OP we called up St David's and Jubilee Camp and set out to crack the problem. We brought up a bowser, that's our water-truck. We backed it up so that its wheels were on our side of the CFL, but with the taps hanging over their side. Then they came up, connected hoses and drained off the water. Until the pipes are repaired, we'll keep on doing this.'

An ingenious solution, satisfying all criteria, political and practical, I reply, but I wonder what would have happened if the Turkish boy had not spoken English. Was there anybody in the British contingent who spoke Turkish?

'Yes,' replies Corporal Friday. 'We're very fortunate because two of our lads, who are British now, came from Cyprus originally. One is Turkish and the other Greek. In fact, some of their relatives live around here.'

Did they get along? 'I knew you'd ask that,' Corporal Friday exclaims. 'Yes, they get along very well because, before anything else, they're 2 Queen's, British soldiers.'

One of the BRITCON Land-Rovers is about to leave for Jubilee Camp with a party of off-duty soldiers collected from several OPs. They've agreed to squeeze me on board the rear of the vehicle. Although I know my recordings will be very noisy, I still switch on my machine.

'I'm Corporal Thomas from Bromley.'

Are you spending an evening in Nicosia?

'Na, dahn town we're resented,' Thomas replies.

'"Bleedin' soldiers" they call us. I don't think they appreciate we're bleedin' well putting our necks on the line for them,' another soldier interjects.

'Betcha you won't tell your listeners what we really think. It's all bloody bullshit here havin' to salute fuckin' helicopters an' all because they're fuckin' UN.' That was the voice of a private with a Millwall scarf round his neck. 'What he says is true. We can be standin' in a fuckin' OP when this helicopter comes over at a tharsand feet and we 'ave to jump to attenshun and fuckin' well salute it, all for that bleedin' jumped up Austrian bastard who's the Force bloody Commander. The only fuckin' fighting he's seen as a soldier was in a bloody opera, I'll bet. Toy soldiers, that's what they are. There was this bloke who didn't salute and he got reported.'

'Hey mate.'

Yes?

'Have yer been to BRAVO 28?'

No.

'Yeah, well, you bloody well should. See how they live out there.'

'A squaddie is a squaddie. It don't matter where you are. You get paid to do a job, and you do it.'

'Na, it ain't. Dis ain't wot we wos trained for. We wos trained for war.'

'You're wrong, son. You fuckin' well know there'd be a bloody blood-bath if we wasn't here. It's the same bloody job, just a different-coloured beret.'

CHAPTER 15

SNAKES AND STONES

UNFICYP Helicopter Landing Site
United Nations Protected Area
Nicosia International airport
20.15 hours

White light floods a square of Tarmac at the edge of Nicosia International airport. Night is descending rapidly. I'm with a crowd of UN soldiers. A few minutes ago a Wessex helicopter of 84 Squadron, RAF, raced the dusk to land here. Its rotor blades had barely stopped turning before a UN ambulance rolled quickly and quietly to its side, accompanied by a small handful of officers from HQ, including a photographer. A man on a stretcher was eased smoothly from the helicopter and placed in the rear of the ambulance, which sped off into the darkness of the United Nations Protected Area.

From the time of the helicopter's touch-down to the disappearance of the ambulance, no more than 30 seconds could have passed, but it was enough for the photographer to click off several shots of the stretcher-case. The picture-taking seemed to confuse the patient, although he continued to smile and nod. If he were a bit apprehensive, it was understandable, for he was a Turkish soldier alone amongst a gaggle of UN personnel.

Flight-Sergeant Jones doesn't find the situation remarkable. For him it's simply the successful conclusion of another routine *medi-vac* mission, the last 84 Squadron will fly before its UNFICYP tasks are handed to the 'new boys' — the 18 members of the Army Air Corps stationed at Blue Beret Camp. Their squadron flies the Allouette, a smaller helicopter considered more suitable for aerial surveillance of the BZ than the Wessex or the Whirlwind.

Flight-Sergeant Jones: 'At just after 18.00, UNFICYP HQ received a request for assistance from the Turkish military, relayed through DANCON, to evacuate a seriously-injured Turkish soldier from the Kokkina enclave, up on the north coast west of Xeros. The sea was very rough and the Turks couldn't remove their man by boat. As you know, there are some very strong winds in Cyprus and they can blow up quite unexpectedly, and this is what happened at Kokkina during the afternoon.

'We heard about the request, and our briefing took place at 18.40, after it had been agreed by everybody that we could pick up the soldier. It gets quite complicated because we're not allowed simply to fly the

most direct route, even though we're going to their aid. They may feel
we'll take advantage and gather military information if we went our
way. So the Turks tell us the air corridors that they'll allow us to fly
and we suggest various landing sites we'd like to use. A sort of
contingency plan to cover all eventualities. We also have to be familiar
with the names Turks give to their places. For example Kokkina is
Erenköy.'

'Anyhow, we managed to get airborne at 19.00. When we reached
Kokkina, we found the soldier was a walking patient and so we decided,
with the Turkish army's agreement, to fly him to Delta Echo, which is a
night-landing site by a technical school in northern Cyprus. Here we
met a Turkish ambulance and one of their doctors, plus a UN ambulance.
After a short chat with the doctor we concluded it was in the interests
of the patient that we bring him to Nicosia International for transfer to
a proper hospital.

'As you saw, a UN ambulance was standing by and it picked up the
Turkish soldier. By now, it'll be at the Ledra Palace check-point. The
Turks will probably collect their soldier on their side and take him to
North Nicosia General for treatment. I reckon he'll be there by 20.30 or
thereabouts.'

While Sergeant Jones prepares to return to Akrotiri in the Western
Sovereign Base Area, one of his crewmen tells me that 84 Squadron has a
good record of responding to calls for assistance from both sides,
although the majority involve picking up Greek Cypriot civilians from
the Troodos mountains. He and Jones are disappointed that from now
on the army will handle most UNFICYP missions.

Sergeant-Major Tony Davis of the Army Air Corps is determined
that my documentary should reflect equally the efforts of his men and
so I've been invited to their crew-room for a soft drink. Tony is a short,
energetic man in his late-thirties. I met him last year when I was
producing my Christmas show for Radio London and so I don't have to
explain the types of anecdotes I want to record on this trip. A
Welshman, Tony is never short of words.

'The Army Air Corps team out here is highly experienced,' Davis
begins without prompting. 'But everybody will have to keep their wits
about them. In the Buffer Zone of Cyprus, you have to fly to very
precise limits. You can't afford to make an error of a single metre with
your map-reading. Mistakes can cause serious repercussions. *Both* sides
have threatened to shoot us down if we stray over the cease-fire line. Or,
as they put it in their protests, they "cannot be held responsible" if
anything happens. In fact, there is an instance of an RAF Whirlwind
having been shot at.

'From every viewpoint I believe UNFICYP service is worthwhile.
For the British, it is an investment. You are bound to become a very
good pilot and spotter out here, and those who are very good become
even better. That must be of value later when we return to our

conventional military duties, whether we're in Northern Ireland or Germany.

'For UNFICYP, we're able to confirm very quickly whatever the OPs report, anywhere along the 500 kilometres of the CFL. You get to know where everybody is supposed to be, and whether X or Y have moved forward, even by two metres. Anything which could blow up into a major incident can be spotted.

'When you look down, it's quite amazing to see all the defensive positions, zig-zagging all over the place. Some people say it's the nearest thing to what the World War I trenches in France must have looked like; just as static, too.'

But why do UNFICYP soldiers in their watch-towers have to salute your helicopters as they buzz the line?

Sergeant-Major Davis pretends not to hear the question and offers me another Seven-Up.

Tape 11

BRITCON
Ferret Scout Car Squadron HQ
Blue Beret Camp, United Nations Protected Area
Nicosia International airport
21.30 hours

Major Peter Rogers: 'Only when you travel the entire cease-fire line on the ground can you be aware of how important the UN task is in keeping the two sides apart.'

Rogers is the OC or Squadron Leader of the most visible show of force that UNFICYP musters. He and I are standing on the edge of Blue Beret Camp. Tonight it's the turn of the Blues and Royals to parade the UN flag along the entire length of the Buffer Zone, travelling through all sectors, irrespective which national contingent holds the ground between the Turkish army and the Greek Cypriot National Guard.

More usually associated with ceremonial parades in London and Windsor, this unit of the Household Cavalry is dismounted for six months, steeds and polished saddles exchanged for grey overalls and a seat in the grimy, cramped interior of a squat, four-wheeled Ferret scout car, nick-named 'The Mouse'. It's one of the longest-surviving vehicles in service with the British forces.

Lieutenant Ed Mountain is the commander of the two white Ferrets about to set off in a few minutes at the start of another regular night patrol. Their crews are making final checks on engines and armaments.

'We're fully bombed up, but the only thing we're ever likely to fire though is our Very pistol. We're only allowed to use our weapons as a last resort. To protect our lives.' That was the voice of one of the troopers.

A technician is wiping his hands on a dirty rag, trying to remove black oil from his fingers and nails. 'We have to do oil changes every two days,' he says. 'The bloody dust plays havoc with the filters. We often have to work on our days off to keep the vehicles in an operational state. The ground is so rugged in places that it tears the tyres to shreds.'

An engine, which has been roaring and belching black smoke from its exhaust pipes, is switched off, and a Ferret driver raises his head above the turret. 'We're all set, Mr Mountain, sir. We'll get this one up to 50mph tonight. No trouble at all.'

'As long as you don't roll the damned thing with us inside,' Mountain replies, turning to me and adding, 'David, the patrol-track winds over some damned treacherous terrain, right up to the edge of precipices.'

Lieutenant Mountain is 21.

With UN flags flying and headlights blazing, the two Ferrets pull away into the night, contravening every rule of warfare by their absolute visibility, but observing all the rules of UNFICYP which demand that they project a high profile of potential force without ever actually intervening militarily.

Major Peter Rogers: 'It's good experience for the men, being Peace Soldiers. It broadens their minds and makes the chaps more mature.'

Trooper: 'Bloody frustrating, more like it. I don't even go down town anymore. I got suckered there once, paying for those birds in Regaena Street. I don't bother now. Just get ratted instead.'

Officer and trooper agree on one thing only: men and machines are tested to the limits of their endurance in the Ferret Scout Car Squadron.

Tape 12

CANCON
Sector Four, OP 'Omorphita', Nicosia
On the Turkish side of the CFL
00.45 hours

The three young Canadian soldiers on the roof of the Omorphita OP in Sector Four sense the two opposing forces are restless tonight in their military positions. Although the Canadians have been here on duty for almost six months, they are nevertheless uneasy.

In daylight the Turkish and Greek Cypriot soldiers stare sullenly at each other across a bumpy track. About 100 yards of open space separates them. When night comes they prove their existence by making the air echo to their national anthems in an attempt to provoke the other side.

Elsewhere along the CFL the only sounds come from Ferret scout cars on patrol and UNFICYP soldiers can sleep undisturbed. But at

Omorphita, the men of the Royal 22nd Regiment from Quebec never have an uneventful night. I've been warned that very soon the singing will stop and shouting will begin. The verbal insults will fly across the BZ until dawn.

The Omorphita OP, located on the extreme eastern end of the Canadian contingent's area of responsibility, clips the edge of northern Nicosia. There's no more potentially dangerous spot in the entire Buffer Zone. Quite literally it's a minefield. Not even wild dogs and stray cats venture here.

Omorphita is both a place and name which stirs violent passions in the hearts of Cypriots everywhere. During Christmas 1963, Nicos Sampson launched waves of EOKA irregulars against the Turkish Cypriots who lived in this enclave. Turkish resistance was tough, but not strong enough to prevent the loss of many lives, including Omorphita's 70-year-old *Imam* and his crippled son. Fifty homes were smashed to their foundations and 250 others were damaged beyond repair. Five-hundred-and-fifty Turkish Cypriots were taken hostage and nobody knows how many people died in the battle.

Several years later, on 17 July 1973, the Greek Cypriot newspaper *Mahi* commented: 'Omorphita was conquered by Greek arms; conquered lands can never be returned.'

In 1974 Turkish Cypriots reclaimed Omorphita and now they look down on the Greek Cypriots from a position of military strength. Both sides can see the remnants of their fathers' actions. 'Sometimes they will hurl boulders at each other, and that is when we have to call a halt,' a Canadian sergeant tells me.

Scanning the darkness I try to spot the worst offenders. It's easier to tell where the Turks sit because our OP is a building which stands on their side of the line. Because the Turks consent to this arrangement, it suggests that they they approve CANCON's ability to referee the nightly game.

Ideally the UN observers should sit in the BZ, but there are no buildings around that are structurally safe enough to house them. They were hit hard by mortars and small arms fire during the 1974 war. As Greeks fell back, they booby-trapped many houses and these have never been cleared.

The Canadians, like the British, are professional soldiers and carry an air of authority which nobody but a fool would question. Even so they still have to accept the nightly taunts that fly across them and wait patiently for the light of morning. Only then will they get some peace and quiet to relax again.

Tape 13

BRITCON
Sector Two

Liaison Post BRAVO 36, at Peristerona
In Greek-controlled southern Cyprus
07.00 hours

Dawn comes early to Cyprus during the summer months and, for centuries, farmers have been at work in their fields by 04.30, taking advantage of every minute of light, before the heat of the day makes their labours unbearable. But today many Greek Cypriots are unable to follow their parents' traditions and must wait until well after 07.00 to begin their farming chores. These are people whose fields and orchards lie within the Buffer Zone. Without UNFICYP's determination to restore 'normal conditions wherever possible', they would not be able to farm at all.

Here in Peristerona — a tiny market town, perhaps better known for its Byzantine churches, Ayios Hilarion and the five-domed Ayios Varnavas, than its geographical position half-a-mile behind the Greek Cypriot National Guard's front-line — two farmers, Andreas and Michael, are engaged in an animated conversation outside a house with a chicken-run and a UN flag-pole. They're awaiting the arrival of a squad of BRITCON soldiers who will be their escorts for the day, accompanying them in and out of the BZ.

Colour-Sergeant Roger Furlotte and Sergeant John Foster are the two senior NCOs in charge of this operation centred on Liaison Post BRAVO 36. It's their office and home for six months of UN service. They play the role of 'farming agents', one of the most unusual jobs found in the British army.

Sector Two is a rich agricultural area divided into two distinct halves. To the east, an open valley, used by farmers to graze animals and grow vegetables, can be overseen and supervised easily by the BRITCON soldiers. They keep Greek Cypriots working behind a precise line of blue-and-white barrels, the northern limit of allowable civilian activity in the Buffer Zone. To the west, the task is more difficult. Because the land is ideal for citrus crops, the orange groves can hide farmers from view and sometimes they move too close to the cease-fire line. To ensure nothing goes wrong, BRITCON's Western Company Commander assigns 'escorts' to every farmer who wants to work his land. He does this partly to allay the fears of Greek Cypriots, but equally to prevent a headlong rush into the zone which Turkish soldiers in their watch-towers could regard as a provocation and answer with force.

While Greek Cypriots are eager to regain as much of their pre-1974 wealth by cultivating every square-inch of territory up to the cease-fire line, relying on a UN shield to protect them from the Turkish army, Turkish Cypriots view the value of the Buffer Zone differently. They prefer to keep their side of the BZ uncultivated, an open defensive strip ahead of their fixed military positions. Few Turkish Cypriot farmers are, therefore, allowed access to the area.

Officials of the Greek Cypriot administration, always quick to score points in the propaganda battle, encourage guests to look down on the Buffer Zone from their side of the line. On the Greek side, all appears green and flourishing. The Turkish side, by contrast, looks brown and dead. As a result, casual observers conclude that Greek Cypriot farmers are industrious and competent, while Turkish Cypriot farmers are not.

Far less concerned with the propaganda issues and much more with getting results in the battle to stop the entire BZ from becoming a desert, UNFICYP and BRITCON follow a steady policy, tempered with caution, of gradually re-opening more fields close to the CFL.

A few minutes ago Colour-Sergeant Furlotte took me inside his spartan accommodation and pointed to large-scale maps which identified the owners of the plots of land in the BZ. All are colour-coded. White areas may be farmed at any time without prior consent from UNFICYP, he explains, but the ones in blue must not be worked unless a farmer is escorted by a UN soldier, booked the day before. 'It may look very simple on the map, but it's very hard to differentiate one farmer's field from another when you're on the ground and it's covered in yellow flowers and long grass, or in winter when it's very slushy and boundaries get blurred.'

A truck pulls up and five soldiers get out to be paraded by Sergeant Foster, who checks their weapons and reads them a set of instructions before handing out individual assignments. 'The grass is very long out there at the moment. So don't leave your rifle on the ground. You may lose it, or you may return to find it's been run over by a tractor,' Foster warns his men. 'And I won't accept back any rifles that are bent. Do you all understand? Good. Now, have you read your white card? This is it. Right. Now you must show it if any civilian not assigned to you enters the BZ. Okay? Good.'

The white card mentioned by Sergeant Foster is *UN Field Guidance* on 'the restraint and temporary detention of civilians in the Buffer Zone'. In Greek, Turkish and English, large letters state: 'YOU ARE WITHIN A DANGEROUS PART OF THE UNITED NATIONS BUFFER ZONE. UNLESS YOU LEAVE IMMEDIATELY YOU WILL BE HANDED OVER TO THE POLICE.'

If offenders refuse, UN soldiers are expected to detain them until 'appropriate civilian authorities' arrive, which, in this sector, means Australians in UN service. Force, the card declares, must be avoided if possible. Only as a last resort may 'minimum force' be used, its level determined by 'common sense'.

UN soldiers also carry a yellow card. This tells them how to tackle 'non-UNFICYP military personnel' entering the Buffer Zone. It categorically prohibits the use of any force 'to get the violators to leave the UN BZ' but insists that UN soldiers 'will stay in place and, if required, be reinforced until the violators have returned to their own positions'.

Sergeant Foster: 'Remember, you are to stay at all times *between* the farmer or farmers and the patrol-track. If the farmers offer you beer, you may accept, but you must bring it back here for consumption later. And if I catch any of you asleep, you'll be for the high jump. Right then, off you get.'

For each UN soldier there's one or more Greek Cypriot to escort. Private Fleming, barely 19, collects his charges. They are Andreas and Michael. Fleming alone will be responsible for their welfare until 17.00, or earlier if the farmers want to go home.

Michael speaks English in slow, fractured phrases but I record him nevertheless. 'I was very afraid from the Turks before I went to irrigate my orchard, because I was arrested by Turkish soldiers. I remember very well. It was 20 of July 1974. I hope I am safe now with a UN man,' he says. 'Since British come we have no more problems.'

Andreas has told Fleming he intends to take his children with him to pick oranges, but he has promised to keep them well away from the forward edge of his field as there's a Turkish OP 30 yards from the far side of the patrol-track and he does not want them to be seen.

'There are lots of farmers like Andreas who are still very frightened by what happened in '74,' Colour-Sergeant Furlotte says. 'They'll work quite happily if there's a UN soldier with them. But when they get close to the forward positions of the Turkish army, they talk in whispers. During the picking season the women actually hide inside the trees. All you see are oranges disappearing *into* the tree!'

Armed with their cards, a rifle with a magazine containing 20 rounds of ammunition, a canteen of water and Sergeant Foster's orders still ringing in their ears, the young BRITCON soldiers trundle northwards with their motley collection of men, women and children in a convoy of battered tractors and spluttering trucks. I'll follow later in a mud-splattered Land-Rover.

'When you get there, watch out. They'll keep offering you peeled oranges which they'll want you to eat,' Furlotte warns. 'One of our soldiers ate about 80 during a single day and had to be rushed to hospital with citrus poisoning.' For the time being I settle for a breakfast of bacon and eggs cooked by the sergeant.

On the way to the Buffer Zone, Colour-Sergeant Furlotte waves to a passing Greek Cypriot on a bicycle. The man smiles and returns the greeting. 'Some of our work is like being a village bobby, because the local police aren't allowed in the BZ. Before we came out, we took a crash course in Greek, but we needn't have bothered. Farming Greek out here is very different and more people speak English than we expected. They've all got relatives in London.'

Furlotte retires soon from the army and plans to settle in Norfolk, where he hopes to build a small market garden, something he had never thought of doing until he came to Cyprus and became involved in the local agricultural scene. He says he has learned a lot out here.

BRITCON policy allows the farming NCOs to work with a minimum of supervision. Both Furlotte and Foster appreciate this. They consider their mission at BRAVO 36 one of the most interesting to have come their way in their entire army career. Watching fields being re-opened gives them great satisfaction, they say.

Because of the summer heat, the two farming NCOs, like others in BRITCON, are concerned about the risk of fires in the BZ and the need to cut fire-breaks. 'Out there, in the west side, there was a very serious fire recently. It burnt more than 400 orange trees,' Sergeant Foster tells me. Colour-Sergeant Furlotte adds, 'When the people want to cut fire-breaks they tell us and we inform the Company Commander, who, in turn, informs his Turkish opposite number to let him know what's going on. As yet we've never had a refusal from the Turks.'

Sergeant Foster: 'Everybody seems to get together on the common problem of fire. There's never any hesitation about coming across the line to put them out. Of course, they don't want a fire spreading any more than we do. After all, their OPs are wooden towers surrounded by dry grass.'

It's 07.55. Soon senior staff at UNFICYP HQ will be assembling again to hear the morning report. I expect the Canadian major to conclude once again: 'It's been another quiet 24 hours. There have been no violations of the cease-fire by shooting.'

CHAPTER 16

THE NORTHWIND PATROL

WHEN Captain Hurley's Land-Rover with Carter aboard roared to a halt outside Kyrenia's only police station, of more concern to the policemen on duty was how much red mullet had been caught the night before, and what profits they were likely to collect from their moonlighting activities, than the state of crime and punishment in northern Cyprus or even the arrival of UNFICYP on their doorstep. Like their uniformed colleagues the world around, they subscribed to W.S. Gilbert's lyrical notion that a policeman's lot was not a happy one. Not even this attractive location offered them adequate consolation, nor did the sight of empty cells lessen their determination to add a few more legitimate lira to their families' bank accounts.

Hurley and Carter's presence was merely a minor interruption in the smooth flow of business ideas designed to improve their financial status. For this task a pocket calculator was far more useful than whether or not they had the right to carry weapons. Of course they knew how to use guns, but they never carried any. In fact they would be hard pressed to remember the last time they had arrested a law-breaker, let alone chased one in hot pursuit.

Their most dangerous assignments these days were sorting out infrequent arguments over land rights between veteran Turkish Cypriots, residents of nearby villages, and the more recent arrivals from the south since 1974. The next most taxing tasks were escorting UNFICYP officers to routine meetings with elderly Greek Cypriots and Maronites who continued to reside in the immediate vicinity, and checking the documents of visitors like Carter to ensure that the security of northern Cyprus was not being endangered.

As Detective Nafi had made it his special business to handle the UN, and he was out on his rounds, both Constable Sönmez and Sergeant Görmüş decided Carter's papers were in order and there was nothing much more for the two policeman to do except to welcome the Britons with traditional, open-hearted Turkish Cypriot hospitality.

Coffee and conversation having been exhausted, as far as Captain Hurley was concerned it was 'time to get cracking — don't want to get behind schedule'. But Nafi had not returned and his current whereabouts were not known. Without him nobody would be allowed to move on, and so BRITCON's Economics Officer would have to exercise patience while the policemen practised their rusting English.

Sergeant Görmüş, the policeman turned fisherman (or was it the other way round?), wanted Carter to tell him what he thought of life in the north since the Turkish Cypriots had taken charge. He was surprised to hear that the man from the BBC was not a newcomer nor seeing Kyrenia for the first time. As Carter had spent the previous three days in the resort, Görmüş was surprised that the police had not known of the producer's presence.

'You are very lucky and must be highly trusted,' one of the two policemen remarked, giving a knowing smile as if to suggest Carter had friends in high places. 'Most journalists have to be watched. Some of them are very untrustworthy. They are sent here to spy for the Greeks.'

These policemen were pleasant fellows, but their views were not original; many officials in northern Cyprus held them. They were paranoid about journalists breaching military security and revealing the north's secrets to the enemy. Turkish Cypriots gave media people abilities which few possessed. Moreover, if Greek Cypriots wanted classified material, they definitely did not need Fleet Street hacks and the BBC to do their dirty work.

Nevertheless the discussion made Carter feel uncomfortable, a bit like waiting to pass through Customs. His camera and tape-recorder, the tools of his trade, appeared to threaten these Turkish Cypriots whose company he enjoyed. To lessen the effect, he discreetly moved the equipment out of sight, sliding his bags under the UN Land-Rover, and pretended to be relaxed as they continued to wait for Nafi.

The morning air felt crisp and clean as they stood by the edge of the empty moat which separated the police station from the bulky mass of Kyrenia's Byzantine castle. The tiny harbour below was filled with rows of brightly painted-yachts and motor-cruisers, outnumbering many times over the drabber, but no less picturesque, fishing boats which were moored where tourists would not notice them. One of the craft belonged to Görmüş, his insurance against the rising cost of living. The scene was one of peace and beauty. It deserved publicity, not confidentiality.

To the left of where the group stood, a grey stone wall curved round to meet the entrance of St Andrew's Anglican church, open, empty, and as quiet as the cells in the prefabricated police station. Both had outlived their colonial builders and both had known busier times.

'May I see your permission from the PIO to confirm you are allowed to be here this morning to join the Northwind Patrol?' The question was framed politely, but coldly stated. Nafi had arrived. He was an olive-skinned man with bright, penetrating eyes. His civilian clothes were scruffy, both open-necked shirt and crumpled grey trousers past their wear-by date.

Nafi took Carter's document, unfolded it slowly and studied carefully the type-written lines of Turkish and the several stamps and signatures which adorned the sweat-stained piece of yellow foolscap paper. It was no more legible than a British doctor's prescription. To make certain he did not miss a single vital point, the policeman ran his forefinger along every line, seeming to count each comma and full-stop.

The more he read, the less happy he became.

Something had proved unsatisfactory because he took Captain Hurley by the arm and walked him a short distance away, out of earshot. Glancing in Carter's direction from time to time, they whispered together. Then they returned, frowning.

'Nafi says you've got to stay here,' Captain Hurley said, hardly disguising his irritation with the Turkish Cypriot plainclothes policeman. 'It appears you must be accompanied, not only by us and Nafi, but by somebody from the Public Information Office in Nicosia.'

'If the Turkish Cypriot PIO wants me to have one of its reps, then don't you think that Nafi had better telephone Nicosia and get one here as soon as possible,' Carter replied. 'Whatever he thinks, I'm coming with you. The TFSC administration has given me its word and this official documentation.' He took the paper from Nafi's fingers and added, looking him in the face, 'I don't recall any occasion when a Turk has broken his word and I'm sure you won't allow that to happen today.'

Hurley waited for Nafi to respond, but it was Sergeant Görmüş who broke the silence. He suggested that he make the telephone call to Nicosia. Nobody disagreed.

While they waited for him to return, Carter reflected on how Major Tim Whitehead at UNFICYP had warned that the chances of securing permission to meet the Maronites in the north were very slim. 'That's because the Northwind Patrol goes through Turkish military areas,' he said. 'And then there's the business of how Turks are supposed to treat the Maronites and Greek Cypriots left in the north. These are very sensitive matters for the Turkish Cypriot administration.' Which was, of course, why Carter wanted to see for himself and not rely on second-hand impressions collected from UNFICYP drivers employed on these missions.

Two different Northwind Patrols took place on a fortnightly basis, part of the humanitarian relief programme assigned to UNFICYP and the Red Cross to fulfil the Security Council's mandate. One patrol was the responsibility of AUSCON, the other was conducted by BRITCON.

Both patrols, although supervised by the relevant sector's contingent, relied entirely on British army drivers and vehicles from either UNFICYP or the Sovereign Bases.

AUSCON concerned itself with the diminishing population of elderly Greek Cypriots who were in the Karpas. They numbered about 850 people, mainly over the age of 65.

What exactly went on in the Karpas was largely a mystery because, since 1974, very few Cypriots, Turkish or Greek, had been allowed to visit the rugged area at the eastern extremity of the island, and representatives of the foreign press and broadcasting organizations were banned completely.

'The Karpas is really a beautiful place,' one of the UN drivers had told Carter. 'When we get to the villages the people wave and are very happy to see us. We get a meal, which they don't have to provide. Most of them are very old. The youngest that I've seen is about 60. I don't think they'd survive without us.'

A typical Northwind Patrol to the Karpas consisted of three UN vehicles which carried about 12 tons of foodstuffs and fuel oils donated by the UN High Commissioner for Refugees, as well as individual parcels and mail from relatives, collected by the Greek Cypriot Red Cross.

BRITCON looked after the six or so Greek Cypriots still living in Kyrenia plus the three Maronite communities in the vicinity of Cape Kormakiti on the northern coast. It also transported medical supplies from various international agencies to the Turkish central hospital in Nicosia.

One UNFICYP driver to the hospital said, 'They are great to us. They give us a meal, and they take care of us very well.'

Despite the regular UN visits to these isolated communities of non-Turkish Cypriots, Greek Cypriot officials continued to insist that their people were being harshly treated and expressed concern for their welfare. They argued that the TFSC was pressurizing these people to quit their properties in the north. Understandably the Turkish Cypriot authorities denied these charges and told Carter that, if anything, the Greek Cypriots and Maronites were often better off than their own people because of the Red Cross aid.

However, one Turkish Cypriot army officer admitted candidly, 'If I were a Greek Cypriot living in the Karpas, I would not feel comfortable. I would be unhappy knowing that my own people were not the government any more and that if there were more troubles, my movements would be restricted.

'But, having said that,' he continued, 'remember it was much worse for my people when the Greek Cypriots tried to control us. We lived in constant fear of our lives. At least these people do not have that worry.'

For both sides it had been an awesome task after the war to re-settle the island's 250,000 refugees. For the Turkish Cypriot administration the burden was extremely heavy as northern Cyprus received financial support from Turkey only. The Greek Cypriot side fared better due to massive amounts of foreign aid which it received because the international community recognized the state.

While UN agencies monitored the precise numbers of Greek Cypriots and Maronites in the north, they had less accurate figures on how many Turkish Cypriots remained in southern areas. Their estimates suggested there were fewer than 200, of whom about 80 lived in the area of Limassol.

'One day you should try to see our people in Greek Cyprus and report on whether they are treated as well as we treat their people in the

north,' a TFSC official had challenged Carter. He had sounded like
George Tsigarides's friend who made similar remarks about the north
four years earlier. 'Judge for yourself who is telling the most truth,
Mr David. Them or us.'

Carter had asked UNFICYP to arrange for him to meet Turkish
Cypriots in the south and the Greek Cypriots and Maronites in the
north. His request was put to both administrations by the MPIO.

The Greek Cypriot PIO replied that permission would not be
granted for Carter to accompany UNFICYP officers on the Southwind
Patrol, organized by DANCON, because Turkish Cypriots were
integrated citizens of the Republic of Cyprus and *they* did not want to
be singled for special attention.

Major Tim Whitehead was surprised by the Greek Cypriot side's
reaction. He had expected the Greeks to agree and the Turks to refuse.
He speculated that the Greek Cypriots' refusal could have been due to
the fact their government insisted the Turkish Cypriots in the south
were not refugees, *officially*. Granting a journalist permission to
accompany the Southwind Patrol would be an acknowledgement of UN
aid and an admission that Turkish Cypriots were experiencing
difficulties, thereby undermining the administration's claims to the
contrary.

There was another possible reason why the Greek Cypriots had
refused. It was an open secret that there were several young Turkish
Cypriots in the Limassol area. They had run there to escape military
conscription in the north. After being used for propaganda purposes,
the Greek Cypriot authorities turned their backs on them. Some
returned to the north chastened by their experiences.

Unable to meet and talk to any of these Turkish Cypriots, young or
old, Carter was left to quote other people — neutrals like 2nd
Lieutenant L. H. Truelsen of DANCON. In the April 1983 edition of
The Blue Beret, the journal of the United Nations Force in Cyprus, he
described his contact with Turkish Cypriots in the Paphos district. He
had spoken to 30 while checking their well-being.

'Most of them are elderly single people who were born and have
lived all their lives in Paphos. A few are farmers and landowners, some
with large estates and hundreds of goats and sheep,' he wrote.

Truelsen, DANCON's Economics Officer, described how he
delivered mail and passed on information about their friends and
relatives in the north. He photographed Hassan Hasip, Mustafa Hassan
and his wife, and Emine Ahmet Kommatos, a woman in her eighties.

With his colleagues, Truelsen arranged meetings between the
Turkish Cypriots of Paphos and their relatives in the TFSC. These
meetings took place at the Ledra Palace hotel on 'neutral' ground, with
Australian and Swedish UN civil police present. 'Here, families are
reunited for a few hours, often under heart-rending circumstances,' he
said. 'A family may be trying to convince a son that he should return to

his family on the other side. Whatever the outcome, the meetings end in tears.'

There were cases, too, where Turkish Cypriots requested a permanent transfer to the north. These were investigated by the humanitarian branch of UNFICYP to establish whether the person was making the request of their own free will. Some situations gave cause for concern.

Carter had managed to talk to one elderly woman who left her home in the south to settle in Famagusta. She claimed that Greek Cypriots were determined to absorb Turkish Cypriots so thoroughly that they pressurized them to denounce their Turkish origins and attempted to convert them from Muslims to Christians.

Without permission to meet the Turkish Cypriots in the south, Carter would not be able to substantiate what the woman told him, nor could he accept the statements of the Greek Cypriot PIO without question.

Oktay Oksuzoğlu, who headed the Turkish Cypriot Public Information Office, had been shocked when Carter told him of the allegations made by the woman in Famagusta. He insisted that no Muslim would become a Christian unless they were seriously threatened. No wonder Andreas Sophocleous, the director of the Foreign Press section of the Greek Cypriot PIO, did not want Turkish Cypriots to be seen by journalists, Oksuzoğlu had argued, immediately approving Carter's request to visit the Maronites on the next Northwind Patrol.

Carter's dealings with Oksuzoğlu had always been satisfactory in the past and there was no reason to doubt the Turkish Cypriot's good intentions, but he still wanted the paper granting permission to be signed and sealed before minds changed. Within 48 hours Major Whitehead had collected the document from northern Nicosia. For reasons not given, Carter was not granted *carte blanche*. He was prohibited from *recording* conversations with Maronites or their meetings with the UN observers; nor was permission granted for any photography.

Major Whitehead had advised Carter not argue against these restrictions, but to accept in good grace what the authorities had granted. He would be allowed to see what went on and that was a significant achievement as no other journalist had been allowed before. 'It is the very first time,' he said. 'Be satisfied.'

Now, in Kyrenia, several days later, Carter was running into difficulties because Oksuzoğlu had not explained the Turkish small print in the document. 'There has been a misunderstanding,' Sergeant Görmüş explained on his return from the police station. Turkish Cypriots had the tedious knack of often stating the obvious. Only their generally charming demeanour stopped Carter from reacting crossly. 'Your escort, Mr David, has been waiting for you at the Ledra Palace checkpoint. He did not realize you would be crossing with the UN. He will be here soon.'

'How soon?' Carter asked, aware that time-keeping was not a Cypriot virtue, particularly in the north. 'Soon,' Görmüş smiled back. 'But his car is having difficulties.'

'Don't tell me it's missing a part?'

'Yes,' Görmüş said, 'you are very well informed.'

'How will he keep up with our vehicles?' Captain Hurley wanted to know.

'You will give him a lift in your Land-Rover.'

'Not on your nelly,' exclaimed Captain Hurley, sharply. 'When he eventually gets here, he can hitch a ride with you, Nafi.'

'But I have only a Volkswagen. Very small and very hot,' Nafi said apologetically. 'I was hoping that we may all stay together. It is important that we know what Mr Carter is doing at all times. Do you agree, Captain Hurley?'

Captain Hurley sighed. 'All right.' He knew it was pointless to argue details if the Northwind Patrol were to start rolling today.

Some conversation and a cold drink later, Carter's escort arrived, his dust-covered Murat wheezing its way up to the police station and spluttering to a stop.

The Northwind Patrol was ready to start.

Sergeant Görmüş smiled with satisfaction. He had just heard the market price for red mullet. It was to his advantage.

Passing The Dome Hotel, Carter asked Captain Hurley to stop outside the Barclays bank. He had a long overdue promise to keep. He dashed inside, saw Mr Sami behind the counter and passed him a small collection of Victor Sylvester dance music albums. 'Better late than never,' he exclaimed breathlessly. 'Can't stop. I'm with the UNFICYP patrol outside.'

'But Mr Carter,' replied Mr Sami, 'you have kept only part of your promise. You also promised to share hospitality with me. There are so many questions I wish to ask you. Does UNFICYP think our government will declare proper independence soon?'

'I think UNFICYP would like to know the answer as much as you,' Carter laughed. 'But I promise, Mr Sami, I'll be back one day to have coffee with you. On that day, perhaps you'll promise to give me Turkish lira for my sterling travellers' cheques.'

'Ah,' said Mr Sami, shaking his head, 'that will be the day when Barclays will not be here any more.'

At a location west of Kyrenia on the coastal road, agreed in advance by the Turkish authorities and UNFICYP, the Northwind Patrol formed a convoy. Under the command of a weather-beaten Turkish sergeant, a former paratrooper with 14 years' service, a Jeep-load of soldiers led the way to Kormakiti. Next came a Land-Rover driven by two Australians, UN civil policemen, followed by a 10-ton Bedford truck with Driver Ralph Cresswell of Muswell Hill at the wheel; on board were Red Cross supplies of fuel and food. The last vehicle was another Land-Rover. It carried Captain Hurley and Carter in its front seats and Nafi, the Turkish Cypriot policeman, and the PIO escort in the rear.

By noon the convoy reached the first of the three Maronite villages, passing a Turkish army camp on the outskirts. Even there, fields were cultivated, green and watered. The village itself appeared little different from any other Carter had seen in the rural areas of Cyprus, except there was nobody of his age. This puzzled him because they had stopped outside a nursery school packed with bright, beaming youngsters, aged between three and nine. Where were their parents?

'Working in the south, making a very good living,' Captain Hurley replied. 'When the children reach secondary school age, they will move to the south for their further education. Meanwhile, their grandparents bring them up.'

Driver Cresswell of the Royal Corps of Transport started to unload his truck. The rest of the Turkish and UNFICYP representatives entered the village hall where the Maronite headman sat at the top of a long table. Hurley and he began checking names, supplied by the Greek Cypriot Red Cross, against a list of rations brought by the convoy. When both were satisfied that names and quantities of food matched, the Maronite signed on a dotted line — proof that he had received everything sent from the south.

Next on the agenda was hearing complaints. Prohibited from recording these conversations on tape, Carter scribbled, 'If there are any complaints, it will take a brave Maronite to voice them when there's a Turkish officer present,' he wrote.

The only complaint declared on this occasion was directed against UNFICYP and Captain Hurley. The headman claimed they were receiving insufficient food supplies, that their colour television set should have been a better model, and, with the advent of Easter, no poster paints had been delivered for the children to colour their eggs. As a concluding thought, the Maronite leader suggested Hurley investigate the possibility of getting them UN-style boots for use by the men of the village.

Captain Hurley made copious notes; so did the Turkish army officer and the civilian policemen from Australia and north Cyprus. Within half-an-hour the meeting was over and everybody was on the move again for the next village, where the exercise was repeated with little variation.

The final destination was Kormakiti itself, less a village, much more a small town by the standards of Cyprus. Today it was called *Koruçam* by the Turks. The inhabitants here ranged from babes in arms to elderly folk on sticks, who looked as if a slight breeze would blow them away.

By this stage of the Northwind Patrol Carter had established a friendly relationship with the Turkish soldiers and they turned their attentions to other things when he set up his Uher to record the sound of children at play outside the Maronite church. However, they were still not willing for him to interview local people, even less a very lively café owner called Lorenzo, who had a perfect grasp of English.

The firm decision of the Turkish officers appeared not to upset Lorenzo, who had been eager to talk. Instead he invited everybody into his café for cold drinks and coffee, including Driver Cresswell.

Carter assumed the drinks were 'on the house' and without paying went outside again to help unload Cresswell's Bedford, which still carried half its load. No sooner had his feet touched the pavement than Lorenzo presented a scribbled bill for the refreshments, payment demanded in Greek Cypriot currency, not Turkish lira.

Meanwhile Cresswell had rolled up his shirt-sleeves and was already lifting off crates from his truck while a healthy bunch of Maronite males stood by idly observing the sweating British soldier. Carter had no authority to intervene, but he told the RCT driver to stop until the villagers showed some willingness to help.

Failing to get any response from the Maronites, Carter grabbed Lorenzo and told him to organize a working party or else the truck would remain loaded.

The Maronites believed the threat and the removal of flour sacks and boxes of apples and tomatoes began at last. Why the Greek Cypriot Red Cross thought it necessary to send these to the Maronites was a puzzle; similar fruits and vegetables were growing in profusion everywhere in the immediate surroundings.

'We also have crates of sardines, corned beef, cheese and macaroni on board for individual families,' Cresswell remarked. 'They always want extras, which we can't supply, and sometimes they come to you and try to make private deals.'

The Turkish army officer watched the Maronites unloading the truck with wry amusement before joining the two Britons on the church steps, where he added some comments of his own. 'They sell on the black market,' he said. 'They have so many things which Turkish Cypriots do not get. Sometimes these people become very spoiled. It is good to see them working today. Usually your UN soldiers have to do all the hard work. We are not allowed to order the Maronites, but you can.' He smiled broadly.

Once the Bedford was empty, Captain Hurley asked the headman to sign for the supplies, but the headman refused. A sack of seed-potatoes had gone astray and, unless it was found or replaced, there would be no Maronite signature.

At UNFICYP HQ in Nicosia, an officer had warned Carter that 'a love-hate relationship exists with the Maronites' and now he could see why. He recorded his feelings in his diary: 'I can't understand why aid is given to a fit and healthy community, when that aid consists of the very items the people grow and sell here for themselves. They're also given cash, which makes them richer than the Turkish Cypriots who live alongside them. Who can blame the Turkish Cypriots for feeling resentful? I shouldn't mind being a Maronite refugee in Kormakiti.'

(Much later, Carter raised these matters with George Tsigarides of the CTO. 'You don't understand,' George replied impatiently. 'These people are a minority group and it is the duty of our government to ensure their welfare.' Carter decided not to ask why, if that were the case, Turkish Cypriots had not been treated better by the Republic in the days before 1974).

In Kormakiti, agreement was reached at last between UNFICYP and the headman over the missing potatoes and the Northwind Patrol scurried away in a swirl of dust. Toots from the Turkish army Jeep signalled a farewell as it peeled away from the convoy on the road back to Kyrenia.

'Well, that was a pretty typical set of incidents you witnessed today,' said Captain Hurley. 'Sometimes the patrol is easier, sometimes a little more complicated. It depends whether we have to intercede with the Turkish authorities on behalf of the Maronites and report back our results.'

Captain Hurley explained that Maronites were Lebanese Roman Catholics who observed the teachings of *St Maron*. Most of them lived in the south, but those who remained in the north held title to land. For the most part, the Turkish Cypriot authorities imposed fewer restrictions on them than the Greek Cypriots of the Karpas, he said.

Arguments with the Turkish Cypriot authorities sometimes took place however, because the Maronites frequently could not produce deeds and establish their rights to the land they farmed. They were three-generation families. The middle generation worked in the towns, leaving the senior generation to cultivate the land and bring up the children of the third generation. Land was passed from one family to another as a dowry, the arrangements rarely formalized.

'Because many Maronites are trying to make a living from land which technically belongs to a son-in-law living in the south, there can be trouble for them,' said another UN officer, explaining why. 'Under Turkish Cypriot *Equivalent Property Laws*, the land can be confiscated and given as compensation to Turkish Cypriots who have fled from the south and lost their properties. But the northern authorities have agreed to prosecute any trespassers on Maronite land, if the Maronites lodge formal complaints and provide documentary evidence to support their claims of ownership. Few Maronites are prepared to do this as their way of life relies on private understandings between family members, and sometimes even different families, as to where boundaries actually lie.' Therefore it was left to UNFICYP officers to maintain the status quo where possible by using tact and persuasion.

'As far as getting back Maronite fields from Turkish Cypriots, I think UNFICYP has been fairly successful,' Captain Hurley maintained. 'Sometimes their problems simply arise because they live in the middle of a military area and it wouldn't matter who was in charge.'

The Maronites also complained of 'religious persecution' by the Turkish Cypriots, but so far UNFICYP had found no evidence to substantiate these allegations. 'It may sound callous,' said Captain Hurley, 'but the Maronite villages can't last for ever. The elderly people are dying off and the youngsters are moving to the south, never to return. In time, the problems will solve themselves.'

The Northwind Patrol was over for another two weeks. Captain Hurley folded his notes, which included a request for UN-styled boots, powder-paints for colouring Easter eggs, a complaint about the size of a colour TV set and the solution to the mystery of the missing potatoes. The humanitarian aid mission had been fulfilled again.

Back in Kyrenia, Captain Hurley and Carter rested at a restaurant on the harbour front, eager to enjoy a late lunch of fish kebabs and chips, guests of Sergeant Görmüş. The PIO escort sat with them. He had given up the struggle to start his vintage Murat, which remained parked by the castle wall, missing an engine part and unable to move until one was found.

Sipping an Efes beer, the escort turned to Captain Hurley for help.

'Sorry,' said the UNFICYP officer. 'You know the rules. You'll have to catch a bus.'

While UNFICYP could ferry colour television sets to isolated Maronites, its aid programme did not extend, officially, to carrying spares to keep Turkish Cypriots mobile or to returning them home after a day's work.

The bill for lunch was presented and Major Hurley chose to pay for everybody. He was charged twice the going rate.

The restaurateur winked at Sergeant Görmüş; the United Nations could afford the price.

CHAPTER 17

JULIA'S DIARY

EVEN a recent heart attack had failed to slow Major David Emmett, the jovial new MPIO at UNFICYP headquarters, and during Carter's latest two-week stay as a UN guest he was determined to show the BBC producer everything in the Buffer Zone and re-introduce as many people as possible in the various contingents.

'I know that Cedric Mercer and Tim Whitehead gave you the grand tour before and you're a veteran of the Cyprus scene,' Emmett told Carter on arrival, 'but you may still find something different on this trip to trigger a new angle for another programme.' There was no aspect of the UN force in Cyprus which Emmett was not going to reveal and explain in depth.

The UN was David Emmett's current mission, the British army was his way of life, and radio was his hobby. All three were tied together neatly by Carter's visit. Had Emmett not been an officer, he would have wanted to be a BBC interviewer or writer. Tapes, microphones and recording machines fascinated him and his knowledge of how they worked far exceeded Carter's.

From early Monday morning until late Thursday evening, Emmett kept Carter on the move, dashing from one OP to another. Between appointments he quizzed his BBC guest incessantly on the comparative merits of various bits and pieces of broadcasting equipment. When technical matters were exhausted, he wanted to hear about the production of radio documentaries, the techniques of interviewing and how Carter proposed to edit and compress the material which was filling his spools of tape.

At the end of each day Emmett insisted on sharing the hospitality of 25 Sycamore Road, his home at Blue Beret Camp in the United Nations Protected Area. Here Carter met Anne, Emmett's wife, and their teenage daughter, Charlotte. After pouring everybody large drinks, the UN officer played recordings of *The Goon Show*, his favourite radio programme from the fifties.

Emmett was particularly proud of his Japanese stereo system, which filled a large space in the corner of the living room. It had been acquired, duty-free, from the Canadian contingent's Post Exchange, their upmarket equivalent of the NAAFI. Because the system was still brand new, he had not yet mastered all of its controls, with the result that the classic verbal antics of Peter Sellers and Spike Milligan were drowned frequently by passionate broadcasters screaming through the system's twin loudspeakers from one radio station or another in the Middle East. When the gags of the Goons and the propaganda of the Arabs combined in a cacophony of bizarre sounds, it became hard to tell where fantasy ended and reality began.

At moments like these, Emmett replaced his vinyl records for taped cassettes of Carter's radio programmes about Cyprus, all given to him by his MPIO predecessors for reference purposes. He played and analysed the content of each documentary, which the BBC producer found flattering but also exhausting, as he was expected to explain every sound and how it had been recorded.

Aware that Carter had had little time allocated to spend on his own in the busy schedule arranged by her husband, Anne decided to become his 'big sister', ensuring that his domestic needs and obligations were fulfilled. Helping her in this work was Julia Sinclair, one of the UNFICYP civilian secretaries at Blue Beret Camp.

Between them they ensured Carter remained on track, making certain his meetings were kept and his appearance was correct for all occasions. Regular telephone calls to his family in Welwyn Garden City were organized by Anne, who also compiled his diary of social events, checked his meal arrangements and took charge of his laundry. For her part, Julia created his network of business contacts, primarily on the Greek Cypriot side of the cease-fire line. To help him further his research, she gave him her diary which recorded the events she had witnessed in the days immediately before and after the coup of 15 July 1974 and the Turkish intervention, five days later.

Because there had been little time for Carter to read during the week, Julia's diary remained unopened alongside a pile of pamphlets about the Cyprus problem lying on a dressing table in the house he was sharing with John Sharp. Sharp was one of the Australian police officers attached to the UN and dealt with civil matters in the Buffer Zone. A tall, friendly man, he was returning to Australia soon to take up a senior appointment in the Federal Police.

By 13.00 on Friday, all Carter's official work had come to an end until late in the evening when he was giving a small dinner party in a local restaurant. After that there was nothing scheduled for either Saturday or Sunday. The next 48 hours were for him to spend as he wanted, although, this being Cyprus, the chances were that somebody was bound to invite him out, perhaps to sail off Akrotiri or picnic in the Troodos.

How busy he became socially would depend on his will-power to resist and his ability to muster adequate, but diplomatic refusals to kind invitations.

John Sharp had already served notice that during Saturday night he intended to go 'on the town' with Carter. Together they would 'do the rounds' of several clubs where 'hostesses entertained' visitors to the Greek side of Nicosia. 'David sport, you've been working too hard,' Sharp said. 'So I intend showing you a side of Cyprus that will make your eyes water.'

Many of these 'hostesses' came from Poland, Czechoslovakia and Romania, not as refugees fleeing from behind the Iron Curtain, but as willing members of the world's oldest profession. After a six-month stay in Cyprus, they returned home aboard Aeroflot jets flying from Larnaca.

Carter *knew* that *three* club hostesses had spent the night in the UN Protected Area on at least one occasion.

They had entered the base hidden in the back of an official vehicle and were smuggled past the Canadian guards on duty at the main gate.

To what extent these eastern European bar girls monitored the observers and eavesdroppers was anybody's guess, but their presence certainly explained why southern Cyprus was called a hotbed of spies.

A leading figures behind this efficient traffic in 'cabaret artistes' was Artin Bahutourian, a 66-year-old Armenian who would later figure in a spy trial involving British servicemen at an intelligence centre on the island, and then die in mysterious circumstances, allegedly murdered by one Andreas Aristodemon, *alias* Youroukis, a convicted killer.

Western intelligence feared Cyprus would become a major Russian spy base as more and more homesick British servicemen found themselves meeting Bahutourian's ladies who wanted to know about their work. At the Sovereign Bases, army counter-intelligence uncovered a network operating sex traps for the unsuspecting. Several young soldiers and airmen had been invited home by the bar girls, only to find a 'husband' crashing down the door and threatening to report the incident in a blaze of publicity unless . . . Alternatively an entrapped soldier might receive compromising photographs taken with the prostitute . . . Either way, he was invited to provide a bit of information here or there 'in the interests of peace'. In Cyprus, blackmailers found it an easy way of life.

Few people could be unaware that Nicosia was a thriving centre for trading military and political secrets. All the major powers were players. *Izvestia* and *Pravda* journalists outnumbered *all* the others who represented foreign publications and used the local press club. To operate its limited number of flights to and from the island, Aeroflot, the Soviet airline, needed so many staff from Moscow that an entire building was dedicated to their needs. Meanwhile, an American U2 spy-plane flew regular daily missions from RAF Akrotiri and highly sensitive British listening-posts in the south transmitted information to GCHQ, the UK government's top-secret communications centre at Cheltenham, in England.

These posts, one of which was located on Mount Olympus in the Troodos mountains, eavesdropped on communications traffic in the Middle East and the Soviet Union. Another was operated by 9 Signals Regiment at 'Ay-Nick', or Ayios Nicolaos, on the edge of the Western Sovereign Base Area, where it touched the Turkish military front-line, not far from Dhekelia.

It was also rumoured strongly that various terrorist groups trained on the island. These groups included Armenian activists who collaborated with PLO members, many of whom had been ejected from Beirut and Jordan. They were now located outside Larnaca, under the eyes of the Greek Cypriot National Guard.

Unless Sharp was involved in more discreet duties outside his officially-declared role as a UN policeman, it was unlikely Carter would find himself involved with any of this intelligence activity, in or outside the clubs. Unlike many British military personnel from the Sovereign Bases, and some off-duty staff from UNFICYP, he would be present only to look and listen, and enjoy some 'rest and relaxation'.

For the time being Carter's thoughts were focused on more mundane matters, like the dinner party to which he had invited David and Anne Emmett, Julia Sinclair and Dinos from the Greek Cypriot Public Information Office, with his wife.

The choice of the latter two people surprised Major Emmett, because he detected a distinct chill in the PIO's office when Carter had last visited earlier in the week. 'Dinos is usually a very helpful chap,' Emmett remarked. 'I've never before seen any of them so correctly polite. Certainly never when I've taken an official UN visitor to meet them.'

'I expected it,' Carter replied blandly. 'They don't like me spending time in northern Cyprus. They don't mind somebody popping over the line for a few hours to meet President Denktas and see Turkish Nicosia, because they know it contrasts badly with Greek Nicosia, but they get suspicious of anybody who takes opportunities to chat up Turkish Cypriot folk and ex-pats who live elsewhere in the north. I guess we draw different conclusions from the propaganda line pushed by the Greek PIO.

'It's really no different in the north. Their officials, too, look suspiciously at western journalists if they come up from the Greek Cypriot side. They're just as cool and correct towards them. In a way, I should be flattered by the way Dinos has acted. The PIO staff on both sides credit me with far more influence than I'm ever likely to have. I'm as dangerous as a pussy cat.'

'Nonsense,' Emmett interrupted. 'Your programmes have contained bits and pieces which nobody else has found. They've been exclusives.'

'Maybe. But if nobody sees or hears a race run, who knows who came first or last? I haven't won any gold medals for my work in Cyprus. That's the truth of the matter.'

'If that's how you feel, why ever did you invite Dinos and his wife for dinner?'

'I wanted to see if they would accept. I'm trying to prove that I really am objective. If they both show, it means they've accepted my definition of objectivity. If he comes alone, it will suggest that I'm not as "objective" as he would prefer, but perhaps I can be turned to his point of view. But if neither comes to dinner, then, quite simply, I'm not worth a candle or I'm a lost cause. In which case, forget any co-operation in the future.'

Since there was no message to confirm that the Greek Cypriot PIO and his wife would be present, Carter had to remain in suspense until the actual moment he entered the restaurant to discover what game, if any, Dinos was playing.

Carter used the next few hours to catch up on a backlog of personal matters. He lay down on his bed, switched on the radio and tuned it to the BBC's World Service. Then he began reading Julia's diary, starting with the day after the Turks landed in Cyprus.

21 July 1974

We sat on our balcony last night waiting for instructions from the High Commission. Fires were burning all around us in Nicosia from napalm bombs and rockets dropped by Turkish planes, which flew too high to be hit by Greek anti-aircraft guns.

This morning we heard from HC (the High Commissioner) Stephen Oliver on BFBS. He said British and foreign nationals should go to the Hilton Hotel and form a convoy which was leaving for Dhekelia at 13.00. *Cypriots were excluded.* Over 4,500 people arrived, but the start was delayed because the Greek Cypriot National Guard still held 300 people hostage at the Ledra Palace Hotel. These people included journalists and television cameramen. They were released only when a British officer, supported by an armoured car, threatened to attack.

We got away eventually, escorted by Ferrets of the 16/5 Lancers. Helicopters flew overhead for protection. Those who did not have their own transport were conveyed by lorry.

It was very hot; temperature 106 degrees.

Arrival at Dhekelia was very orderly, but many more people came than had been expected, including holiday-makers from Famagusta who fled when Turkish aircraft bombed.

We're all parked in a valley which is generally used as sports fields. Only a handful have made it to accommodation in the army barracks.

23 July 1974

The army has worked miracles during the past two days. Tents have appeared in orderly rows on the cricket pitch and toilet and eating arrangements are vastly improved since Sunday when the Paras set up kitchens and served soup, tea, coffee and milk for the babies.

Everybody is being processed at the barracks. Nobody is being forced to leave, although there has been some encouragement so as to make room for others, who are still arriving.

There's a shuttle-service of Hercules aircraft between Dhekelia and Akrotiri, carrying those who want to fly back to UK.

Yesterday HC announced that British and foreign nationals in

Kyrenia and surrounding districts should assemble on the beaches for evacuation by RN. HMS *Hermes* and *Devonshire* are part of the operation.

Evacuees are being flown to *Hermes* by helicopter. They have left most of their possessions behind, including their cars on the beaches. Some people have been brought straight here, while others have gone to Episkopi. Everybody is praising the Navy lads. Tons and tons of supplies are arriving now. There are eight ships in the bay. What a grand lot the soldiers and sailors are. They don't moan about the long hours they work or the shortage of beer and cigarettes. One wishes the same could be said for the refugees. Some of the Greek Cypriots who flocked here so eagerly for help are reluctant to do anything to help themselves -- except taking army supplies! When they get a place in the barracks, they complain about the 750 mils charged each of them every day for their food and shelter.

26 July 1974

About 10,000 refugees have come through Dhekelia, but only a few remain. Some of us have been used to maintain order, working at a variety of jobs. I've been helping in the canteen, where sometimes we've fed 500 people at a time, three times a day. We've been swimming between meal-times. Susie has met many of her old chums, but most of them are leaving for home. We're hoping to return to our flat in Nicosia very soon.

20 August 1974

We were home exactly two weeks when Turkish planes started bombing Nicosia again (14 August at 05.00). This time we had received instructions from HC the night before that in the event of further hostilities we were to *make our own separate ways* to the SBA. Hence, at 06.00 we were on our way, having packed away all our small breakables of any value and covered the dining-table with old curtains. We were sad at leaving Sandy (our cat!) behind.

This time we went to Anzio Camp and joined others in 'Coronation Street'. Within ten minutes of arriving, I had my old job back — in the canteen!

There were serious anti-American riots in Nicosia yesterday, because the US hasn't done more to support the Greek Cypriots against the Turks. The Ambassador was shot dead. The news of Roger Davis's death came as shock to those of us who had met him.

The refugee problem is acute. As the Turks advanced on Famagusta, Greek Cypriot civilians rushed to the SBA and, once more, tents have gone up everywhere. There are 2,000 people here.

We've been getting up at 04.30 to give breakfast to our army shift-workers who have been given a time limit by the Turks to clear out the NAAFI warehouse in Famagusta.

24 August 1974

It's 10 days since the Turks began their second military offensive and eight days since a second cease-fire. So far it's holding quite well as far as we can tell, allowing the tense situation to ease a bit.

We returned home today to take our chances here in Nicosia.

Fortunately the flat is exactly as we left it, except that it's very dusty, because we left our windows open in case there was a bomb blast nearby.

How hard we worked at Anzio. But I have a feeling my real work will be starting now.

Sandy was pleased to see us.

Christmas Eve 1974

Archbishop Makarios returned to Cyprus this month and Greek Cypriots cheered his arrival, believing he'll be able to solve our problems. It will take more than him alone to do that. Not even divine intervention can help the children who went to visit their grandparents in Cape Andreas last summer. They're still trapped there with only their hot-weather clothing.

We hear there are Greeks hiding in Kyrenia, their homes looted and fouled. Their cars have been 'exported' to Turkey by the invaders. We're told 240 Greek Cypriots are held captive in a school in Morphou. For water they have only one outside tap. In Lapithos, which I loved, 120 Greek Cypriots are forced to live in 10 houses. They rely on food delivered once a week by UNFICYP. Even worse is the lot of those in the Karpas. Many will surely die in the winter weather as they urgently need warm clothes, shoes and bottled gas for heating.

Here, 10,000 Greek Cypriots are living under canvas, while 7,000 have accommodation in shacks.

The Red Cross has set up a tracing agency to find those who have not returned to their families. It has not had much success so far.

Given the events in Cyprus this year, I can't see how it can be a happy Christmas.

16 January 1975

There were anti-British demonstrations today, because we allowed thousands of Turkish Cypriot refugees to leave RAF Akrotiri in civilian aircraft for Turkey. We know all of them will come back to Cyprus very soon — to settle in the north, probably in homes left by Greek Cypriot refugees. Last November, the UN carried out a huge evacuation of two villages in the north where Greek Cypriots were isolated.

9 February 1975

At last (those of us living in the south) have an air link to the outside world. The only way of leaving has been by sea, but yesterday Cyprus Airways began operating a shuttle-service to Athens, using Viscounts from an airport at Larnaca. Meanwhile, the Turks have re-opened an old RAF airfield at Timbou, which the French used during the Suez war. They have named their airport Ercan and are advertising flights to Turkey!

20 February 1975

I haven't felt up to writing recently. Bill's decided to leave for London. He says he wants to see what PR opportunities there are for him in UK. He would like to represent British newspapers in Cyprus. 'The Cyprus story will run for years,' he says.

A week ago (on the 13th), the Turkish Cypriot side declared itself 'The Turkish Federated State of Cyprus' with Mr Denktaş as president.

Both sides have been accusing the other of mass rapes and looting.

Our friend who owned the mushroom farm at Yerolakkos has decided to live in Greece. His farm has been taken over by Turkish Cypriots. The same has happened to many other industries and businesses in the north.

In some Greek Cypriot-controlled areas, Turkish Cypriots are harassed and are leaving to make their difficult way to places like Kyrenia and Morphou.

Sometimes UNFICYP can help, sometimes not.

There have been violations of the cease-fire.

2 August 1975

In Vienna, Mr Denktaş and Mr Glafcos Clerides have agreed that all the Turkish Cypriots in the south can move to the nórth as part of an exchange of populations supervised by UNFICYP. Many Turkish Cypriots may want to quit their properties, but I don't think the Greeks in the north have the same desire. Who will force them? One of my chums in the UN says Mr Denktaş will allow them to stay, 'free to lead a normal life and to practice their own religion'.

20 October 1975

Eight thousand Turkish Cypriots have chosen to start a new life in the north. Like the two communities in Cyprus, Bill and I have decided as well to lead separate lives, but without any formalized agreements. He spends half his time in London, the other half here.

I hear that UNFICYP is experiencing a lot of difficulties in getting aid to the Greek Cypriots who have remained in the north. Red Cross parcels to people in the Karpas have been opened by Turks who confiscated the contents of brandy and cigarettes, 'pending payment of duties'. Because Turks are Muslims, they've allowed pigs to die, even though their Greek owners could have continued to care for them. UN teams have covered scores of rotting carcasses with lime to reduce the risks to health from flies breeding on them.

One of Susie's friends in the UN has promised to find me a job at headquarters. I'm sure I could be very helpful and, let's face it, the pay would come in very handy.

New Year's Day 1976

Despite all the troubles, 1975 has flown by. Bill and I have parted for good and Susie has gone to live with friends. At first I wondered if I'd be able to cope on my own, but I've surprised myself by how well I've managed.

Of course, working as a secretary at UNFICYP HQ has definitely helped. Although I'm described as a 'local' employee and not supposed to get perks which are given to the girls hired in New York, I do all right. There's always somebody willing to get me duty-free things. They all help to keep the cost of living down.

I have lots of new friends and I've had so many party invitations this year. It's lovely being able to pick and choose again. The Christmas holiday was a ceaseless round of parties, not just in Nicosia but at the Sovereign Bases as well, but I'm about the only person who remembers those sticky days and nights in 1974.

Re-housing Greek Cypriot refugees continues to be a problem, but the New Year starts with a lot of promise. New houses are going up in leaps and bounds. These utility homes are entirely locally produced, having cement-block walls, cement floors, and timber from the forests of Cyprus. They are available to displaced persons on easy HP terms. The first sites are in Larnaca, Limassol and Paphos.

All Greek Cypriots are contributing a percentage of their income to refugee relief and there's a special 'refugee stamp' for letters and postcards which serves a dual purpose. The stamps keep the Greek Cypriot case in front of the eyes of tourists and generate income for the administration as well.

Now, at the start of 1976, I look back to the old year with mixed feelings and forward with optimism. I intend to pick up the pieces and re-build something worthwhile for myself. There's nothing to be gained from looking back and thinking of what could have been.

The diary stopped suddenly. Only now did Carter realize that Bill Sinclair, the man who brought him to Cyprus in the first place, was Julia's husband.

He closed the folder of loose-leaf pages. Julia had given him a fresh perspective on herself and Cyprus. Had he read them without knowing Julia, he would have imagined a far different character, somebody dull and insecure. Ever since he had been introduced to her in Cedric Mercer's office, she had only radiated confidence. The Julia Sinclair with whom he would be eating dinner tonight was nothing less than self-assured, vibrant and liberated.

Carter dressed for dinner, thinking how tiny the world really was and how small, almost insignificant, incidents could bring about so much change in a person's life. A chance telephone call from Bill Sinclair several years earlier had started his preoccupation with Cyprus. The island was now a major part of both his personal and professional life. Julia, too, was part of it.

Unless Carter was very careful, any objectivity he still possessed would be compromised by him becoming too closely involved with the people he met.

David and Anne Emmett arrived a few minutes before 20.00 to drive Carter to Theo's restaurant on the old Larnaca Road in Nicosia. Julia had said she would make her own way there. They all reached the restaurant at the same time with the exception of Dinos. He kept the party waiting for another half an hour.

Then, just as they were about to sit down and order their meal, Dinos appeared, expressing apologies for his lateness and the fact his wife would not be joining them as she was at home packing for their holiday in Greece, due to start the next morning.

Throughout dinner Julia and Dinos hardly said a word to each other, something Carter noticed. With her obvious support for the Greek Cypriot cause, he had expected the PIO spokesman to be more attracted to her than the others at the table.

Of course, everybody tried hard to avoid talking about 'the Cyprus problem', but if Anne spoke about the difficulties of having a son at boarding school in England, Dinos could add nothing. When Julia discussed some recent party at which mutual friends had been present, Carter was left out. David Emmett, ever the military diplomat and gentleman, tried to find a unifying topic of conversation by raising his hobby: radio and stereo-systems. But this led to broadcasting and that only brought up the subject of documentary-making and reporting, leading inevitably to the very subject the group was attempting to stay off: Cyprus.

At last they gave up trying.

Dinos wanted to know what Carter had seen on his visits to the north and Carter wanted to know where Dinos's original home had been and if he had lost any property.

No, Dinos replied, he was not a refugee, but he said his wife had been ejected from her family's home in Lapithos. Because the BBC producer was more familiar with the Turkish names of the smaller villages, he called it *Lapta*.

Emmett, still trying to be diplomatic, stressed the Greek originals by saying they were the most commonly-used place names, and ended up compounding Carter's lack of political sensitivity and general consideration for his guest's feelings. But, seemingly, Dinos did not take offence, even when the BBC producer inquired whether he wanted more *Turkish* coffee.

Unlike his Turkish Cypriot opposite numbers in the propaganda game, Dinos kept a tight check on his emotions. He was shrewd and sophisticated. While he never deviated from the main thrust of his government's policy aims, he did concede many minor points in the argument, which rarely happened in the north when similar discussions took place.

Grabbing small victories or scoring technical points from minor skirmishes was unimportant in his agenda; Dinos wanted only to win the war decisively. He took an intellectual approach to offer solutions. He was a fine advocate who presented an effective case for his clients, the Greek Cypriots. Nothing said was a falsehood, or even exaggerated, but neither was it the whole truth. However, had his arguments been transcribed on paper, they would have read easily and appeared reasonable, convincing anybody who was far removed from the heart of the matter. Not that the Turkish Cypriot PIO teams offered the complete story either. Despite their claims of being open and direct, they merely baffled listeners with a barrage of statistics and minor details, few of which helped clarify the causes of the tragedy or the justice they claimed.

Then there were those on both sides who preferred to follow Mark Twain's maxim that truth, being such a valuable commodity, should be used economically.

A lot of ground was covered during dinner, but, as both Carter and Dinos knew both the questions and the answers, their conversation did not advance the Cyprus argument at all. Then, just as he was about to leave, the Greek Cypriot asked, 'Do you think we will ever return to our homes in the north?'

'No,' Carter replied. 'Never.'

Dinos stood silent and expressionless for almost a minute before adding, 'Using your contacts in their government, is it possible for you to arrange for my wife to visit her home in Lapithos, just once, to collect a pot of soil from her garden? It would mean a great deal to our family.'

Carter shook his head.

'I'm sure you could fix it. It's a small thing, and I give you my word that there would be no propaganda.'

Carter suspected Dinos of probing to find the level and strength of his relationships in northern Cyprus. 'I'll do my best. I'll pass on your request when I'm next in the TFSC, but, quite honestly, even if I had any influence, and I don't, I can't see how the Turkish Cypriot administration could grant your request. The ramifications would be enormous. If she, the wife of a Greek Cypriot government official, were given permission simply to re-visit Lapithos or Lapta, and if there were nothing behind the trip, why shouldn't every other Greek Cypriot with connections in Morphou, Famagusta and Kyrenia not be given approval as well? What would the Turks gain from any of this? What concessions would Greeks make in return?'

Dinos did not answer the questions, simply repeated his request as he left the restaurant after thanking Carter for dinner. Emmett noticed that the Greek Cypriot did not shake the BBC producer's hand.

'You don't mind if we drop off Julia at her flat before we return you to camp, do you, David?' Anne Emmett said, walking towards their Toyota.

Before Carter could reply, Julia cut in, 'It's such a pleasant night, I thought David could walk me to Metaxas Square where I'll pick up a taxi.'

'Very good. Right,' said Major Emmett, clearing his throat of a non-existent cough.

'You will be able to get back all right, won't you, David?' Anne added, concern in her voice, her maternal instincts aroused. 'Don't forget there's a party of Commonwealth journalists going on a tour of "The Green Line" tomorrow, and I'm sure that my David would like you to meet them.' She glanced at her husband for confirmation, although this was the first Carter had heard about it.

'Yes. Yes, of course.' From Major Emmett's tone it was clear he did not want to interfere with any arrangements Carter may have made to spend the rest of the evening, or Saturday morning.

'I'll be there,' Carter replied reassuringly. 'What time is the off?'

'Ten o'clock. Outside my office.' Emmett fumbled with the keys of his Toyota. The car was brand new and he was still not used to it 'Fine. Very good. Yes, well, we'll say goodnight. And thanks very much for a marvellous dinner, David.'

Anne planted a light kiss on Carter's cheek and whispered, 'Don't stay out too late. You haven't had much sleep for a long time.'

As the Toyota pulled away into the main road, Anne waved and Carter felt one of Julia's carefully-manicured fingers run playfully against his.

'Good.' She smiled and gripped Carter's hand. 'I wanted us to have a chat on our own.'

Neither of them spoke much on the way from Theo's restaurant to Metaxas Square or during the taxi drive to Julia's apartment, not far from the Presidential Palace. Her home was much as Carter had expected. Tiled floors made it cool while her choice of pastel colours was attractive. Six floors above the ground, large windows opened on to a balcony which gave an uninterrupted view of Nicosia. The old walled city was to the north and beyond were the suburbs on the road to Kyrenia, where lights twinkled in the darkness.

'Make yourself comfortable while I pour us a drink,' Julia said, removing her silk scarf, which was loosely knotted round her neck. 'Still sticking to Scotch, or would you prefer some brandy? I have a bottle of Three Kings.'

'No, whisky will be fine,' Carter replied, sinking into a large, soft leather sofa. On the way to the cocktail cabinet, Julia passed some framed reproductions of Cypriot village life.

'Those paintings, aren't they by Victor Joannides?' Carter asked. He had met the artist in his Limassol studio during his very first trip to Cyprus.

'Yes, they are,' said Julia. 'I think his talent deserves international recognition. His style is very similar to the French impressionists, don't you think?'

'I'm fairly ignorant about paintings,' Carter confessed, nodding in the direction of Julia's bookshelves. They were filled with volumes on Cyprus and *Readers Digest* editions of the classics. 'That's quite a collection of books.' The comment was obvious, designed only to continue conversation which remained stilted.

'Do you read much?' Julia replied with a question, handing him a large tumbler of whisky and ice-cubes. She sat down next to him.

'I've read your diary,' Carter said.

'Did you find it useful?' For a brief instant Julia paid him close attention, then ran her fingers through her hair. 'Well?' she said, lowering her face without lowering her gaze. 'You still haven't told me what you thought.'

'I found it interesting. Very.'

Julia ran the tip of her tongue over her upper lip, adding a sheen of saliva to her lipstick. 'Has anybody told you, David, that you're too pro-Turkish?'

Holding his whisky, Carter stood up and walked slowly to the far side of the room where a framed photograph rested in an alcove. 'Is that Susie?' he asked. 'She's very attractive.'

'Some people say she takes after me. What do you think?'

Carter nodded. 'What did you mean about me being pro-Turkish?'

'At dinner tonight everything you said was a hymn in their praise. You were really very unfair to Dinos.'

'Hmm,' Carter grunted. 'I noticed you weren't very talkative to each other.' He returned Susie's photograph to the alcove shelf. Julia took his tumbler and refilled it to the rim with another malt. Facing him again, she said, 'Yes. How observant. Well, it's like this. My ex has done something naughty. One of his business deals has gone badly wrong and he's facing legal proceedings. Because Dinos knows Bill professionally, he doesn't know how to cope with the situation. It's a bloody mess, really.'

'I meant to thank you for all the secretarial help you've given me,' Carter said, hastily changing the subject. He sat beside her again. She removed one of her high-heeled sandals. Again there was silence between them; then she removed her other shoe. Holding both spike heels in one hand like a weapon, she exploded without warning, shouting, 'Has anybody told you that you're an unromantic little bastard?'

Carter, expecting Julia to use her shoes to hammer his head, asked, 'What have I done?' He was genuinely baffled. He rose slowly and took hold of her shoulders.

'Don't touch me,' she said, pulling back. Carter's brain raced, trying hard to find a reason for Julia's irrational behaviour. He wanted to get away quickly from this awkward situation, which he was sure could only become worse.

'Let me tell you something, little smart arse. You come out here and everybody goes out of their way to help you and you can't even say thank you nicely. If only they knew what I know about you. They think you're a big-time BBC producer, but you're not. You're just a little guy who works for a radio station that nobody listens to. How do I know? I know, because Bill told me.'

Carter made no effort to silence Julia's outburst.

'Bill gave you a free trip to Cyprus just to make up numbers and to show the CTO he had a few BBC contacts. He was doing it for himself, not you. Your programmes aren't worth a fig.' Her voice was pitched just above a loud whisper, which made it more disconcerting. Without pausing for breath or an answer, Julia pressed on with her verbal assault. 'You're very fond of talking about truth and objectivity, you pompous shit, but when were you last objective about yourself or even truthful, David? You come to Cyprus, not because you care about the place or the people, any more than the others of your kind. You come because you get free hospitality and air tickets. You're pro-Turkish because they've given you more free tickets than the CTO, and you calculate you'll get more by being "nice".'

Carter had always felt uneasy about accepting 'freebies', although he made a point of having them approved by his superiors, in case there were ever charges like those Julia was making now. On the other hand, without the free facilities provided by various organizations, there would have been no way at all he could have made programmes about Cyprus. That was the reality, but was she right? Was he finding angles to get tickets, or did he accept tickets to make programmes?

If Julia were correct, then he was taking even more advantage than she had suggested. After all, when he accepted free flights and accommodation, he could never guarantee his programmes would be broadcast. And, if the programmes were transmitted, would anybody be listening?

Julia had made the evening end painfully and he still did not know why. All he could do was listen glumly. Any defence he put up would be too late; her mind was made up. Perhaps in the morning, when the effects of her Three Kings brandy had worn off, she would not remember, or prefer to forget.

Just as suddenly as she had started her attack, Julia stopped, threw her arms around his neck, rested her head on his shoulder and bit the collar of his jacket. Her eyes brimmed with tears. His and her anger subsided. 'I think I'd better go,' Carter said.

'Do you find me attractive?' she gasped, pressing him to say something reassuring.

'Yes,' Carter said, his body stiffening, his mind rigid with indecision.

Julia lifted her head, looked at him through wet eyes and gripped his wrists. She tugged him slowly towards the sofa, but they stumbled and he fell awkwardly across her body.

'Stay the night,' Julia pleaded. 'Please.'

Carter shook his head and pulled himself away.

There were no more words to be said.

Her body fell limp as if all passion had been spent, leaving only total exhaustion.

Carter stood up, paused, and then walked to the door, turning to look back briefly.

Julia was fast asleep. And Carter was tired.

THE UNFICYP BRIEF

EVERY visitor to UNFICYP headquarters received a briefing on Cyprus and the Commonwealth journalists were treated no differently when they arrived at Blue Beret Camp on Saturday morning for their tour of 'The Green Line'.

As their convention was being held under the auspices of the Greek Cypriot authorities they had already received graphic accounts of the events of 1974 and heard powerful arguments to substantiate the Greek Cypriot case. Many of the journalists had accepted what they were told without question, which was not surprising as they knew little about the island's difficulties prior to their arrival. A few had been unaware that Cyprus was partitioned or even that there had been a war.

Now some of them were showing signs of apprehension by being so close to the Turkish front-line positions and wondered if they were in danger, almost urging an affirmative response so that they could file vivid copy to their newspapers and broadcasting organizations back home.

When Carter remarked that the journalists would visit places where they could shake hands with Turkish soldiers and the Greek Cypriot National Guard at the same time, their eyes rolled with amazement.

For the moment, however, they were to be briefed by the UN and that would be the nearest the Commonwealth journalists would come to hearing an objective summary of the facts, and so they crowded the conference-room where senior officers usually heard 'the morning report'.

On this occasion all maps displaying the military dispositions of the Greek Cypriot National Guard and the Turkish army had been removed. Only a screen and a projector remained to illustrate the four-part lecture which was to follow.

When the journalists were seated, a UN officer opened his remarks by stating that whatever he said was not to be regarded as necessarily the *official* United Nations' position and, therefore, recordings were prohibited and no transcripts would be issued.

Aware that this particular briefing document had never been published, Carter acquired a copy after the journalists left the room.

He found it interesting because of the careful use of words by the UNFICYP writer and his listing of some facts which were not heard often in any discussions of the Cyprus problem. For example, it recorded that Nicos Sampson had ordered the Greek Cypriot National Guard to attack Turkish Cypriot villages immediately following the coup of 15 July 1974. It revealed that Britain had abdicated some of its rights under the Treaty of Establishment by withdrawing from positions in Famagusta harbour (now under Turkish control) and allowed Turkish encroachment at the Eastern Sovereign Base. Furthermore, the document called the Turkish military action of 20 July 1974 an intervention *not* an invasion.

None of these points was raised by the Commonwealth journalists in the session of questions which followed. Nor did anybody ask the UN briefer to develop a statement about the force's relations with the opposing sides on the matter of freedom of UN movement. Even in the south, UNFICYP faced restrictions. Blue beret soldiers were kept away from Greek Cypriot National Guard installations.

What most journalists wanted to know was how life differed between north and south. Was it true, one inquired, that Turkish Cypriots were confined by the Turkish army? Another asked, would Turkish Cypriots return to their home villages in the south if the Turkish army withdrew? Could UNFICYP confirm that Greek Cypriots were subjected to harsh treatment in the north? And, of course, all expected an UNFICYP view on when the two communities would be re-united.

All their questions were answered deftly by the UN officer and the civilian spokesman, but none of their statements was worth quoting directly. They talked diplomatically and made optimistic noises about talks between the two sides leading to more talks. About the quality of life in the TFSC, they suggested that the journalists find the answers for themselves by visiting the north.

'But how do we get permission?' The question came as a chorus.

Carter told them to go to the Ledra Palace check-point with their passports. Providing the Greek Cypriots agreed to let them cross and promised to have them back, he had no doubts about them receiving a welcome from the northern authorities.

'Your problems won't be with the Turks,' said Carter. 'Trouble will come from your hosts, the Greek Cypriot administration. If they let you out, they'll want you back within eight hours and without goods bought in the north. Any you bring will be confiscated.'

The UN representatives greeted Carter's comments with wry amusement and the journalists expressed scepticism. Nevertheless they were raised at the next session of the convention and angrily refuted by its organizers.

Throughout their stay in Cyprus, the Commonwealth journalists had their ears bent by both sides in a vigorous war of words. Particular attention was given to the representatives of the Third World whose countries virtually controlled the UN General Assembly. This was where the Greeks usually won the battle of the resolutions.

In part this was due to the 'Republic' side holding a seat in that forum and by receiving international recognition as the official government of Cyprus. Because several newly-independent

Commonwealth countries were politically left of centre, it was also hard for them to show sympathy for the TFSC, or any other administration with the slightest hint of right-wing bias. The 'non-aligned' states had much more in common with the large socialist and communist electorates of Greece and the Greek side of Cyprus.

The Turkish Cypriots and mainland Turks, therefore, found themselves, more often than not, out on a limb at UN and Commonwealth functions.

The drive through 'The Green Line' of Nicosia began at the Paphos Gate of the walled city and finished at Omorphita, the end of the Canadian contingent's area of responsibility in Sector 4.

The convoy trundled through two-and-a-half kilometres of narrow streets, stopping several times along the way so that the UNFICYP guide could point to places of particular interest. Because some buildings straddled the cease-fire line, they were empty on one side while occupied and functioning on the other.

Near OP MAPLE 1, the Commonwealth journalists saw a large warehouse which had a garage below ground filled with Toyotas, Mercedes and children's bicycles; all had been brand new in 1974.

'According to what I heard, they were valued then at more than 350,000 dollars,' said Captain André Reoux, a French Canadian of the 3rd Battalion, the Royal 22nd Regiment. The cars were coated in a thick layer of dust, their tyres completely flat, but otherwise they looked road-worthy. 'The Turkish forces will not allow them to be removed from the BZ. Therefore, we look after them and keep this warehouse locked,' the officer continued. 'Once a week their officers come with us and count them to see none has been removed. The Greeks do the same.'

Carter picked up a faded Union flag from the bonnet of one of the cars. 'May I take this?' he asked.

'No,' replied Captain Reoux. 'This place must stay as it was when the cease-fire was agreed in August 1974.'

A British major added: 'At that time a senior Turkish officer said that if he were given one of these cars, the Greek Cypriot owner could take away the rest from the Buffer Zone. The Greek Cypriot refused and so the cars and bicycles remain here. If and when there's a settlement, they won't be worth renovating. Over at Nicosia International, there's a Customs shed filled with bales of rotting tobacco. They belonged to Turkish Cypriots in Famagusta and the Greeks have refused their removal. Like this lot, they're also checked every week by both sides. It's a silly game of tit-for-tat.'

The journalists continued their journey, passing a small restaurant, where tables still carried the remains of the last meals that were served before customers ran in panic when the war moved closer. There was even a half-bottle of milk.

At the foot of Ledra Street, the Olympus Hotel, once used as a brothel, was still as a grave. The buildings at that spot were badly damaged, their walls pocked with bullet holes and marked with signs saying that they were booby-trapped.

'During the hostilities the Turks supposedly put mines here. They said they wanted us to know because we are their UN friends. Are the buildings really booby-trapped? We're not sure, but we don't take any chances,' the Canadian captain emphasized, but added, 'There are so many dogs and cats, especially cats, here, that if there were booby-traps, I think they would have exploded some by now.'

His British colleague disagreed. 'Cats have nine lives. We don't, even if they're neutral like us. When there's a settlement, this place is going to take a major clearance, because, sadly, it's so dangerous. The buildings will have to be blown down to make the area safe. They're far too dangerous even for our bomb explosives squads to disarm.'

The major pointed at another shell of a building. 'That was called Beaver Lodge,' he said. 'It was the Canadian headquarters in '74. The Turks claimed it was in an area where they were meeting resistance from the Greek Cypriot National Guard and they intended to start heavy shelling. They gave the Canadians 20 minutes to leave. Exactly 20 minutes later the shelling began. It wasn't an idle threat. This place really was splattered.'

A British officer turned to Carter: 'I think it was around here that the *Daily Mirror* correspondent, Donald Wise, gave Jonathan Dimbleby some good advice. He spotted young Dimbleby beating a hasty retreat with his camera team when they came under mortar fire from the Turks. Above the noise, Wise shouted, "We never run when the Greeks can see us, my boy." He then took charge and everybody withdrew as if they were heading for the cricket pavilion for a cup of tea.'

All along 'The Green Line', Turkish and Greek Cypriot forces sat glumly behind sand-bagged emplacements, guns pointing at each other. In places they were separated by less than 10 metres, the width of the patrol track which the convoy was using. At one spot in the line, soldiers of both sides were chatting with each other.

'Very unusual,' the British major observed. 'Those chaps are probably trying to start a bit of aggro. They usually throw stones at each other, shout obscenities and often lower their trousers and perform dirty acts. We have to cool them.'

The tour ended at the Omorphita OP and several journalists raised their camera to photograph a Turkish position nearby. Their UNFICYP escorts stopped them immediately. 'They fear us taking photographs. They like to keep their defences secret. Because we are located on *their* side of the CFL, we notified them who you are and why you are here, but there are no concessions for picture-taking.'

During the tour of 'The Green Line' Carter talked to several conference delegates from Asia and Africa. Their views echoed those of their governments. They saw Cyprus subjected to a new form of colonialism by a large nation that had grabbed part of the country through force, actively encouraged by a super power, the United States.

Despite their UN briefing, many believed still that the UN was in Cyprus to *protect* Greek Cypriots alone and to fend off Turkish 'aggressors'. The journalists became confused when it was pointed out that UNFICYP had been in Cyprus for a whole decade *before* the Turkish army 'invaded'. They were also at a loss to explain why the UK, other white European countries, and Canada were providing the manpower for the force and not their own anti-colonial 'Third World' governments, if the Cyprus problem were a 'Western plot'.

Carter wanted the Commonwealth journalists to ask more questions, seek more independent answers, and, most of all, open their eyes and see for themselves. Because the UNFICYP officers could not take sides in these discussions, they kept a low profile and allowed him to play devil's advocate.

'Go and see for yourselves what Turkish Cypriots are all about and why,' Carter insisted, his words duplicating what he himself had been told by Greek Cypriots many years earlier.

Soon afterwards Rauf Denktaş, the Turkish Cypriot leader, extended an official invitation to the correspondents to visit northern Nicosia to meet him and his team.

Some convention delegates accepted, but, at the insistence of their Greek Cypriot hosts, returned to the southern side a few hours later, without talking to ordinary people or travelling beyond the divided capital.

But then it was easy for Carter to be critical; he, unlike them, carried official UN identification documents, stayed within the United Nations Protected Area, and was able to move freely, without fear, to observe the observers observing.

CHAPTER 19

THE SLAUGHTERHOUSE

A MONTH later the emerald grass would be dull gold, but that spring afternoon it still glistened in the warm sun, sprinkled by a shower of red tulips and crown anemones of yellow, white, pink and lavender. It was a gently undulating carpet stretching northwards to the almost-bare, angular outline of the Kyrenia mountains, purple peaks which stabbed a bright blue sky. It was the final day of Carter's sixth visit to Cyprus, and he was fulfilling a promise made a long time ago to a bunch of 'squaddies' in the back of a Land-Rover. They had challenged him to visit Observation Post BRAVO 28 and he had agreed. So now here he was, three miles west of Nicosia International airport in Sector Two of the Buffer Zone.

'Let's see what's going on at the mushroom farm,' Corporal Tanner of the 2nd Battalion, The Queen's Regiment, suggested casually, pointing at a framework of wooden stilts holding up a corrugated metal roof. It stood on a small hill about 100 yards ahead. Was this the mushroom farm mentioned in Julia Sinclair's diary?

Tanner's five years' military service had taken him from barracks in Colchester to Germany and Northern Ireland. Carter had lived in Asia, Europe, Africa and the Americas. Neither had seen such serenity before.

Together they strolled up the slope, their steps disturbing bees and butterflies that buzzed and fluttered amidst an intricate patchwork of stems and tiny petals. A lizard scurried off to avoid being squashed by the corporal's army boots. In ancient times small elephants and hippopotami had grazed here. Now tiny birds, Cyprus warblers, were everywhere, rehearsing for concert performances that took place regularly at dusk; their voices sharp, scratchy and thin as they ran up and down the musical scale.

The birds could be heard, but not seen, perhaps intentionally because they always had a hard time in Cyprus. Migrating with the seasons, they used the island to rest and refresh themselves. For many the stay became permanent. Trapped by farmers, they were pickled in bottles or turned into paté, both considered culinary delicacies by Turks and Greeks alike

Carter and Tanner's path was blocked suddenly by two Turkish soldiers, their body-language hostile.

They had stepped from below a ridge on the far side of the hill. In their olive-green uniforms they looked little different from Corporal Tanner in his combat fatigues; but his Sten gun was slung on his shoulder while the young Turks had their rifles ready for action, right hands covering the triggers and left hands gripping the barrels.

'UN, you are not allowed here,' barked one soldier.

As a gesture of friendship Carter took a pack of cigarettes from his pocket and offered it to the Turks. They shook their heads. The first soldier grunted again. 'Go back,' he ordered, emphasizing his two words by using his rifle to prod the air ahead of himself.

Without any argument Carter and Tanner obeyed, turned and started their way down the well-trodden path they had just used, their feet crunching thick slivers of green glass, the unmistakable remains of shattered Coca Cola bottles.

'When the cease-fire took place in 1974 the Turks had quite a drinking session here,' Tanner remarked. 'They threw their empties everywhere. But nobody bothers to tidy up because the whole area was mined, and who knows what could happen if we tried?'

Amidst the beauty of Cyprus, danger always lurked.

Those shards of glass scattered in the middle of a minefield were graphic symbols of how carefully UN soldiers trod in their dealings with the opposing forces along the cease-fire line.

'The only safe place to walk is the patrol-track,' Tanner said, interrupting Carter's thoughts. 'We have an agreement to visit the mushroom farm, although it's on the Turkish side of the line. You obviously worried them today, because they're not used to seeing civilians at this location. That's why they turned us back.'

Carter ground the stub of his burning cigarette into the gravel at his feet.

The top of the hill was still and silent again. The Turkish soldiers had returned to their fortified positions and Tanner and Carter were returning to theirs. For UNFICYP the task was to maintain the status quo, providing time for politicians, if they cared, to talk and talk again in the search for a satisfactory solution. Year after year, observers were assured there were signs of an imminent breakthrough, the hint of a settlement, but none came.

Turkish Cypriots, however, could not afford the status quo for ever, even if the Greeks could.

Mr Denktaş and his ministers were a *de facto* administration in the north, but because they had not declared the area under their control an *independent* state, it did not exist officially. At the same time northern Cyprus was definitely not a part of the internationally-recognized 1960 Republic of Cyprus.

Therefore the time could not be far off before the Turkish Cypriots would have to do something, and then how would the world view them?

The tenth anniversary of the Turkish intervention was on the horizon and there was a distinct probability that the Turkish Cypriots would use the occasion to declare northern Cyprus a new and independent state. If an opportunity arose, perhaps they would act sooner.

When that declaration came Carter hoped to have a programme ready to tell the Cyprus story, filled with exclusive material. During his current trip he had again spent time in the north and secured promises of co-operation which had never been given before, not even to Turkish journalists. Now he needed BBC approval for the project and he expected both Radio 4 and the BBC Local Radio Network to be interested as they loved marking anniversaries with special features.

The two men crossed the UN patrol-track, a narrow strip of rugged ground carved by the heavy-duty tyres of the Ferret Scout Cars and Land-Rovers of the force.

Ahead was a whitewashed building, its sides and roofs marked with two large letters: UN. To their left a watch-tower rose precariously from uneven soil. It flew the United Nations' flag. A wall of sandbags protected a deep trench on their right. Laundered underwear fluttered from a string line between a pair of stunted trees.

Until 1974 the building had been a Greek Cypriot slaughterhouse. Today eight British soldiers lived there, working, eating, sleeping together during their three-month tour of duty along the thin blue line.

For the men of BRAVO 28 Carter's visit broke the monotony of their routine and they invited him inside for tea as only the British army made it: strong, thick, and very sweet from condensed milk, poured liberally into large mugs.

The main room measured 15 metres by five. It doubled as an operational area and living space. A pair of large metal cabinets separated the functions of the two halves. On the near side, large plastic-covered maps were tacked to the wall. A table made from planks of unpainted wood, stained and marked by ink and ball-pen scribble, protruded at right angles and carried an army radio. It crackled every few minutes with instructions and observations, curt and cryptic in the jargon of the military machine.

'Sunray . . . Charlie-Foxtrot-Lima . . . Say again, I say, say again . . . Roger, your last message at One-Five-Zero-Zero hours, Zulu.' And so it went on, making sense to the soldiers.

Stacked away from the radio operator and his equipment were half a dozen standard-issue self-loading rifles, a collection of white helmets and several green ammunition boxes. On the far side of the room, wall-to-wall, there were pictures of leggy, big-breasted females cut from adult magazines.

Asleep on one of three camp beds, a young soldier was stripped to his Y-fronts; a variety of personal possessions, lined pads of paper, shaving equipment, a block of soap, a dirty towel were spewed on the others.

'At least three of us are always on duty,' Corporal Tanner said, 'and so there are usually enough beds for those who want to rest.'

He walked Carter down three steps to a smaller room. 'This is where we do our cooking.' On a tiny gas stove, a pan of grey stew bubbled, its smell permeating the building. The stew was being stirred by a burly black soldier whose bulk filled the space between the cooker and two compact refrigerators. A lavatory was tucked in the corner, shielded by a sheet of hardboard and plumbed to a cesspit a few yards further along. A shower, constantly dripping, had been improvised by connecting a pipe from a tank to a tin can punched with holes, which discharged water on to a slab of pitted concrete. For privacy, it was hidden behind a tall sheet of blue metal.

'We have enough water for three people to have a two-minute shower every night,' Tanner said matter-of-factly.

While the governments of Austria, Canada and Sweden went out of their way to make life as comfortable as possible for the men of their contingents, the British government took the view UNFICYP was 'a normal posting', no different from one at the Sovereign Bases. Carter was not fooled. He had seen what Base personnel enjoyed. They had good accommodation, proper recreational facilities, fewer rules and regulations, the freedom of not having to wear uniform at all times and, perhaps most important of all, space to be alone.

Whitehall and the UN demanded that Turkish and Greek Cypriots were treated equally, but at the same time applied less-than-even-handed treatment to its own young soldiers.

For the men of the other contingents, UN service in Cyprus had become known as 'The Volvo Posting'. Even the Canadians, the only other full-time professional army wearing blue berets, had 'perks'. The Canadian government went as far as dispatching Customs officers to the island to check soldiers' baggage before they returned to Canada, so that the men would not be delayed a minute longer than was necessary before reaching home.

During their tour of duty the Canadians lived in the air-conditioned splendour of the Ledra Palace Hotel with its marble-floored lounges, restaurants, 200 bedrooms, swimming pools and tennis courts. Prior to the start of the 'troubles' in 1963, the hotel was considered one of the best in the Levant and was used as a base by journalists visiting Cyprus.

To their credit, the British soldiers expressed few complaints. Officers and junior ranks alike set about their extraordinary business with determination, making the most out of very difficult conditions, regarding them as challenges to overcome rather than handicaps to be endured. Without these men, and the massive logistical support from the Sovereign Bases, it was unlikely UNFICYP could survive.

'The British contingent provides a widespread contribution to our peace-keeping role, and UNFICYP logistics are entirely based on the British system,' Major-General Gunther Greindl, the UN Force Commander told Carter. 'Your Scout Cars are the heavy weapon, our show of force; and your helicopter flights are really essential to our mission. As far as the British battalion is concerned, it is always very professional and experienced.'

And yet, who knew of BRITCON in Britain? The British peace soldiers were a forgotten army.

At BRAVO 28 Carter drank tea with the men, sitting on sandbags which protected a large trench.

From the watch-tower, a soldier waved. 'Don't fall down the bunker, mate,' he joked.

'We'd use the bunker in the event something nasty happened,' Corporal Tanner explained. 'That is, if we were shelled. We'd grab anything we could lay our hands on, like weapons, food, water, and throw them down, following fast ourselves.'

Carter switched on his Uher and began taping. What did Tanner and the others at BRAVO 28 feel about their UNFICYP service?

'It gets a bit repetitive at times, having to observe the same scenery every day and night,' Tanner replied. 'Sometimes the troopers get a bit fed up, and this place *is* a bit primitive. But it's what you make of it that matters. I suppose we are stopping a war.'

One-hundred-and-fifty yards ahead of Tanner, in their watch-towers flying the Turkish flag, other soldiers were looking at the UN Colours above BRAVO 28.

Five hundred yards to the south, the flag of Greece fluttered in the slight breeze of the evening. Beneath it sat the Greek National Guard, much more relaxed, playing cards. They knew they were not gambling at all because Corporal Tanner, and men like him, stood between them and the Turkish army.

It was just another day along the cease-fire line in Cyprus; one of many since 1974.

There would be more.

CHAPTER 20

PERMISSION GRANTED

DERRICK Amoore, the station-manager most recently appointed to run Radio London, was a brilliant, but erratic and emotional man, whose reputation had preceded his arrival at the studios in Marylebone High Street. Although many members of the station's staff were apprehensive about the changes Amoore would undoubtedly introduce, Carter was optimistic about the future.

His hopes were soon dashed.

Amoore's plans to revive Radio London's flagging fortunes did not include Carter and he was dispatched to Broadcasting House to help organize the BBC's annual display at the *Daily Mail* Ideal Home Exhibition in Earl's Court, a chore designed by the corporation for those not usefully employed elsewhere. When this took place, Carter believed he would never return to Radio London and would have to discontinue his work on his Cyprus documentary.

To everybody's surprise, including his own, Carter was back six weeks later to serve under Amoore again. What his new role was, nobody knew. He became a producer in search of programmes to make. Whether the new station-manager valued him or not was hard to determine, for there were occasions in the weeks that followed when Amoore did place major projects in Carter's hands, allowed him freedom to execute them, and then ignored him completely for long stretches of time.

During this up and down relationship, Amoore invited Carter frequently to share bouts of generous hospitality in his office late into the night, often continuing into the small hours of the morning.

After both had drunk several gin and tonics, Amoore would tell Carter how he had served in Cyprus during the mid-fifties. He claimed he had performed several SAS-type operations against EOKA terrorists, spending weeks hidden in the Troodos mountains waiting to strike. The two BBC men found that they had both served in the same branch of the British army, the Royal Signals.

Against this background, Carter tried to persuade Amoore to support his plans for a documentary to mark the tenth anniversary of the Turkish intervention in Cyprus.

While Amoore never rejected the project out of hand, he never greeted the idea with more than mild enthusiasm and always promised to consider it, later.

During this period, others at Radio London were being overworked and they resented Carter's easy life. They saw him spending several weeks at a time doing nothing and then, suddenly, with permission, travelling to foreign locations which, to them, appeared to have little or no relevance to the station's broadcasts.

Rumours began to circulate that Carter could be connected to the security services because he always appeared in places immediately prior to something happening which involved the military or the government. On his foreign trips he was then granted facilities denied other journalists, many with better track records of achievement.

Before long Carter was nicknamed 'The Colonel'.

His critics catalogued a series of examples to argue their case. They pointed out, for example, that while others had been told by the Ministry of Defence they could not go to the Falklands unless the BBC paid several thousand pounds to cover the costs of their transportation and accommodation, not only did Carter travel free, he was given priority treatment. He was always at the right place at the right time.

In the Falklands he was taken to watch and photograph a Royal Navy nuclear submarine surface. Now he was able to confirm its presence, something which until then had only been a rumour. On another occasion Carter had been flown to Ascension Island by the RAF, just when the world's media was trying to track and speak to Guardsman Philip Williams, the soldier who claimed to have lost himself for six weeks at the height of the South Atlantic campaign. And where did the army take Williams after his reappearance? Yes, said Carter's critics, it was Ascension Island. Moreover, Williams's parents shunned other journalists, turning down large cash offers for their 'story', but were prepared to talk to Carter and gave him a letter to carry to their son.

Carter's critics were also suspicious because he had secured a visa for Beirut when the Lebanese authorities were rejecting applications from other reporters; and why, they asked, had the Ministry of Defence allowed him to be the first producer to work alongside the Multi-National Land Force, flying him to Beirut in a C-130 Hercules to arrive immediately after the American Embassy was bombed and US Marines had suffered heavy casualties?

Carter's explanations were simple: he said all his opportunities were due to careful planning and a lot of luck. His critics were not pacified and, in Radio London's newsroom, they responded by refusing to use the material he gathered during his travels abroad. Not to be trusted as an objective professional annoyed the BBC producer more than being labelled 'a spook' for an intelligence agency.

Then two incidents occurred which frightened Carter.

On his way home one evening from Baker Street to King's Cross station, two Englishmen, whom he had never seen before, pushed him into a corner of the tube train and warned him to drop his interest in the Cyprus problem, threatening the safety of his family if he did not.

At first Carter thought he was involved in a bizarre practical joke, but the men convinced him of their seriousness by revealing details of his background, proving that they had studied him carefully and demonstrating they had access to information known only to very few people.

Immediately on his return to Welwyn Garden City, Carter contacted a friend in the police.

A meeting followed soon afterwards with a Special Branch officer at which all members of Carter's family were present. They were told that a thorough check had been made of their lives to ensure that the BBC producer was not involved in a publicity stunt.

The officer, a man over six feet in height, promised them that all reasonable precautions would be put in place for the Carters' safety. They were given a special telephone number to use day or night if anything unusual happened or they felt insecure.

Special Branch took the matter seriously.

A few days later, a news producer at Radio London asked Carter to meet a friend of his, a Member of the European Parliament. The invitation was accepted in the belief the meeting would be purely social, but that was a wrong assumption.

At 18.00 the news producer arrived at Carter's office with the MEP, Richard Cottrell, who represented the Bristol and Bath constituency. With them was the MEP's female aide.

Without waiting to be asked, they settled themselves in chairs and placed the microphone of a cassette tape-recorder on Carter's desk.

Cottrell said he was investigating the death of Ann Chapman, a freelance reporter who had worked for Radio London in the early seventies. She had been murdered in Greece in October 1971. Ever since, her parents had campaigned for a thorough and impartial inquiry into the controversial circumstances leading to her death and the subsequent police inquiries. This investigation was being conducted at the behest of the European Parliament, the MEP added. He wanted Carter to answer a set of questions, which had been 'authorized'.

Carter replied that he was willing to help in any way possible, but he doubted if he had anything worthwhile to reveal as he had met Ann Chapman on only a couple of occasions, and these he could barely remember. Most of what he knew about the case had been gleaned from newspapers, he said.

Cottrell, who had been a journalist before becoming an MEP, raised a quizzical eyebrow and asked if Carter objected to having his answers recorded.

No, Carter replied, he did not, although he felt Cottrell was suggesting that he was somehow personally involved in the Chapman case and should be interrogated as a hostile witness. But a witness to what?

The questioning began.

How well do you know Cyprus?

'Quite well.'

Have you spent time in northern Cyprus, the Turkish-occupied area?
'Well, yes. But I dispute the *occupation* part of your question.'

Cottrell's line puzzled Carter. What did Ann Chapman's murder in Greece, 13 or more years ago, have to do with his visits to northern Cyprus, and why had the MEP chosen to question him?

Cottrell replied that a former member of the British security services had suggested Carter would be a source of valuable information about the girl reporter. He added that there was evidence to suggest Ann Chapman had stumbled on secrets involving Turkish intentions towards Cyprus. This was a possible reason for her murder, he said.

Carter was bemused and said so: 'I don't think she was capable of uncovering a banana if she peeled it. As for anything big or of international significance, come on . . . Perhaps she stumbled on something and, in her naivety, she tried to bring it home.'

But why would the Greeks kill anybody who had information about the Turks, Carter asked? If Ann Chapman had discovered Turkish plans for Cyprus, then somebody must have deceived her because even the Turks themselves did not decide to intervene militarily until 1974, three years after her murder.

What sort of person was she?

'A dull, boring girl,' Carter replied, never one to pull his punches. 'Thick as two short planks, with stars in her eyes.'

The MEP was not put off. He continued to question, his attractive aide continued to record, and the Radio London news producer continued to listen; all were eager to pluck something 'significant' from Carter's responses.

Describe the last time you saw Ann Chapman.

Carter did. It had been the weekend before her final journey to Greece on 11 October 1971.

You say she was carrying a Uher tape-recorder?

'Yes, that's the model we use at Radio London.'

But a Uher wasn't found with her possessions. Nor were there any tapes.

'I wouldn't know,' Carter snapped, adding that he had nothing more to say and he was going home.

The trio of investigators left his office and, as soon as he was alone, Carter dialled the telephone number given him by the Special Branch officer. He described what had just taken place. The officer's reply was polite and to the point. He had no idea who could have put Cottrell on to Carter and he advised him to tell the MEP to 'bugger off' if he returned. To refuse to answer any more questions, legal or otherwise, was Carter's absolute right. Members of the European Parliament could not force people to do anything against their will, and to say questions had been 'authorized' was a 'load of crap'.

The officer ended the conversation by promising to deal with the matter.

Next Carter raised the incident with his station-manager. Derrick Amoore knew Cottrell had visited Radio London, but claimed he did not know that one of reasons was to interview Carter. He expressed surprise that Special Branch had been notified.

Later Carter would be quoted in Richard Cottrell's book, *Blood on their Hands — The Killing of Ann Chapman.*

Carter never found out who was behind the two incidents or whether they were connected, but if they had been designed to deter him from pursuing his interest in Cyprus, they had failed completely. He was determined to probe deeper and produce an in-depth documentary. His efforts were supported by Charles Murray, another Radio London news producer, who, at the time, was responsible for the station's early morning current affairs programme, *Rush Hour.*

Murray was not concerned by what others said about Carter. So what if he were a 'spook'? Good news stories mattered to him more than where they came from, providing they could be verified. For that reason he promised to carry Carter's material on northern Cyprus, which, so far, had never proved incorrect.

Murray particularly wanted a 'live and direct' interview from Nicosia with Rauf Denktaş, the Turkish Cypriot leader. If Carter could arrange this, then Murray was prepared to use it in his programme. He also suggested that Carter waste no time in contacting Alan Rogers, BBC Radio's Head of Current Affairs Magazine Programmes, better known as CAMP. The latter was in a strong position to commission a full-length documentary to mark the tenth anniversary of the island's partition and have it broadcast by Radio 4. Murray was certain that Rogers would give the idea a sympathetic hearing as he had worked at Radio London and knew Carter of old.

'What about offering the programme to Greg Ainger as well?' Murray said. 'He's always on the look out for good stuff to syndicate to other stations, providing it doesn't cost him an arm and a leg, and let's face it, David, you come cheap.'

Ainger was the BBC's Local Radio Programme Services Editor. His potential market was enormous, but his budgets were minute.

'I'm sure you'll persuade them both of the value of the project,' Murray said ordering Carter another large whisky and a pint of IPA beer for himself.

The two men spent a lot of time in a public house not far from Radio London, swapping gossip.

'The BBC will send you to any trouble-spot where the hazards to your health are greater than from your cigarette consumption,' Murray continued. 'Come on, let's have another fag.'

Murray helped himself to one of Carter's Marlboros. 'Have you ever thought that maybe Amoore and the Beeb are trying to tell you something?'

While Alan Rogers at Radio 4 rejected Carter's first suggestion for a series of three programmes, one each devoted exclusively to the Greek and Turkish positions, and the third for the world view, he did accept the alternative: a single documentary designed to report and evaluate what had happened to *Turkish Cypriots* since the formation of the Republic of Cyprus in 1960, why the Turks had intervened in 1974, and how the Turkish Cypriots were managing their affairs today in the TFSC, a state recognized by Turkey alone. He insisted, however, that the programme must contain information never broadcast before. To help Carter achieve his ends, Rogers wrote a letter to the Ministry of Foreign Affairs in the Turkish Federated State of Cyprus.

Over at Local Radio headquarters, Greg Ainger was even more definite about the Cyprus programme. Because he had supported Carter's work in the Falklands and Beirut, he knew what the Radio London producer could deliver.

The two BBC executives had given Carter what he wanted. With their letters he hoped the Turkish Cypriots would convert their promises of assistance into something more tangible. He needed their written guarantees that he would have complete freedom to operate in northern Cyprus without constant 'supervision', and he wanted access to so-called 'forbidden areas' like Varosha, which had been closed to Cypriots and the media since 1974.

Carter sent his requirements to Fikri Direkoğlu at the Ministry of Tourism in Nicosia and copied them to Mustafa Adiloğlu, the press officer at the TFSC offices in London, and to Vural Türkmen, another official who was friendly and efficient.

At the same time Carter wrote to Trevor Taylor, the British expatriate he had met during his first trip to the north. He also contacted 'The Cave Ladies', Majors Phyllis Heymann and Betty Hunter Cowan, and Major Cedric Mercer, the former MPIO of UNFICYP who had introduced them. All were asked to exert influence on their contacts in Cyprus and to persuade the 'ancient Brits' of Kyrenia to co-operate.

Within days Radio London's Editor, John Murray, received a reply from Dr Kenan Atakol, the TFSC Minister responsible for Foreign Affairs at the time, inviting Carter to make his seventh visit to Cyprus.

In the letter, the TFSC provided the necessary guarantees for the making of the documentaries and acknowledged that editorial content would be shaped by the BBC alone. Sending the invitation to a senior BBC executive to vet was another positive action by Dr Atakol. Whatever Carter produced for Rogers and Ainger now, nobody could accuse him of playing an underhand game. Everything was out in the open.

Carter felt secure.

CHAPTER 21

TRUTH AND CONSEQUENCES

A FOUR-year-old boy dressed in military uniform and carrying a wooden rifle dug the rubber heels of his boots into the pock-marked asphalt outside the war-damaged Famagusta district offices. From vintage loudspeakers martial music crackled through the hot August afternoon air. The youngster stepped forward, his movements jerky and out of time, but his awkwardness did not inhibit the Turkish Cypriots from cheering. They stood, four and five deep, along one side of the Greek Cypriot-named 'Democracy Avenue', which did not seem inappropriate as they were there to watch a celebration parade to mark their liberation by the Turkish army in 1974.

Nine years later they remained unrecognized by the international community but their resolve stayed firm to remain apart and independent of the authorities of the original Republic of Cyprus founded in 1960. Or that was what Carter heard wherever he went gathering material for his Cyprus tapes. No wonder that they had not bothered to repair the Law Courts opposite or clear the charred remains of a police station down the road. Both were places where once Greek Cypriots exercised their brand of law and order.

Behind the boy came marching lines of smartly-dressed Turkish soldiers, followed by rumbling tanks, armoured personnel carriers and mobile rocket-launchers. On the VIP dais the political leaders of northern Cyprus, including Rauf Denktaş and the Mayor of Famagusta, stood shoulder to shoulder with representatives of Turkey, all standing to attention as the Turkish flag passed and was dipped in salute.

Across the road Arif Gürbüz, the director of the municipal water department, wiped sweat from his forehead. The temperature was more than 100 degrees. He smiled in relief as the parade went by smoothly. He had been delegated to help organize the festivities. His particular job was to ensure all microphones, loudspeakers and amplifiers worked perfectly when the Turkish Cypriot leaders made their speeches. It was always worth reminding the local populace of the long siege that Famagusta had endured and how they had been liberated by the Turkish army.

With the parade reaching its conclusion, Gürbüz now had time to search for Carter in the crowds, for he had been tasked additionally to provide any assistance the BBC man required. He wished he had been given warning of Carter's visit because he would have arranged for him to be seated alongside the dignitaries. As it was, all he had been able to fix were some ice-creams and cold drinks for the Carter family.

'I'm sorry I cannot give you better hospitality,' he had apologized, 'but, as you can see, we are all very disorganized today.'

Carter knew exactly what Gürbüz meant. During the preceding week he had become used to having his plans go wrong and official arrangements drastically altered at the last minute. But the trip had started promisingly.

Before departing London he had asked permission to record Turkish Cypriot air traffic procedures on the approach to Ercan so that his documentary could deal with Greek Cypriot charges that the northern Cyprus airport was unsafe by international standards. Permission was granted and all his questions were answered by the Turkish captain in the pilot's seat.

The aircraft had arrived on time and Carter and his family were greeted warmly by Fikri Direkoğlu and Ali Özel, his long-time friends from the Ministry of Tourism. Pleasant hotel accommodation had been provided in Famagusta and in Kyrenia. A car was at his disposal and he was able to travel to most places he wanted, but there was no formal itinerary to follow.

Whenever Carter pressed the authorities to take him to the Karpas peninsula to meet Greek Cypriots who still lived there, or the 'forbidden city' of Varosha, literally a quarter-mile from where he was standing today, Fikri, looking more worried than usual, replied that permission would be granted 'soon' or was 'under consideration' by one ministry or another.

While Fikri had promised all would be well, Carter saw nothing happening. What worried him, too, was not having a date or time for the 'live' interview with President Denktaş which Charles Murray wanted for his radio programme. Nor was there a meeting scheduled with Dr Kenan Atakol, the Turkish Cypriot Minister of Foreign Affairs.

Turning to his other friend, Ali Özel, for assistance had not proved much more useful. Ali was no longer a civil servant. He had taken early retirement to set up a tourism agency in Famagusta and, understandably, he was always busy trying to make Özel Tours a successful business. It left little time for him to chase the government ministries of Nicosia on Carter's behalf.

'I never thought that starting afresh would engulf all my energies,' he told Carter in his quaint English. 'I am placing all my efforts in starting the business, encountering difficulties and wracking my brain to find solutions. You must see and use my office for your work, my friend, David. I am located in the square, flanked by the mosque and the palace.

'You remember the café where we drank coffee with Bora, who was the Mayor? Well, my office is in the domed building behind the bust of Namık Kemal. It is from the thirteenth century. I have a chandelier hanging from the middle of the room and I have decorated it as a place European travellers would like to visit. I have a telephone.'

Carter took up Ali's invitation and found the office much as it had been described, give or take some twentieth-century layers of dust. Most of the time, however, the office was locked, with Ali's whereabouts not always known.

Telephoning London from Famagusta was no easy matter either. It took hours of patient dialling to reach the studios in Marylebone High Street, only to find Charles Murray was out having a drink somewhere and that nobody else was prepared to take the call.

But Carter had not wasted his first week entirely. With Ron Kendall, Matthew's godfather, an energetic 77-year-old at the wheel of the family's rented Renault, he had raced through the north, stopping here and there to record interviews with ordinary Turkish Cypriots, young and old.

Carter found these people consistently philosophical about their administrators and their country's lack of recognition abroad. They were fatalistic about not having any direct flights between Europe and northern Cyprus, and tolerant of their constantly-devalued currency, the Turkish lira. But no matter how hard he looked or how carefully he framed his questions, he had failed to find even one Turkish Cypriot who believed there could be a unified Cyprus again. The withdrawal of the Turkish army would not make any difference to their beliefs, despite what Greek Cypriots claimed.

The interviewees vigorously denied that the Turkish forces controlled their lives, that northern Cyprus had become a province of Turkey, and that their press and political parties were strictly controlled.

Amongst those who talked was Okan Avni, a 25-year-old teacher from the Jewish Beis Shammai Grammar School in north London. He was a British passport-holder who had grown up in England, his family having fled Cyprus to escape the intercommunal conflict of the sixties. He had returned voluntarily to northern Cyprus to do military service.

'I think I should do this service because it's still my country,' Avni explained. 'The mainland soldiers won't stay for ever and we have got to be able to defend ourselves. We are secure today and no longer fear being suddenly killed. We would prefer to be economically worse off than the Greek Cypriots, rather than return to the pre-1974 conditions of Cyprus.'

That feeling of patriotism and security had also persuaded 21-year-old Gurnal Yavaş, from Southgate, to come back to northern Cyprus. As a switchboard operator at The Dome Hotel, she often connected Carter to his radio station, without the London switchboard realizing that the call was coming from abroad.

What did Gurnal miss from London, Carter asked?

'The wages,' came her quick reply in a chirpy cockney accent. 'I earn £25 a week. That's the average weekly wage out here.' For this she worked a six-day week. 'And of course, I miss the junk food. Things like McDonald's.'

Gurnal told Carter that because she, too, held a British passport, she had had to obtain a work permit from the northern Cyprus administration, something she found very amusing. She said she was also having to learn a new language:'*Türkçe bilmiyorum*. I can't speak Turkish.'

There had been changes since Carter's last trip, but much stayed the same. At The Dome Hotel, the fresh-water swimming pool was still unfinished, but, across the road, the Barclays bank was shut. Mr Sami had moved on and Carter had never had coffee with him after all.

Next door to the bolted bank there was a shoe shop and its owner was Mustafa Reisoğlu, a quietly-spoken man in his late fifties. He had been an inhabitant of Limassol, where, as a young man, he was employed by a Greek Cypriot shoe-maker. They had worked together, he told Carter, until EOKA threatened his colleague's life. For both their safety, he had left.

Then, in 1974, Reisoğlu had been forced to flee northwards, leaving behind his home and all his possessions. In the chaos of war, his 10-year-old daughter went missing for a period of six months.

While Mustafa continued to shape and trim his leathers, he talked to Carter's microphone, paying tribute to former Greek Cypriot friends, one of whom had driven his car to the Sovereign Base at Dhekelia from where the shoe-maker had collected it after the war.

Mustafa expressed sadness for 'the ordinary Greek Cypriot people who weren't involved in attacking us', but he was pessimistic about future relations with southern Cyprus. 'Once our generation is off this world, the young people will know nothing about Greeks, and the Greek young people will know nothing about us,' he said sadly. 'So we can't come together.'

'The Cave Ladies', the retired Majors Betty Hunter Cowan and Phyllis Heymann, were the next to contribute to Carter's Cyprus tapes. They took him to *Yavus Çıkartma Plajı*, where the Turkish army had come ashore in 1974. The beach-side restaurant was still there, but now it was called The Golden Rock. Its owner was Sami Otcuoğlu, a former Turkish Cypriot 'Freedom Fighter', one of those who had controlled the Kyrenia-Nicosia road prior to the intervention. During this period he had lived for 11 years at St Hilarion castle, without once being able to see his family.

Children were playing on the beach while 'The Cave Ladies' talked. 'They are the new generation,' Betty remarked, reminding Carter that until 1974 many Turkish Cypriots, like Sami, had been prevented from setting foot in the sea; held hostage in their own country by their fellow citizens of the old Republic, the Greek Cypriots.

'Of course, David, there's still a lot the Turkish Cypriots have to learn before they get things right,' Phyllis added, 'but you must realize that these people have had less than a decade of experience in governing themselves, and without very much help.'

Both women spoke of the Cypriots' affection for the British and their bewilderment at why the British government had not given more help in resolving the problems of island. In the view of 'The Cave Ladies', the biggest danger to the island's stability was 'the rubbish both sides talk about the other. The real trouble is that both sides believe their own propaganda. Neither knows what's really going on in the minds of the people on the other side, and a whole new generation has been taught to distrust their peers on whichever side of the line they live.'

The subject of the war of the words decided Carter to meet Kemal Aşık in Nicosia. A journalist for the past 36 years, he was the director of TAK, the official news agency of the Turkish Cypriot administration. In his air-conditioned office, a quiet haven next to a bustling newsroom, Aşık expressed himself enthusiastically on the subjects of democracy and press freedoms in the north, as he saw them.

Slapping a pile of Turkish newspapers on his desk, Aşık pointed out that all of them were published in the divided city. 'You would be amazed how outspoken they are,' he declared. 'I don't think there are so many different points of view expressed in the British press.'

Aşık said there were eight political parties in the TFSC, ranging from the extreme right to the extreme left, all trying to win the hearts and minds of the population of almost 160,000 Turkish Cypriots.

Questioning Aşık for his BBC radio programme, Carter suggested that as TAK was funded entirely by the government, how could its news coverage be objective? 'Nobody, nobody controls the news before it goes out,' Aşık replied emphatically.

If the northern administration believed so strongly in the freedom of the press, Carter continued, why were foreign journalists escorted by government officials?'

'We are still at war, and until there is a stable peace, any government must take precautions,' Aşık retorted.

Surely, by the same token, the Greek Cypriot side was still at war, too, but journalists there were not restricted, Carter countered.

'I disagree with you that journalists are more free in the south,' came Aşık's reply, registering clearly on Carter's tape. 'But I agree that we are naturally more suspicious than the other side, because we are the people who have suffered most over the years. However, even if a journalist is escorted, he can still see everything, even our prisons. Only military areas are restricted, just the same as in Portsmouth. But a journalist who comes to the north with an open mind will find us more free, more democratic than anywhere else.'

Carter smiled.

He hoped Aşık would be proved right and that the delay in getting permission to visit 'forbidden' areas in the north was due only to the administration's inefficiency, the kind 'The Cave Ladies' had described.

During the Carter family's first week in the TFSC, they also sought out a Turkish Cypriot youngster who had befriended Matthew on the beach at Salamis five years earlier. Emir was now 11 years old, tall, dark and rapidly growing into a young man, while Matthew remained blond and, at the age of eight, still a boy.

The two recognized each other immediately when they met again in Famagusta. Although neither spoke the other's language, they embraced as brothers and disappeared into the kitchen of 'The Cyprus House Restaurant and Art Gallery', their little fingers linked according to Turkish custom.

The restaurant was owned by Emir's father, Hüssein Herbsoy. It was filled with customers, more than Carter had seen elsewhere.

At the start of the war in 1974 Herbsoy had been employed at a hotel in Varosha, where he was being taught his catering skills by Greek Cypriots.

Because Herbsoy was a non-combatant throughout the period of hostilities, serving instead as a medical orderly, Carter thought his views might be different to those already captured on tape.

Herbsoy answered questions softly, but precisely, in clear English. He conceded nothing in favour of the Greeks. 'I am a Turkish Cypriot and I am proud of that. I don't want to lose my identity and if I met a Greek Cypriot today, I would tell him, "You asked for it, the war and everything, and you've seen what's happened."'

A fine-featured man with sad brown eyes, Herbsoy believed in Cyprus the place, but argued there was no such being as a Cypriot. Carter was reminded again of something one of 'The Cave Ladies' had said. 'There never has been a *Cypriot* as such. Think of the United Kingdom and look at us. I'm Scottish and always will be, while Phyllis is English. It's a similar sort of thing for the people out here. They are Turks or they are Greeks.'

As the last tanks roared past to end the Turkish army's display in Famagusta, Arif Gürbüz found Carter and his family amongst the onlookers. Glancing at Matthew's Kodak Instamatic camera, loaned him by Ali, Arif asked, 'Did you get some good pictures of the parade of our soldiers, my young friend?'

'Yes, thank you,' Matthew replied. 'May I have another Coke, please?'

'*Evet*. But of course, my friend.' Arif placed Matthew on his broad shoulders, turned to Wendy and said, 'Madam, please, if your husband and Mr Kendall will follow me, I will take you to the school where our folk-music group rehearses. We have refreshments there.'

Like many other Turkish Cypriot officials, Arif was unaware that Carter had visited northern Cyprus before and on the short walk to the school, he quizzed the BBC producer about what he planned to put in his documentary. Every Turkish Cypriot felt that their side of the story was never put fairly by European reporters; the Greeks were always favoured.

'I insist that you do not call the events of 1974 an "invasion of Cyprus by Turkey". It was an intervention to save lives,' the tubby official said, his voice friendly but firm. Passing an old colonial building, he added, 'You know, during the British period we were all having a jolly good time, until EOKA began killing innocent English ladies, like Mrs Cutliffe, here in the streets of Famagusta.' He waved his arms in many directions as if each incident had taken place everywhere. Somehow Matthew remained balanced on his shoulders.

Arif stopped and lowered the youngster to the pavement, running his hands through the boy's curly hair. 'I was only a little older than your son, Mr *Dyvid*, when I first had to carry a gun for protection. I was 13.' Carter listened. He didn't tell Arif that he had been only nine when he first fired a gun in anger.

'I am 42 years now, and three times in my life I have been made a refugee.'

From a short distance away came the sound of a choir performing a Turkish folk-song. 'That is what the youth should be doing,' Arif declared. 'Come, let us go inside and talk. I wish you to meet my friend İsmail. He teaches in the technical school and helps with the choir. Please forgive him his poor English.'

İsmail was waiting inside, acknowledged everybody's entrance with a desultory nod, exchanged a few words in Turkish with Arif, and disappeared to return shortly with a tray of Turkish coffees and a Coca Cola for Matthew.

While İsmail had been out of the room, Arif explained that his friend still suffered from the effects of war. He said that the man had escaped with two other Turkish Cypriots from a village in the Karpas which had been over-run by the Greek Cypriot National Guard, found a small boat and sailed in search of safety. But during three days and nights at sea, İsmail's friends had perished from heat and exhaustion. Just as he had begun to give up too, a warship spotted him and her crew hauled him from the sea, saving his life. Only when he had regained consciousness did he realize that his rescuers were Russians. Later they put İsmail ashore at İstanbul.

Arif asked İsmail to show Carter his photographs of the Russian sailors. From his wallet he produced two cracked and faded black-and-white pictures of him with his arms around his rescuers, all of them wearing Soviet navy sweaters. 'He spoke very good Turkish,' İsmail said, tapping one of three figures in his photograph.

Arif, too, had tales to tell of his own experiences during the 21-day siege of the walled city of Famagusta. 'I got very very cross with the Greeks,' he recalled, his understatement contrived. 'They kept cutting off our water supply and it was jolly hot. So I went up to this one UN man who was observing and told him that we would get on our radio and ask the Turkish air force to come and blow them away if we didn't get our water back. He arranged for me to have a meeting with my opposite number in the Greek Cypriot water department to see what we could sort out between ourselves.

'The Greek Cypriot told me that the decision to cut the water supply was not made by him, but by the mainland Greek officers who were leading the Greek Cypriot National Guard. He himself was very sorry, but then the Greeks tried to arrest me, although I was under the protection of the UN for these talks. I owe my life to a very brave man, a Swedish captain. I wish I knew his name to tell you. But this man, he took out his pistol and said to them, "You will have to shoot me as well unless you immediately release Mr Gürbüz." They released me. You can imagine, those were very trying times.'

'Yes,' İsmail added. 'Mr Arif's wife was pregnant as well.'

Arif put down Carter's new camera which he had been examining. Turning to Wendy, who had showed concern, he said, 'Our baby came on the first of September. She is a girl. I will, of course, tell her the circumstances in which she was born. We must teach our children to recognize their enemies.' Arif spoke calmly, no emotion in his voice which made his last remark more chilling. 'I cannot trust the Greeks at all. They are good actors to your face, but they will kill you when your back is turned. Sorry, that is all I can say.'

'Are you enjoying your visit, Madam,' İsmail asked shyly, trying to change the subject.

'Yes, but I think my husband is finding it very frustrating.'

'Why?' Arif wanted to know immediately.

Carter explained his tight schedule and how he was facing a number of delays in getting confirmation to see various parts of the TFSC which was necessary if he were to gather fresh material for the Radio 4 programme.

'I will do my best to chase the ministers for you,' Arif promised, laughing for the first time. 'But I think you are spending too much time, if I may say so, on what has gone before and not showing enough interest in what we are doing now as a free people. May I suggest Mr *Dyvid*, that you and your charming family come with us tomorrow evening to one of our villages to hear our folk society performing. We will be taking our orchestra with us. What do you say?'

'I think that will be very enjoyable and a pleasant change from politics,' Wendy replied before her husband could say a word.

'I agree,' Ron Kendall added, at last feeling able to make a contribution to the conversation.

'Yes, we'd love to come,' Wendy continued. 'Where do we meet?'

'We are going by bus at three o'clock, but you may bring your car and follow us later if that time is too early,' Arif replied.

'No, let's go on the bus,' Matthew chipped in, blowing through the drinking-straw in his bottle of Coca Cola. 'Uncle Ron won't have to drive then like James Bond.' Wendy smiled, relieved, for Ron Kendall was a sprightly pensioner with a fondness for fast driving. 'Will there be enough seats? We don't want to put you to any trouble.'

'Plenty,' İsmail confirmed. 'It will be our pleasure.'

'Forgive me,' said Ron, clearing his throat, 'but what sort of clothes ought we to wear if this is a special occasion?' He was a stickler for correctness at all times.

'Ow do you say?' Arif replied, his voice suddenly taking on a stronger cockney inflection. 'Come as you are.'

'Is it okay for me to bring my tape-recorder?' Carter inquired. He liked ground-rules to be established and understood in advance, never wanting to hurt local feelings later.

'Yes, of course, Mr *Dyvid*, but I have some good recordings of our choir which I will give you for your programme. Bring your camera as well, because I wish to try it. Photography is my hobby, you know. It is one thing I have in common with our President, apart from this.' He rubbed his stomach. 'Perhaps later you would like to swap your camera for mine.'

CHAPTER 22

AN ARRESTING CELEBRATION

PRECISELY at 15.00 the next day, the Carters and Ron Kendall arrived by taxi outside the Famagusta school. It was blistering hot and humid. As usual, because this was Cyprus, the whole group was far from complete at the agreed time, but Arif Gürbüz was determined to demonstrate his control of the situation and vigorously ordered out search-parties for the missing musicians and singers, only to find the missing appeared while the searchers were away.

As the performing company grew in strength, Carter felt damp patches developing under his armpits. He should have worn something light and airy. Instead, for reasons of vanity, he wore his favourite checked shirt and had squeezed himself into a pair of tight denims, his waistline already beginning to show the effects of his love for Cypriot food; his only companion in the dress stakes was Arif of the municipal water board, whose large chest pulled apart the buttons on his small shirt and whose trousers exaggerated the size of his rear.

Wendy and Ron felt smug. They had chosen to dress comfortably but smartly, she in a colourful print dress matched with low-heeled sandals, and he in a crisp shirt and carefully-pressed trousers. Matthew wore neat shorts and a tee-shirt, his hair washed and combed. Around them stood the Turkish Cypriot ladies of the choir, wearing long white dresses trimmed with lace, while the men of the orchestra wore black ties and dinner suits, seemingly unconcerned by the heat.

At last, all were present and correct, according to Arif, by now definitely the self-appointed officer in charge. 'Right,' he said forcefully, ordering everybody to board the bus, 'Let us proceed.'

With a wheeze from the handbrake's release, a cough from the engine, and a squeal from grinding gears, the vehicle dragged itself forward to the main road and headed away from Famagusta. By this time Ron and Wendy were beginning to envy Carter and Arif's sturdy denim jeans, for the plastic seat-covers on the bus had begun to stick to those whose bottoms were not as well protected.

Wendy dabbed her face with a tissue, trying to absorb the streaks of perspiration which had started to smudge her elegant and carefully-applied eye make-up, while Ron fidgeted, undid his shirt to the waist when nobody was looking, and still grew more florid by the minute.

Noticing their discomfort, one of the Turkish Cypriot girls, all of whom still looked cool and composed, produced a bottle of lemon fragrance and sprayed the English party. It did nothing to make them feel any cooler, but it did make them smell nicer.

Along the route the bus driver made several detours, stopping to collect additional members of the Famagusta philharmonic and folk society from places without a sign of habitation. At a minor crossroads, he waited for more than five minutes. Here, as far as eyes could see in any direction, there were only flat fields of wheat, yellow and ready for harvesting; nothing else, or was there? In the distance, a wheat field was moving. The movement came closer. There, ploughing his way through the stalks, was a Turkish Cypriot musician in full evening dress, a double-bass resting on his shoulder. He boarded breathlessly and offered Arif profuse apologies for his tardiness, and so, once again, the vehicle lurched into a sort of half-life, leaving a trail of black diesel smoke and white dust in its wake.

Some two hours later the bus reached the outskirts of its destination, Yiğitler. Before 1974, it had been a mixed village of Turkish and Greek Cypriots. Then, if Carter had read his map correctly, the place was called *Arsos*.

Arif explained that as the bus was too large to squeeze itself through the narrow streets leading to the town square, everybody would have to walk. The passengers trooped off and drew deep breaths of fresh air flavoured with the essences of country manure.

'We will walk and I will introduce you to the *Muktar*,' said Arif, much relieved to have arrived safely. 'You will be his honoured guests at dinner. Meanwhile, Mr *Dyvid* we will have cold drinks.'

Arif walked his small party to a nearby farmhouse opposite a large cow-shed. Within minutes the farmer's family had arranged three chairs on the edge of the dusty track leading to the square. Glasses of cold water were offered with shy smiles by the daughters of the household, while chickens clucked and cocks strutted. Cows mooed and ambled forwards. They peered over the fences of the fields, curious to know who the strangers were in their midst.

'Come now,' said Arif, taking Matthew by the hand, while Ron Kendall had his picture taken quickly with the farmer and his daughters. The picture, he said, would be of great interest to his friends back in south Devon.

They strolled to the village square, a distance of about 300 yards. It was in the throes of being decorated with streamers, fairy lights and hundreds of flags of various sizes. A video team from Bayrak Television had erected floodlights and camera stands. Carter was glad that they were there. Their lights would help his photography. On the edge of the square a charcoal fire was burning and children were everywhere laying tables and chairs for the celebration dinner.

Arif took his guests to the largest building, a combination of town hall and village café. Its veranda stood several feet above the ground with an unfettered view of the square. This was where the Carters would be seated to watch and hear the folk singers and their musicians. For the moment, however, their duty was to meet the *Muktar* and have another drink.

Weather-beaten faces beamed as the Carters entered, weaving their way past crates of vegetables and piles of watermelons. All eyes were fixed on the pale-faced visitors and all ears were tuned to their words, which were carefully translated by Arif Gürbüz. Special attention was paid to Wendy and Matthew. The hosts felt that the eight-year-old should have a companion with whom to spend the evening, somebody who spoke English. One of the villagers mentioned that they thought there was a young Turkish Cypriot boy on holiday from London staying in Yiğitler. 'Find him,' Arif instructed. The boy appeared within minutes and Matthew was taken off to meet others of his own age.

Chairs were placed on the veranda and the guests were invited to sit and look down on the changing scene in the square and so they did, like a party of visiting officials from the days of empire. But tonight the celebrations were for an independence of sorts, not some strange native ritual of which European missionaries usually disapproved in bygone times.

Because Arif had gone to supervise rehearsals, the English group was left in the company of the headman who stood guard, refilling glasses, replacing bowls of nuts, always smiling.

Eventually Carter left to wander the village by himself, snapping pictures here and there, his tape-recorder ready for action in the event he heard something interesting.

'*Affedersiniz*. Excuse me,' said a soft voice. Carter turned and saw a tall, slim man in a white suit. 'Are you from the BBC in London?'

'Yes, I am,' Carter replied, smiling but surprised.

'I am from London too,' the man continued. 'I am here on holiday in my home village.'

Excellent, Carter thought, the man could be a potential subject for interview.

'Are you here on business?' the man asked politely.

'Partly,' Carter answered honestly.

'Have you been taking pictures?'

'Yes. Your village is a charming place.'

'But you are not allowed to take pictures. This is a restricted area. The military will not like it.'

Carter was surprised by the man's observations. 'I don't think there'll be any trouble. You see, I'm a guest of the government and I was invited here for tonight's concert.'

'Ah, yes,' the Turkish Cypriot from London replied, his voice shaded with suspicion. He walked away slowly, glancing back frequently. Carter shook his head and hoped that London did not affect all Turkish Cypriots this way.

A few minutes later Carter returned to join his wife and Ron Kendall outside the café. Both were sitting bolt upright in their chairs.

'We've been arrested,' Wendy exclaimed, trying to smile, but not succeeding. Carter laughed, thinking she was joking.

'No, it's absolutely true,' Ron stammered. 'They've even taken our passports. Dash it all, it's just not on.' He stroked his white handlebar moustache. 'They say foreigners aren't allowed here. But damn it, we're English.'

A Turkish soldier marched up, saluted and said, 'Excuse me, sir, I am very sorry, but are you Mr Carter?'

'Yes, I am.'

'Then I must have your passport as well. *Lütfen.*'

Carter looked at the private's determined stance and glanced at the rifle he carried. 'Here it is,' he said, removing the passport from his canvas camera bag. 'Why do you need it?'

The soldier ignored the question. 'Please, stay here. Do not go away.' He flipped the pages of the passport, looked up at the BBC producer and said, 'Where is this fourth man? This Matthew Carter?'

On the far side of the square, the boy was running with a group of Turkish Cypriots. 'That's my son,' Carter senior replied, pointing to the only boy with blond hair in the pack of olive-skinned youngsters.

'I will come back,' the soldier promised, turning sharply on his heel and marching off at double time.

While Carter was away several Turkish soldiers had arrived at the café and told Wendy and Ron Kendall they were in Yiğitler illegally. It was a military zone and, as they had no special permits, they would have to be arrested.

Despite Kendall's protests, the soldiers had insisted on taking their passports.

Arif, on his return, had been told the story and rushed off in a fury, muttering, 'It's a terrible and silly mistake.'

'Brandy? Whisky?' the headman inquired, hoping to pacify his guests.

'Have you looked around the square?' Wendy asked. 'Do you see, they've stopped rehearsing? Nobody's putting up any more decorations.'

A silence had fallen on the village. Singers, musicians, and villagers were walking towards the veranda. Within moments the Carters and Kendall were surrounded by concerned people, all expressing a chorus of sincere apologies. 'If this is not sorted out, we will not play,' they said. 'You are our guests. Our honour is at stake.'

Viewing the scene from a distance was the man in a white suit from London. The sod, thought Carter.

Escorted by the private who had taken the passports, a Turkish army captain now joined the group. Both soldiers saluted smartly before the officer spoke. '*İyi akşamlar.* Good evening, sir. You are aware that to be in a military zone, you must have permission. Do you have such permission?'

'Yes, I have permission to record and photograph in northern Cyprus without restrictions,' Carter replied.

'May I see that permission, please?'

'It's back at my hotel. But captain, we are guests of the government and we were invited to attend these celebrations by a civil servant in Famagusta.'

'What is his name?'

'Arif Gürbüz.'

'Where is he?'

'Gone to see one of your officers,' Wendy replied. The captain smiled, bowed in her direction, and continued: 'I see from your passport, Mr Carter, that you have entered Cyprus many times?'

Carter nodded. He was intrigued by the officer's American accent.

'Are you associated with the military, Mr Carter?'

'No, not any more. I was an officer in the British army a very long time ago.'

'Then,' said the captain, 'how is it that you have come and gone so often from the British Sovereign Base at Akrotiri?'

'Because I've made programmes about the UN in Cyprus and once my passport was stamped at Ercan, it seemed easier to use Akrotiri than provoke the Greeks at Larnaca.'

'I see.' The captain nodded and re-examined Carter's passport, turning each page slowly as if deep in thought. 'As a brother officer, you will appreciate, sir, that I am obliged to do my military duty.'

'Yes, of course.'

'Well, sir, we have been told that you have been taking pictures of our military installations here in Yiğitler. If this is the case, you will not be charged with spying, providing you will allow me to take the film from your camera.'

'Military installations? What military installations?' Carter exclaimed incredulously. 'I've only taken pictures of the village square. I can't believe the pretty girls here are members of your special forces aiming to lull the Greeks into a false sense of security by hiding their weapons under their long dresses.' Immediately he regretted his sarcasm.

The Famagusta folk society pressed closer to catch every word of the exchange between the Turkish army and the BBC. Both were formidable organizations. Carter was armed with his tape-recorder. The officer was equipped for combat. The BBC had its Uher, the Turkish private his M-16 rifle. Today Carter accepted discretion would definitely be the better part of valour.

Fortunately the captain laughed.

'May I have your word that you did not take any photographs of military value? Your word, sir, as an officer?'

'Sure.'

'Good,' the captain replied, 'but should we discover otherwise, then the consequences will be very serious.' He nodded at the private who handed back the passports. 'Now you must go and we will make nothing more of this matter.'

'Captain, quite frankly we would love to oblige, if only to allow the concert to take place, but we can't leave unless you provide us with transport. You see, we came on the bus with the musicians,' Carter told the officer. 'Will you book us a taxi?'

Darkness was settling on the village square and somebody turned on the fairy lights, but the atmosphere remained black with gloom. 'Please understand that I am very sorry about this, sir,' the captain apologized again, not failing to notice the unhappiness of the local people who were still crowding around. 'I will go back to my commanding officer and seek fresh orders.' He saluted once more.

Arif returned, accompanied by the *Muktar*. 'This is very silly,' he fumed. 'I have told the Turkish commander to telephone Nicosia and speak to President Denktaş. Mr Denktaş will be very cross when he hears. Don't worry Mr *Dyvid*, all will be sorted.'

Far from worrying, the Carters were now finding the whole incident mildly amusing, even Ron who was gripping his passport to his chest.

Fifteen minutes passed and they heard the stamp of marching feet coming closer. A squad of Turkish soldiers was moving in their direction from out of the blackness. They halted below the veranda. At the head was the captain, accompanied by a major and the Turkish Cypriot in the white suit. The officers saluted.

Up the steps came the officers, leaving the civilian on his own. The major extended his hand to shake Carter's, bowed in all directions, and uttered a series of sentences in Turkish. The crowd began to smile and started to thin rapidly, people dashing in all directions.

'My commander says that he wishes to apologize most sincerely for any inconvenience you and your family may have suffered here tonight,' the captain translated, waiting for the major to speak again, which he did. 'My Major says that he has been in touch with Nicosia and with the President's office and we understand now that you are honoured guests with permission to move freely in northern Cyprus.'

More words in Turkish flowed from the major and the captain beamed. 'My major says that had he been notified, he would have arranged proper hospitality and comfort for your family in our officers' mess. He wonders if you will stay now and be our guests.'

The white-suited man appeared uncomfortable, but nodded.

Carter glanced at his family and the Turkish Cypriots on the veranda of the café. They had welcomed him warmly and supported him completely and he had no intention of leaving them.

'Please tell your major that I fully understand that you were doing your duty and that I appreciate his offer of hospitality,' Carter said, 'but I want a question answered. If this is a restricted military area, why then are there no signs to warn us? It's possible that other visitors, equally innocent as ourselves, will come here, get arrested, and eventually leave northern Cyprus with a very poor impression of the people in general and the Turkish army in particular.'

The major flushed on hearing the translation. He and the captain exchanged more words in Turkish and waved in the direction of the farmhouse where the bus had drawn up earlier. 'My major says that there is a sign, but accepts your point. The sign is written in Turkish only. He promises it will be replaced first thing in the morning.'

'Thank you,' said Carter. 'Now will you please have a drink with me and my family as my guests?' He introduced Wendy, Ron, and Matthew to the major and another a round of handshakes followed.

'My major says he will be delighted to join in one half-hour. We are in uniform and we wish to return as human beings.'

Even an American-trained Turkish officer could sometimes make an ill choice of words. 'Good. I look forward to seeing you.'

Once more there were salutes. This time Ron and Carter felt they should return the mark of respect by standing to attention themselves.

'*Goodbye*,' said the major, using English for the first time.

'*Güle güle*,' Carter replied.

The festivities began.

Food was spread on tables, the choir sang, the musicians played and the audience danced. Suddenly the two officers were back, almost unrecognizable in their civilian clothes. They were clutching bottles of Rakı, an aniseed-flavoured alcohol. They poured liberal quantities of the transparent liquid into tumblers and passed them round the table.

'*Şerefe!*' Toasts began to ring out; first the Queen, then the Carters, next the Kendalls followed by the British contingent of UNFICYP for its high standards of discipline and the BBC for its honest World Service broadcasts.

Carter responded by raising his glass to the Turkish army, Mr Denktaş and the Turkish Cypriot people.

Wendy added a toast to peace, and Ron, as a fully-paid-up member of the Newton Poppleford Conservative Association shouted, 'Mrs Thatcher.'

'The Falklands,' Arif added.

And so it went on until the earth moved under Yiğitler.

'I say,' Ron remarked in a slurred whisper, 'isn't that the driver of our bus pouring himself another?'

Carter saw two drivers and searched for words with which to reply. 'Don't worry Ron, there's not much traffic on the roads of northern Cyprus. Less at this time of night. Or is it morning?'

Suddenly the narrow street leading to the square looked much wider and the driver decided his passengers should not attempt to walk to the farm to board his bus; somebody could trip and fall in the darkness, hurting themselves. He insisted on bringing the veteran vehicle to the jolly party instead. And he did, without adding a scratch to the fading paint-work.

Through the quiet countryside of northern Cyprus the bus meandered with the Turkish Cypriot equivalent of 'She'll Be Coming Round The Mountain' ringing out across the plains, every passenger performing with vigour. The girls squirted lemon fragrance at anybody who dozed, while the men called for frequent stops along the way to clear their systems.

'I guess if I have to be arrested again, I'll pick the Turkish army to do it,' Carter remarked to Arif, before the family reached their hotel a little after 05.00 ready to throw themselves on their beds for a good day's sleep.

Only minutes later it seemed, the telephone was waking Carter. His arm aimed for the receiver, missed and caught it on the second attempt. 'Hullo,' he growled, trying to shake himself awake.

'Hullo, David. *Günaydın*. Good morning,' the voice crackled. 'This is Fikri. I'm hoping I'm not disturbing you.'

'No,' Carter said. 'I was getting up. The 'phone woke me.' He looked at his watch. It was 08.30.

'I have good news,' Fikri continued brightly. 'The President has agreed a date for your BBC interview, Dr Atakol wants to see you, and I am getting your pass to visit Varosha and the Karpas.'

'*Teşekkür ederim*,' Carter responded, thanking Fikri in Turkish.

'Ah, very good. Can you come to Nicosia this morning?'

'*Evet*. What time?'

'Any time,' Fikri replied.

'By the way,' Carter added, 'we got ourselves arrested last night in Yiğitler.'

'Yes, I know,' Fikri said without concern. 'Did you have a good time?'

CHAPTER 23

TWO DEAD CITIES

Summer 1983

A MILE north of where the waters of the Pedios river trickle into the broad curve of Famagusta Bay during the rainy seasons, a wire fence straggles its way round the remains of many bygone civilizations, including the original capital of Cyprus which lies half-buried in the sands along the eastern shore. This is Salamis, founded by Teucer, a hero of the Trojan wars who named the place after his original home, a small island off Piraeus in Greece, ruled by his father, King Telamon.

During the period of British colonial rule and immediately following the independence of Cyprus, the world's archaeologists excavated the area and discovered an enormous treasure-trove. They uncovered a Bronze Age city of the second millennium BC and scraped the sand from a vast necropolis containing the tombs of Greek warriors with their chariots, complete with skeletons of horses; all buried according to customs described in Homer's *Iliad*. Nearer the sea they found the greatest forum of the Roman empire, measuring 200 feet by 700 feet, and the largest Christian cathedral to have been built in the fourth century, the basilica of *St Epiphanius*.

When they visited Cyprus, Carter always explored the ruins with his young son, Matthew, whose imagination, still unfettered by the problems of adulthood, would take wing and carry him to ancient times. Carter's mind, cluttered with the realities of the present day, was less able to escape to worlds of fantasy.

Because Wendy, Matthew and Ron Kendall had returned to England a few days earlier, Carter wandered alone now within the unguarded perimeter of Salamis. In his solitude, he thought about another Greek city, which was firmly secured by the Turkey army; its interior closed to prying eyes. The world wanted to know more about both places: Salamis to the north of Famagusta and Varosha to the south.

Varosha had been at the heart of the Greek Cypriot tourism industry, and whenever there were discussions on the future of Cyprus its name appeared near the top of the agenda. Greek Cypriots wanted Varosha returned immediately, arguing that its former 35,000 inhabitants, none of whom was a Turkish Cypriot, deserved to have their properties and possessions given back. On the other hand, Turkish Cypriots insisted that the city's future could only be settled within an overall agreement on Cyprus.

Stalemate.

So Varosha stayed empty, probably the only city in the world of its kind; just another pawn on the chessboard of Cypriot politics.

To stroll through Salamis was easy, but Varosha was another matter. The media had never been allowed to set foot inside. Even the UN was prohibited from taking pictures, although UNFICYP had an observation post within the cordoned area.

Since 15 August 1974, when the Turkish army took control, Varosha had been the basis of many rumours, some exceedingly strange. That was why Carter pressed his Turkish Cypriot hosts for permission to enter. He did not expect to uncover any mysteries, but his eyewitness account could be that 'fresh material' Alan Rogers wanted for the Radio 4 documentary. Other BBC correspondents and American network producers, too, had tried to persuade the TFSC administration to open up 'the forbidden city', but none had got closer than Carter.

Over the years Carter had succeeded in seeing most of the areas which Turkish Cypriots decreed were no-go places for journalists. By now he had seen the Maronites in Kormakiti and questioned their need for Red Cross aid; he had been shown the poverty which existed in parts of northern Nicosia; he had been taken to places where small Christian churches stood forlorn, their crosses broken by Turkish Cypriots when their hatred for the Greek Orthodox Church took the better of them during the 1974 war; and he had toured 'The Green Line' that divided the capital. Not always using the official check-point at the Ledra Palace, he had crossed frequently between the Greek and Turkish sides. His dozens of tapes and hundreds of photographs testified to his movements.

As recently as last week Carter had added another 'first' to his collection by travelling beyond Dipkarpaz, or *Rizokarpasso*, the place where Bishop Philon in the fifth century established Christianity and where almost 2,000 Greeks lived still in the so-called 'pan-handle'.

With government authority Carter had gone to the very end of the almost deserted peninsula, the last three or four miles of which remained under military jurisdiction and were off-limits to visitors of any nationality. On the way, he had stopped and talked privately to Greek Cypriot farmers whose pigs he photographed. All pigs had allegedly been destroyed during the 1974 war.

Carter was accompanied by Fikri and Sevilay Direkoğlu, a young Turkish army officer, and Dr Noel Kennedy Thomas, a professor from the University of Birmingham. Dr Thomas had been a lecturer at the British government's Training College in Nicosia during the mid-fifties and Carter took him on the journey as an independent witness who could verify what changes had taken place in the Karpas since the Turkish military intervention.

At the very end of the road, where the land ran out and the sea came together, stood the Monastery of Apostolos Andreas. It was a comparatively modern church with a rectangular collection of houses used by its Greek caretakers, their families and pilgrims who came to see the remains of an ancient chapel. Here, according to Christian Orthodox history, St Andrew cured the sick with the water from the chapel's well.

An elderly Greek Cypriot woman invited Carter into the church and proudly showed him a lectern which carried an enormous Bible opened at the Gospel of St Mark. By the door was a gold collection plate on which the BBC producer placed a 5,000 lira note, but she returned it.

One of Carter's escorts, the young Turkish army officer, explained that she did not wish to receive money from Turkey, but would be willing to accept Greek Cypriot pounds instead. 'If you have any with you, please leave some with her,' he said. Carter obliged and they went back outside, where the Greek Cypriots had prepared coffees.

They sat together on the veranda, the Turkish officer chatting in Greek. The women laughed at something he said and embraced him as if he were a son returning home from a long journey.

Before Carter and his party departed, they were offered a second cup of coffee. They drank it to honour this Cypriot custom of friendship.

Only the 'forbidden city' remained to be investigated.

Next Carter produced the 'live' interview with President Denktaş for Charles Murray's *Rush Hour* programme on Radio London. The circuits were crystal clear and John Waite, the interviewer, handled the Turkish Cypriot leader well, but the emphasis of their conversation was on the historical reasons for the divisions between the two communities of Cyprus and a key question was overlooked: when did Mr Denktaş plan to declare northern Cyprus an independent republic? Not that the wily barrister would have answered directly, but his words may have given a clue to his intentions.

At the end of the transmission, London wanted to know when Carter planned to return to the radio station in Marylebone High Street. He replied that he was working in Cyprus in his own time and his annual vacation which had another two weeks to run.

'But Greg Ainger at Local Radio headquarters has you down to cover his round-England cycle race which starts next Monday,' one of the Radio London people declared. 'What's more, Vin Bootle says you're producing an outside broadcast from an exhibition at Olympia, John Murray's billed you in the *Radio Times* as presenting a new jazz programme, and Derrick Amoore wants a fresh jingle package recorded with a 27-piece orchestra in Manchester.'

'And I suppose I'm doing all these different things at the same time in different places?'

'Hang on. I'll check the dates,' came the reply.

There was a slight pause. President Denktaş and Fikri Direkoğlu looked on. The affairs of northern Cyprus were on hold, too, because Carter was still in the presidential office.

'Yes,' said London eventually. 'Some of the dates do appear to overlap.'

'Well,' Carter sighed, 'I'm continuing here. Anyway, there aren't any

flights available for me to take for at least 10 days. It's the peak
holiday period and every seat is taken by Turkish Cypriots returning to
London. They booked months ago. Sorry. Vin and the rest will have to
make alternative arrangements.'

Carter's reply did not please his BBC masters.

President Denktaş smiled and observed: 'I see that the various
departments of the BBC are not dissimilar to our ministries; highly
political and just as organized. But then the BBC is almost the same
size as our country.'

On the road back to Kyrenia, where he was staying at The Dome
Hotel once again, Carter reminded Fikri of his real need to visit
Varosha. Fikri's response was only an enigmatic smile. It was always
difficult to know what the man from the Ministry of Tourism was
thinking.

That September evening Fikri returned to The Dome Hotel and took
Carter aside. Glancing to right and left, the Turkish Cypriot official
spoke in a conspiratorial whisper. 'David, my friend, your pass to visit
Varosha has been agreed at last by the President and the general in
charge of Famagusta district. We *must* be there at 10 o'clock tomorrow
morning.'

'Great,' Carter exclaimed loudly. 'You crafty old fox, you've done it
after all.' He slapped Fikri on the back.

'Not so loud,' Fikri coughed. 'We have another journalist staying
here at present. We must keep this information to ourselves. You see,
he is not permitted, although he has been making many demands.'

For nine years Varosha had been a dead city. What would Carter find
there? He fell asleep pondering the question and wishing the air-
conditioning unit in his room worked, even occasionally.

The next day Fikri and Carter arrived at the military check-point at
the entrance of the 'forbidden city' precisely at 10.00. Fikri had
demonstrated that Turkish Cypriots did have the capability to be
punctual when they searched their souls and glanced at their watches.

Armed Turkish soldiers, once again dressed in combat uniforms, took
the pass from Fikri and studied it line by line, counting every signature
and noting every official stamp. Satisfied the document was authentic,
they moved to Carter, comparing his face with the photograph in his
passport. Then they walked slowly round Fikri's car, peering inside and
underneath. Politely, but emphatically, the soldiers asked the two
visitors to step out. They explained they would now telephone the
officers detailed to conduct the tour.

When the officers arrived, they said their unit's commanding officer
wanted to meet Fikri and Carter before anything else took place. One
escort was a captain, a career officer; the other was a lieutenant, midway
through his compulsory military service. The latter spoke fluent
English, the former claimed he spoke only Turkish. Neither wore
badges that could identify the military formations to which they

belonged, and only reluctantly gave Carter their names.

The CO was waiting for them on his veranda, a short walk away. Like his two junior officers, the lieutenant-colonel was dressed for combat, armed with a pistol slung low and strapped to his thigh. From his thick rubber-soled boots Carter concluded the big man probably was a member of an airborne unit.

Pointing to the courtyard, the lieutenant-colonel commanded everybody to sit in the shade of a tree, its branches spread like an umbrella over a tidy tiled space. As they sat down, Turkish privates, their heads completely shaved, placed bottles of cold Bel-Cola on a low table, followed by a small silver tray laid with packs of cigarettes and a lighter.

A civilian joined the group, appearing out of nowhere. His name was Gorgon Fenercioğlu, a bureaucrat from the TFSC's Ministry of Finance, somebody Carter had not met before. Within seconds the new arrival was telling of his year-long stay in Stoke Newington, words spitting from his mouth as if they were bullets from a rapid-firing machine-gun.

The lieutenant-colonel spoke more slowly, in short sentences, which Fikri asked to have repeated or clarified before translating. All the time the senior officer chain-smoked, watching Carter intently. First he emphasized the conditions under which Carter would be allowed access to Varosha. He could go anywhere during a two-hour period, but would be accompanied by his junior officers, Fenercioğlu and Fikri. Carter could choose to enter any buildings and make notes about what he saw, but was not permitted to quote directly anything said by the soldiers or identify by name or unit any other military personnel he encountered. Nothing was to be recorded on tape. Still-photography was acceptable, but cine-filming was banned. Was this satisfactory, the lieutenant-colonel asked?

Carter nodded his agreement. In these circumstances there was little to complain about, although he wished he had swapped his Minolta 110 Zoom SLR for the 35mm camera offered him by Arif Gürbüz.

Next, according to Fikri's translation, the lieutenant-colonel said he could not understand why anybody from the media needed to visit Varosha, because there was nothing to see and all his soldiers behaved properly. To him, reporters and spies were synonymous. But, because his superiors had ruled it was appropriate for Carter to enter the city, he promised to make the BBC producer's stay as interesting as possible. Ominously he added, 'I expect you to behave yourself.'

Carter understood now why Fikri had been taking great care with his translating, trying to use diplomatic phrases to create a better public relations image for the senior Turkish officer who had probably said something along the lines of, 'I'm a military man and military men don't mince their words. So why should I?'

If Carter were correct in his assessment, then he welcomed the lieutenant-colonel's frankness and felt they would get along very well, once they stopped sizing up each other and put aside caution and suspicion.

How many visits had Carter made to Cyprus? What did he think of Turkish food? Did he think it was amusing that the Greek side served 'Oriental' or 'Greek' coffee, refusing to admit it was Turkish? Did Carter know the purpose of 'the Peace Operation'? Whereupon, without waiting for an answer, the lieutenant-colonel launched a detailed presentation of the Turkish case, peppering it liberally with his personal reasons for disliking Greeks. Not once did he mention Cypriots. It was clear he regarded himself and Fikri as Turks.

Noticing Carter was smoking his own cigarettes, the lieutenant-colonel clapped his hands and issued a short, sharp command to his orderlies lurking to attention in the shadows. Seconds later, two packs of Marlboro cigarettes were placed in Carter's hands with the compliments of the Turkish army.

While the lieutenant-colonel's dissertation on the history of Cyprus was interrupted by his greater concern for Carter's nicotine addiction and welfare, one of the two junior officers returned the conversation to the purpose of the visit. He wanted to explain the reasons the Turkish army held the city and how it was protected. He claimed that once Varosha had been secured in August 1974, Turkish soldiers had not looted buildings, least of all Greek churches. Greek Cypriots and foreigners had fled as the Turks moved closer and he hinted that they, perhaps, had taken things themselves and now wanted to lay the blame on the Turkish army. If Carter wanted to check the contents of any building, he was most welcome. He would see exactly what the Turks had found; everything was catalogued and held behind locked doors.

CHAPTER 24

BEHIND CLOSED DOORS

EXPLANATIONS over, the lieutenant-colonel escorted Carter to a Turkish army jeep which was heating up on the Tarmac outside his shaded patio. His junior Turkish officers would drive, stopping when requested to allow the BBC producer to photograph whatever he chose. They set off.

Varosha was a dead city; water and electricity supplies cut. Or so Fenercioğlu claimed, adding that only basic maintenance was carried out within the boundaries and that work was done by 79 civilians. He was very precise about this figure and he insisted, somewhat defensively, that they were always accompanied by Turkish soldiers. The civilians were employed to shore-up properties in danger of collapsing. They also laid down various pesticides to prevent rats and snakes escaping to populated areas outside the city. Mosquitoes, too, were a major irritant.

Fikri and Fenercioğlu in their different styles provided a non-stop commentary as they went deeper into the forbidden city.

Property damage was extensive, but appeared superficial. Paint-work was faded; metal structures were covered in layers of rust. Buildings under construction in 1974 were still surrounded with their original scaffolding. Tall cranes hovered over them like predatory vultures.

They passed a sign erected by the Lordos company which said, 'Buy a holiday apartment or villa on Famagusta beach. Receive a handsome income and see your property appreciate rapidly in value.'

The claim was disproved by the appearance of smaller buildings, shops, restaurants and homes which were in a very poor state; windows smashed, doors hanging off hinges, interiors stripped bare. Power points had been removed and electricity cables snaked their way uselessly to weeds outside. The pans and pipes of toilets and bathrooms were dark brown with rust; wash-basins were black with dirt and tiles lay cracked and scattered. Plants forced their way through fissures in concrete floors, spewing pyramids of red soil from the foundations.

One house stood out from all the rest. In every sense it remained a home and Carter expected to see people inside.

'Take a picture,' Fenercioğlu suggested, after chiding the BBC producer for only photographing damaged properties. 'That house belonged to Dr Marangos, OBE. He was a Greek doctor and lived here before the war. We take special care of his home.'

'Marangos was a good doctor,' Fikri added. 'He treated everybody the same way.'

Fikri's knowledge of Famagusta was considerable. It went back to his childhood days when his father had been a local policeman with the British colonial administration. His family had been implacable opponents of EOKA, the Greek Cypriot terrorist organization.

But whether, in truth, the Turks took care of the house only because the owner had been 'a good doctor' was open to question. Some cynics could argue that the real reason why the property received attention was because Dr G. N. Marangos had been Austria's Honorary Consul in Cyprus and the Austrians formed the UNFICYP contingent in the Famagusta district with an OP in Varosha.

In almost as good condition were the buildings owned by foreign nationals, the so-called 'third parties' caught in the Cyprus dispute. A small Marks and Spencer shop still had its plate glass windows in place and was intact; a row of parking meters standing sentinel outside.

Carter stopped the Jeep and began taking photographs. Standing on a cracked pavement, he saw several footprints in the concrete. Obviously tourists had not waited for it to set. One had carved her name: 'Jane, 1973'. Would her mark be there still if the city had continued to thrive with thousands of tourists pounding the sidewalks?

Brilliant colour blazed from red and yellow flowers — bougainvillaea and acacia — growing wild in gardens, while aloe plants, usually found in burial places, reached for the sky by the sides of tall buildings. Perhaps it was right that they were there because death was present in the form of the dried-out trunks of orange trees, strangled by weeds and bamboo plantations, all out of control.

Then there were the windmills for which Varosha had been famous, their vanes disintegrating. Some turned aimlessly, creaking in the light breeze. At night their sounds haunted Turkish army conscripts as they patrolled long, desolate avenues and walked past empty buildings which they were there to guard.

At noon, with the hot sun burning down, the simmering stillness was, perhaps, only marginally less eerie than the atmosphere of the dark hours. Occasionally there was noise in the distance, a military vehicle trundling somewhere. From where did it come and where was it headed? An answer came in the shape of a white UNFICYP patrol vehicle with its lights blazing, approaching at speed from the west side of the city where the Greek Cypriot front-line began. Canvas-covered, the vehicle was an Austrian twin-axle Pinzgau, one of 25 in service with AUSCON. It roared past, its UN occupants looking hard at Carter who was snapping photographs from the edge of the broad avenue's sticky Tarmac. Who was he, this photographer?

Carter knew the Austrian soldiers would report him as a stranger in their midst. First their information would go to their colleagues at Camp Duke Leopold V, the AUSCON base located on the road from Famagusta to Salamis. Then, before the hour was out, his movements would be logged at UNFICYP headquarters in Nicosia, alongside all the other messages coming from the UN's thin blue belt of OPs which gripped Cyprus by the waist. Unusual activity was always reported and brought immediately to the attention of senior officers in case the status quo was being endangered.

Carter hoped he would be included in the 'morning briefing' the next day and that Major David Emmett would get to know that despite his gloomy predictions to the contrary, his BBC friend had made it safely into 'the forbidden city'.

Because Emmett wanted photographs of AUSCON at work in Varosha for publication in *The Blue Beret*, the UNFICYP magazine, Carter, his camera ready, asked his Turkish hosts to chase and catch up with the Austrian patrol vehicle.

The vehicle stopped outside an old restaurant, which before its conversion to a UN post, had been aptly named the Edelweiss. The post was easily identifiable by the UN flag hanging from a balcony and the collection of white vehicles parked outside. Stripped to their waists, several soldiers were topping up their suntans, siting in easy chairs on the veranda.

The Turkish army Jeep parked in the centre of the street. Carter and his escorts stepped out, half expecting the Austrians to react immediately at the sight of two Turkish officers, two Turkish Cypriot civilians and a European with a camera. There was none.

Reasoning that good manners demanded they introduce themselves and explain the purpose of stopping, Carter and the English-speaking Turkish lieutenant walked up the stairs of the restaurant. Neither understood German and they doubted the Austrians spoke Turkish. But barely had their feet touched the floor of the veranda when the sound of pop music was cut by somebody switching off a radio tuned to the BFBS station in Dhekelia. Soldiers pushed aside cans of beer and bottles of Coca Cola from their tables, stood up and shouted dramatically, *'Nein, nein.'*

Holding his ground, Carter bellowed back, 'Does anybody here speak English? I'm from the BBC and I want to see the officer-in-charge.'

A burly Austrian, much larger than the rest, edged forward from the rear of the restaurant. 'You vill leave immediately,' he shouted in the unmistakable voice of an NCO. 'You cannot come here.'

From his attitude, Carter and his companion knew they would not be offered cold drinks. They backed their way to the terrace. The Austrian continued his slow stride in their direction.

'Move, move,' he ordered, 'this is United Nations.'

Only when Carter and his Turkish officer were back in the centre of the street was the Austrian corporal satisfied. He still glowered, rocking on the toes of his boots which overhung the edge of the pavement.

'Good afternoon,' the Turkish lieutenant shouted politely from the road, giving a crisp salute, although military etiquette demanded that the UN soldier salute the senior party. 'We are taking Mr Carter on a tour of Varosha and he has asked to meet you so that he may take photographs of your men at work.'

By now all the UNFICYP soldiers were lined up on the terrace behind their NCO, their stance a combination of curiosity and aggression, no doubt recalling the lines on the little white cards they carried at all times: 'UN soldiers will stay in place and, if required, be reinforced until the violators have returned to own positions.'

'Call Nicosia and ask for Major David Emmett. He'll confirm who I am and explain everything,' Carter shouted.

'I cannot,' replied the NCO. 'I have no telephone.'

'Use your radio,' Carter suggested.

'No. I must notify AUSCON first. You must go away. I know nothing about you. I must consult with my superior officers.'

'May we come inside for a moment and tell you about the pictures I want to take?'

'No. This is UN.'

'Yes, I know it is, but will you please contact your headquarters now?'

'Yes.'

'May I have your name?' Carter asked.

'Why?'

Carter shrugged. The reason was unimportant and the matter not worth pursuing.

'Shall we wait while you contact your officers?' the Turkish officer inquired.

'No. Come back in one hour,' came the uncompromising reply from the UN observation post.

The Turk stopped smiling. With Carter he returned to the Jeep where the others had found the whole incident very amusing. They explained that the BBC producer had crossed a thin blue line painted on the road. By stepping over, he had moved from Turkish-controlled territory into space protected by the United Nations Force in Cyprus. Technically speaking, he had advanced the Turkish army by several feet. That was why the Austrian NCO had been so determined to demonstrate his authority. By pushing them back into the centre of the road, he had fulfilled his UN mission. The status quo in Cyprus continued.

Aware that his time was at a premium in Varosha, Carter decided not to return to the Edelweiss restaurant in an hour's time. Major Emmett would have to go without the pictures he wanted, but could not take; the pictures Carter could, but which Emmett's own people prevented.

'Why are you not taking your pictures?' the lieutenant asked, watching Carter return his camera to its case. 'You do not require UNFICYP permission. We have given ours. You may take pictures of anything from *inside* our area.' Click away, he suggested, and Carter did.

The Austrians, spotting what was taking place, suddenly became very active. They tidied up the forecourt of the restaurant and unloaded one of their trucks. Swimming trunks were swapped for khaki military shorts. It was possible, of course, that the UN soldiers' lunch-break had coincidentally ended the moment Carter had started pointing his camera lens in their direction, but the civilian Turkish Cypriots took a less charitable view.

'You see, David, we still have tourists in Varosha,' Fikri declared solemnly, his eyes twinkling. 'But as the Director of Tourism, I must admit there are not many. However, *they* have a long holiday. At least six months. Then they go home, tell their friends, and we get some more. Always from Austria.'

Fikri's sardonic attitude was shared by the others. Once again, Carter was reminded, 'The Turkish army is the *real* force in Cyprus. For ten years, between 1964 and 1974, the UN soldiers were here, but every day Turks were killed, Greeks were killed. Since our Peace Operation, tell me, my friend, how many Turks have died? How many Greeks have died? The whole of Cyprus is at peace now.'

In the centre of a vacant plot between two large dilapidated buildings, a tiny timber shack protruded from a jungle of weeds. There was Greek lettering painted on its side. Fikri, who understood Greek, translated. It was an EOKA phrase, he said. It insisted Cyprus was Greek. Just as the paint remained visible on the wood, so did the Greek Cypriot dream of union with Greece. That sign had not been removed because it reminded patrolling Turkish soldiers why they were in northern Cyprus to defend Turkish Cypriots, he told Carter.

Not far away, scrawled in chalk on the side of another building, were words in Turkish, smaller but clearer. What did they say? Reluctantly the Turkish lieutenant explained. The writer was a private soldier, a conscript, and he had written the name of his mainland village, his length of service in Cyprus, and his desire to return home. This was the only thing Carter was prevented from photographing in Varosha.

To test Turkish claims about the state of the interior of the hotels in Varosha, Carter made his escorts drive up this avenue and down that street until he selected a hotel of his choice, not theirs. There was the Hotel Grecian, the Hotel Troian, the Golden Plage and many more.

In the end Carter settled for the largest he had seen. It was the Golden Sands, a multi-storey complex. Providing nothing had been removed, it was likely to contain some interesting clues to what life had been like for tourists in Varosha before August 1974.

Having made his choice, Carter waited outside while soldiers were sent to find various sets of keys which would open the locks on the doors of the entrance. Six shots remained on his last roll of film and he wanted to use them well.

During the time it took Carter to smoke a cigarette, the keys arrived, accompanied by several civilians, the first he had seen inside Varosha. There were more soldiers with them. There was considerable jostling of bodies as the seals on the doors were broken and the locks were opened; everybody wanted to appear in Carter's pictures.

A flash of light from the camera, a click of the lock, a scratch of a ball-point pen to note the exact time and place for his files, and they were inside the main lobby.

A plaque showed that the hotel belonged to the Trust House Forte Group. It had been officially opened in a blaze of glory by Archbishop Makarios in May 1974. Only three months later it was closed by order of the Turkish army with far less publicity.

Furniture was still in place, covered in a thick layer of fine dust. Several small motor boats were stacked untidily in one corner. Behind the reception desk, rows of envelopes hung limply where room keys should have been. The Turkish officers said the envelopes contained inventories of the hotel's contents and they volunteered to show the lists and the matching items.

On the way to the bar, Carter touched a withered plant held erect by its pot. It disintegrated. He opened a cash register. It was empty, but its roll of paper was there still, giving details of the last drinks ordered by guests as they left, or fled.

Because there was no electricity for lights, Carter stumbled his way up a staircase in darkness to the first floor, reached a corridor, and randomly chose three bedrooms to enter and check. He noticed some handles had been ripped off and doors opened with a light touch of his fingers.

The first bedroom still had suits and dresses hanging in a cupboard. Shoes and slippers were scattered on the floor as if their owners had left in a hurry. In the second room, a lady's handbag lay open on a bed, its contents spread across the covers; a scent spray, three tubes of lipstick and a powder compact. A half-empty bottle of gin stood on a dressing-table next to an unopened bottle of Anglias brandy, produced by Haggipavlu and Son, a firm established since 1844 in Limassol. In the last of three bedrooms, the waste-paper basket was full. To the amusement of his escorts, Carter rifled it.

There, under some dirty tissues, was a clue to the room's last occupants. It was a sheet of yellowing paper, a questionnaire for guests, left untouched for almost a decade. It had been completed by the couple who had stayed in Room 1427. It showed that they had come to Cyprus for a 15-day vacation organized by Exchange Travel Holidays. It was their first trip to the island and they declared 'the most helpful staff members' of the Golden Sands were the waiters and waitresses. Their only criticism of the hotel was its lack of a card-room, which they felt was 'necessary'.

In the space for general comments, the couple had written, 'Under the circumstances of our last four days, we would congratulate you on the combined efforts of all your staff to make our holiday memorable.'

The questionnaire was signed by Mr and Mrs Griffiths of Warwick

Road, Ealing, London W5, and addressed to the Area General Manager of Trust House Forte Limited, PO Box 823, Famagusta.

Watched by the Turkish officers, Carter folded the sheet of paper carefully and placed it in his shirt pocket. In a whisper, the Turkish lieutenant reminded him, 'Nothing is supposed to be removed.' After a pause, he added, 'but I think this will be all right.'

In a third room, lying open on a bed was a book called *You Have Been Warned*. The inside cover said it had been bought for the Hesperides Hotel on 4 April 1936, but a stamp at the bottom of the title page was stamped ' W. C. C. King, Chief Commandant of Police' in dark purple ink. Disputed property?

Back in the sunshine, away from the musty atmosphere of the hotel, Carter saw a pair of dead sea-gulls. They had been brushed to the side of the road, now a gravel-strewn path. The carcasses were being eaten slowly by a vibrating carpet of insects.

Fenercioğlu, anticipating a question, told Carter that the birds may have swallowed poisons intended to kill rats and snakes. These were breeding at a rate which was causing alarm amongst the authorities in Famagusta, fearful that they would spread out of control to the populated areas.

Carter could be given statistics on vermin in Varosha, but nobody would reveal the number of Turkish soldiers based there. Any questions remotely related to military matters were brushed aside politely, although the army escorts agreed eventually to be photographed, standing by a line of empty oil drums that marked the Turkish side of the cease-fire line.

From what he had seen, Carter concluded there was no concentrated military presence in the heart of the city. For the most part the army appeared to keep itself close to the entrance of Varosha, not far from the Ayios Ioannis church.

Of course the military had taken over some buildings. These gave themselves away by the radio aerial arrays on their roofs. However, they had not occupied the old Greek army barracks. These had been allowed to rot and sink in a sea of long grass which rose to the height of the window-sills. Of all the buildings in the city, none was in a worse state of repair.

At the start of the tour Carter had been told all electricity and water to Varosha was cut, but this was not entirely true as there were ample supplies of both for use by the military. It was possible that the army generated its own power locally and that water was delivered to the soldiers by tankers. However, this was unlikely. In fact, Carter knew, from his UNFICYP briefings, that Famagusta received its water from tanks sited in the 'forbidden city'. These tanks were filled by pipes leading to the south. This explained why Greek Cypriots strictly controlled the amount of water sent to the tanks, much to Arif Gürbüz's annoyance. He may have been the director of the Famagusta

water authority but he had no power to change the situation and he faced
the wrath of his fellow Turkish Cypriots when the district's taps ran
dry during the summer months.

Gürbüz claimed that the Greek Cypriot side pumped only enough
water across the cease-fire line to satisfy the basic needs of 12,000
people, the population of old Famagusta in 1974. Since the end of the
war, Turkish Cypriot refugees from the south had almost doubled that
number. Consequently, the amount of water received was inadequate to
deal with current requirements.

Furthermore no water was available for use in Varosha because,
according to Gürbüz, the Greek Cypriots argued there was no need to
provide a city that was notionally empty. What the Greek Cypriots
really meant was, let the Turkish soldiers go thirsty or you, the Turkish
Cypriots, can split your rations with them.

That view was morally wrong, Gürbüz had argued. The water was
not intended for the Turkish army; it was needed to prevent the city's
pipes and joints cracking from lack of use. If there were a settlement
and Varosha returned to Greek Cypriot-ownership, would they want to
spend large sums of money on having to replace all the city's plumbing,
he asked?

Whatever Gürbüz said, the Greek Cypriot side did not believe him.
On several occasions he had asked UNFICYP to persuade his opposite
numbers to increase the flow of water and every time his requests were
turned down. His assurances that any additional water would be used
only to maintain the life of the systems and not the life of the soldiers
were hard to swallow, and the Greek Cypriots were unwilling to try.

But Greek Cypriot intractability was not the only cause for the
water problems of Varosha and Famagusta. With the population of the
entire island on the increase, the growth of tourism in the south, and the
decline in annual rainfall, the *whole* of Cyprus had a shortage of water.
As far as the Greek Cypriots were concerned, it was easy to cut the size
of the problem: simply rid Cyprus of 30,000 soldiers, the 'invaders'
from Turkey.

There was another answer to the water problem, but the Greek
Cypriots did not want to think about it. Turkey, the island's nearest
neighbour, had more than enough for its own needs in the south of the
country, and water went to waste.

To build an under-sea pipeline to carry Turkey's surplus the 40 miles
to Cyprus would be costly, but not impossible. It was well within the
bounds of present-day technologies. But any notion which contained the
merest hint of increased Turkish influence in Cyprus was nothing less
than anathema to the Greek Cypriots.

Yet within Varosha, amidst the desolation, there was an oasis where
the soil was wet and plants green. It stood in front of the Sandy Beach
Hotel, used exclusively by the families of Turkish officers in Cyprus.
Its gardens were lush and cool, the air filled with tiny droplets of

water from innumerable sprays hidden in the flowers.

On the hotel's beach, multi-coloured sunshades dotted the fine golden sand. Women reclined in deck-chairs, while children shouted and splashed in the clear waters of the bay. It was a small reminder of what life must have been like throughout Varosha before the summer of 1974.

Carter was brought to the hotel on the invitation of the lieutenant-colonel who had met him on his arrival. Obviously the BBC producer's behaviour had proved acceptable to the crusty CO for he wanted him to share lunch with his officers and had provided a polished staff car to drive him to the Sandy Beach.

The lieutenant-colonel offered profuse apologies for the poor selection of food awaiting them in the hotel's spotlessly clean, first-floor restaurant overlooking the sea. The kebabs, rice and salad served by army waiters seemed more than adequate to Carter, but not to the lieutenant-colonel. He claimed all the good dishes had been eaten already by the other guests as the hour was late.

Ice-cold Turkish beer arrived, but Carter drank little and ate even less, not through choice but lack of opportunity. Every time he raised his fork or readied his glass to drink, the lieutenant-colonel put another question for him to answer and awaited his reply eagerly.

Again and again he wanted Carter to repeat his impressions of Varosha and discuss whether the Turkish army had been more or less co-operative than UNFICYP. He had obviously been told by his staff of the encounter with the Austrians, but he wanted a blow-by-blow account delivered in the BBC producer's own words and he demanded that these words were heard by his officers sitting at surrounding tables. Throughout the narrative that followed, the lieutenant-colonel expressed concern that Carter was neglecting his food.

At the end of the meal, which Carter had barely tasted, and several toasts, which he had, the lieutenant-colonel, who had only touched water because he was on duty, asked if his guest wanted Turkish coffee or Nescafé.

'I'll try the *Oriental*,' Carter joked, recalling their first conversation.

A mighty roar of laughter came from the lieutenant-colonel. 'Very good,' he said, his first words in English.

Taking advantage of the lieutenant-colonel's current good humour, Carter said, 'I see there are some Greek things you like.' He lifted a knife from the table.

'I also use their plates and their glasses and their cups,' the lieutenant-colonel responded.

Then he added a question, a technique often used by Turks when they wanted to prove a point. 'Did your British government return the Mercedes trucks they captured from the Argentinians after Port Stanley was surrendered?'

Circling the air with both hands, the lieutenant-colonel continued, allowing time for Fikri to translate his sentences, 'This was *our* Falklands. Just as you went to save your people, we came here to rescue ours. If Mrs Thatcher had been in charge of our Peace Operation, what would she say to those who told her to hand back everything? Why should we deny our victory and the justice of our cause?'

The lieutenant-colonel fixed Carter with his eyes, paused, then slapped the table with the palms of his hands. 'My friend,' he said, 'I am sure you know the answers to those questions very well.'

When they left, a flood of thoughts ran through Carter's head. He was the first journalist to walk Varosha's streets since 1974 and, perhaps, the last for some time to come. He had not found any military training grounds, labour camps, or germ warfare experiments; nothing, in fact, to make headlines, nothing to change the status quo, and nothing to substantiate what Greek Cypriots asserted had gone on and was taking place in the 'forbidden city'. But he had stepped in places from which Cypriots were banned, a city they might never again enter and use, and seen for himself.

With each day that passed, the more deeply Varosha fell into a state of suspended animation from which it became more difficult to wake, more costly to revive, and more impossible for either side to inherit. It had become a museum of contemporary history on a grand scale, closed to the public.

How long would it be before the city joined Salamis as another ghostly monument amongst many in Cyprus?

Would some future archaeologists dig beneath the sands and find a piece of wood with the word *Enosis* in Greek lettering, or a slab of plaster with details of a young Turkish soldier's service? And what about the concrete slab with the name 'Jane'?

And if these relics were found, how would the archaeologists interpret their discoveries? Would they be able to explain Varosha's life and death any better than they had those of Salamis?

CHAPTER 25

DINNER WITH THE MAJOR-GENERAL

MAJOR-General Eşref Bitlis of the Turkish army in northern Cyprus was the man in charge of the forces in the Famagusta district which included Varosha, and Carter wanted to thank him personally for authorizing his visit. But Turkish Cypriots, British residents and UNFICYP personnel all told him that Turkish officers were rarely seen outside their own circles, and, when they did meet outsiders, these meetings were formal and held on ground of their own choosing, perhaps an officers' club, like the one at the roundabout in Kyrenia, or in a conference-room at The Dome Hotel. Nobody could explain why. Carter decided to check for himself.

Fikri Direkoğlu agreed to telephone the military headquarters in Famagusta and, on Carter's behalf, invite the general and his wife to dinner at the Abbey House restaurant at Bellapais.

There were several reasons why Carter had chosen this particular venue. First he wanted to meet on ground which had British connections so that there could be no doubt about who was hosting the occasion. Secondly the food had to be good, and finally the place must be close to The Dome Hotel to allow him to reach it easily and on time, ensuring a welcome to match any he had received during his visits to northern Cyprus.

The Abbey House fitted these criteria. It was a short taxi ride from Carter's hotel; the food was rated highly by senior UN officers who came all the way from the south to eat there; and it was managed by a pair of unmistakable Englishmen.

Having established the place for dinner, Carter now had to get his invitation to the general, not an easy task as the telephone lines between Kyrenia and Famagusta were notoriously unreliable. Fikri wanted to call from a different place at a different time, but the BBC producer was used to Turkish Cypriots procrastinating and prodded his friend into taking action, now.

To their astonishment, they connected with Famagusta on the first attempt but, as usual, the line left much to be desired and Fikri began to shout louder and louder, gradually losing dignity, which was very precious to him. Carter wondered why they needed a telephone at all, convinced that the shouting could be heard from one end of the island to the other without any telephonic assistance.

Between shrieks, crackles and whistles on the strand of wire between the two telephone exchanges, Fikri talked and talked. Eventually he replaced the receiver and smiled in victory. 'The major-general,' he said, 'is delighted to accept your invitation. He has decided that eight-thirty this evening will be appropriate, and he will bring his wife.'

'Eighty-thirty Cyprus time or real time?' Carter joked.

'No,' Fikri replied with complete solemnity, 'the Turkish army is always punctual.' Then, with his voice tinged with embarrassment, he added, 'David, you will not mind wearing a tie tonight?'

'For you Fikri, for the Turkish army, and the honour of the BBC, I will wear a suit as well,' Carter promised. Relief spread across Fikri's face. 'Good,' he said, confident once more. 'I will collect you here at The Dome at eight o'clock. I think it will be best if Sevilay comes as well to keep company with the major-general's wife. We know him and his family well. They are good people, but they speak little English. So we will translate for you.'

Fikri left Carter to make the reservations at the Abbey House. Although it was nearing 17.00, his telephone call interrupted Graham Cousens's afternoon rest. Graham, the co-founder of the restaurant, ran his life as precisely as anybody in the Turkish army. Five minutes later and he would have been wide awake.

No, Graham was quite firm, there was no possibility of Carter and his guests having a table on the terrace overlooking the distant sea; the Abbey House was always fully booked many days in advance and Carter should have known this. Fitting five people anywhere in his restaurant tonight would be very, very difficult.

'But it's for Major-General Bitlis and his wife. He's the No 2 military man in northern Cyprus,' Carter pleaded. His words fell on ears used to hearing names being dropped.

Graham Cousens and his partner were very selective in their choice of dinner guests.

'And Fikri Direkoğlu will be with us. He's the Director of the Ministry of Tourism. His wife, Sevilay, is the Angela Rippon of Bayrak Radio,' Carter persevered, hoping to spark some interest in his VIP list.

'Dear boy,' Graham laughed, 'if you were to bring the UN Secretary-General and the Presidents of Cyprus, north and south, we'd still have difficulty in placing them this evening. But, since it's you, Bryan and I will work out something by eight. I expect the major-general will be arriving with the usual escort of Jeeps and soldier boys?' Carter confessed he had given no thought to his guests' travelling arrangements, but it was something to consider.

Because Graham had settled in Cyprus before 1974, he belonged to a diminishing group of expatriates in the north who were allowed to visit the Greek Cypriot side whenever they wished. However, his partner, Bryan Hill, had arrived in Kyrenia two years after the war and was considered an 'illegal immigrant' by the laws of Greek Cyprus, if not an outright collaborator with the 'occupation' forces. As a consequence he could not set a foot in the south without facing arrest.

Outwardly the men were a pair of gadflies, but both possessed a remarkable firmness of purpose. They believed northern Cyprus had

enormous potential as an area for tourism. At first they had worked at
The Grapevine in the late seventies, but they held formal catering
qualifications and decided to establish a place of their own. By the
spring of 1980, they had converted another Englishman's home into a
restaurant, decorated it from floor to ceiling with style, and drawn up
their first dinner menus.

Within three years they had established the Abbey House as one of
the best restaurants in the whole of Cyprus and the two men were
contributing more than money to the TFSC's economy. Their success
allowed them to employ several young Turkish Cypriots, several of
whom were refugees from Mari, a village near Limassol. Most came
with a background in agriculture and had no experience of serving at
tables or behind a bar. Some had introverted personalities, the result of
spending their early years in an enclave where they endured siege-like
conditions. Even so, under Graham and Bryan's tutelage, they had
become fine waiters and, in return, were teaching their employers the
Turkish language.

At weekends the Abbey House was always packed with foreigners,
mainly residents of southern Cyprus. They included UNFICYP
officers and their wives. Usually they arrived at about 20.00 and spent
the next three hours feasting leisurely on smoked salmon, fresh from
Scotland; prime cuts of steak served in French sauces; English puddings,
and the best cheeses from around the world, all washed down with the
finest wines from France and Turkey.

When the two restaurateurs first began operating in northern
Cyprus, many quality ingredients had not been available in the grocery
shops of Kyrenia. To get what they needed for their menus, Graham
would travel to Nicosia and buy in the south. Nowadays there were no
shortages, but if they wanted something in particular, they placed an
order with Fortnum and Mason in London, and the goods would arrive
at Ercan airport on board a Cyprus Turkish Airlines flight in under 48
hours from their initial telephone call.

Graham and Bryan were models of discretion and guarded the gossip
of the local expatriate community from outsiders, such as Carter. But
as easily as they acted the roles of diplomats, they could become tyrants,
dispatching from their restaurant any guest who lacked good manners
and a sense of elegance.

Only recently a gaggle of scantily-clad young women had
unwittingly fallen victim to the men's sharp tongues. Accompanied by
a journalist whom Carter had met briefly in The Dome Hotel bar, the
women had arrived on the doorstep of the Abbey House early one
morning. Carrying an expensive camera, the Fleet Street reporter had
claimed to be on a semi-official assignment for the Turkish Federated
State of Cyprus and wanted to photograph his models in an environment
which promoted the country.

'We can smell *his* sort a mile off,' Bryan had remarked later. 'All he wanted was a free meal and a place to impress his dolly birds. Do you know, he had the audacity to suggest *he* was doing *us* a favour by having the girls drop their tops for his snapshots which, he said, would appear on page three of some tatty rag? If we co-operated, he said he'd guarantee a mention of our place in the little article underneath. I ask you, do *we* need favours like *that*?'

Graham had continued the tale: 'It's quite dreadful really the way that northern Cyprus is a magnet for his sort. Somehow or other they persuade an unsuspecting official here or there to fork out free airline tickets and hospitality in return for promises of all sorts of publicity for the Turkish Cypriots in the papers back home. One chap promised *The Sun* would publish *five* serious articles on *five* consecutive days about life out here. Can you imagine *that* paper publishing five sensible *paragraphs*, with or without girlie pictures?'

Ultra-sensitive about his Turkish Cypriot-sponsored trip, Carter hoped he was not included in their general observations and criticisms.

'No, not at all,' Bryan had assured him. 'You work for the BBC.'

Carter did not reveal that the BBC, despite its reputation for morality, had accepted its fair share of 'freebies' too, but he did make sure his credit cards were always in order to pay bills whenever he used the Abbey House.

A Jeep carrying three armed Turkish soldiers in white helmets swung round the corner of the narrow street and drew up in the car park between the abbey at Bellapais and the restaurant. It signalled the arrival of Major-General Eşref Bitlis and his wife at precisely 20.30.

While dust was still swirling skyward from the speed and rapid braking of the Jeep, the soldiers jumped out and in a well-practised drill movement stood to attention. A moment later a black Mercedes limousine slid to a stop a few paces from where Carter stood. Another Jeep-load of guards completed the convoy.

Standing in the orange light of evening and striped by the long shadows cast by the abbey's grand Gothic pillars, the soldiers in their sharply-pressed uniforms and high glossed boots made an impressive sight. Carter was the only person who appeared out of place, dressed as he was in a pale blue drip-dry suit, creased in all the wrong places.

A soldier marched forward and snapped open the rear door of the limousine. Major-General Bitlis was the first to alight, followed by his wife. Carter extended his hand in greeting. It was crunched firmly by the major-general and then lightly brushed by Mrs Bitlis's fingers. Fikri Direkoğlu and Sevilay, both smiling broadly, bowed slightly in acknowledgement of the guests' arrival.

Major-General Eşref Bitlis was a large man who had passed his half-century, yet carried none of the loose weight which often came with middle-age and a life of inactivity. He wore a dark civilian suit and a lot of confidence, but there was nothing arrogant about his bearing. He was a man used to power, knew the range of his authority, and had no reason to prove himself. Carter had met people like him before, in all those places where military actions had been decisive and commonplace. The major-general, he concluded, was one of the world's professionals.

Before they began dinner Major-General Bitlis asked Fikri to clear the ground rules of conversation. He hoped Carter would understand that in his position he was prohibited from expressing political views. He apologized for not being able to speak English and wondered if Carter could converse in German, the major-general's second language.

When the BBC producer replied in the negative, the major-general laughed, saying that Fikri would therefore continue as official translator at the dinner-table and the unofficial censor in case any of them became indiscreet after the second bottle of wine.

On the subject of wine, the major-general said he had an important question to ask: had Carter tasted a good Turkish wine? If not, then would Carter mind if he took charge and ordered on their behalf? Not at all, Carter replied, but the answer bothered Fikri.

'Maybe they won't have what the major-general wishes for us, David,' he whispered in English.

'I'm sure we will,' Bryan interrupted. He had been standing behind Fikri's left shoulder.

For every suggestion made by the major-general, Bryan had a better recommendation, delighting the military man and compounding Fikri's surprise at the range of wines in the cellar of the Abbey House.

The choice of wine having been settled, the major-general declared that he thought Bryan and Graham were splendid chaps as their Abbey House was better stocked than his own officers' mess and was most definitely better than most Turkish restaurants. He drew more approval from the two Englishmen when he suggested that they serve him the speciality of the house. He may not have been prepared to discuss politics, but he was demonstrating a talent to charm as skilfully as any clever politician on a mission to win hearts and minds.

But if compliments were to be handed out, Carter, as the host, felt duty-bound to add a few of his own. He asked Fikri to put a question to Mrs Bitlis, translating his words exactly. He wanted to know how it was that Turkish ladies always had beautifully manicured hands and polished finger-nails.

Fikri blushed, a victim of his own natural reserve. Sevilay, who understood English perfectly, covered her smile with her own elegant hands, and suggested that the question would come better from her. Mrs Bitlis lowered her eyes, a shy smile spread over her face and she giggled. From the major-general came a throaty chuckle and an answer. 'The reason Turkish girls have soft hands is because they never do any housework!' In that case, said Carter, he would not share the secret with his wife. The major-general acknowledged the good sense of the decision, provoking Sevilay to click her tongue against the roof of her mouth in mock disapproval.

During dinner there were bouts of loud laughter and moments of quiet seriousness as the conversation covered many aspects of Turkish Cypriot life. Major-General Bitlis shrewdly avoided comment on all matters of military security and political sensitivity, although his smiles in response to certain questions provided better answers than a thousand words.

About the UN presence in Cyprus, the major-general said he had to accept UNFICYP as a reality, talked warmly about individual officers and men whom he had met at liaison meetings, but considered the UNFICYP mandate ineffectual as it had not been able to provide Turkish Cypriots adequate protection between 1964 and 1974. He paid tribute to the 'Freedom Fighters' who had defended the Turkish Cypriot enclaves during those 10 years and expressed the hope that northern Cyprus would play an increasingly important role in its own defence.

Cypriots, wherever they lived on the island, had no cause to fear the Turkish army, he said; the last thing soldiers wanted was war; the Turkish army was in northern Cyprus to ensure peace by defending the Turkish Cypriot community.

Carter suggested it was easy to talk in these terms when they all sat in an elegant restaurant, enjoying the companionship of friends, drinking good wines and sampling English trifle, but feelings were very different amongst the Greek Cypriot farmers who worked their orange groves in the middle of the Buffer Zone and saw armed Turkish soldiers looking down on them from their military positions.

'Major-General, those farmers are petrified when they see your soldiers, sometimes just a few feet away,' Carter said. 'They see you as the people who forced them to flee their homes. How can they regard you as "Peace Soldiers"?'

Before the major-general could reply, Fikri answered. 'David, my friend, we talk of the present. If I, as a Turkish Cypriot, have to look to the past and compare what happened to us with what is happening to them now, there is no comparison, and *you* will not have understood the realities at all; our people, our history.

'At night, Turkish Cypriots went to bed not knowing whether we would be alive in the morning. Our children went to school on the bus and we wondered whether they would return. We tried to develop our businesses on our lands, owned legally, only to find that we were denied materials or stopped because Greeks decided to confiscate and make them military areas.

'David, today our young people are safe. We are not threatened any longer. The changes since 1974 have made us *all* safer.

'Remember, we, too, have lost properties, but we did not terrorize the Greeks, and we do not continue to complain, nor do we persist in blaming others for our difficulties. We ask only that we are recognized for what we are.'

Never before had Carter been subjected to so much passion about the

Cyprus issue from his friend. It was true, he had not heard Turkish Cypriots complain about their lot, although the north faced greater economic difficulties than the south. He decided to change the subject and asked if the major-general had been told about the incident at Yiğitler.

Smiles returned to the faces of Carter's guests; only the major-general remained solemn.

'Yes,' he said, 'I was informed. The news reached me during my dinner. An officer came in and said four spies had been captured in a military zone and he wanted to know what action he should take. I said to the major, "If you have spies, then shoot them". I am pleased to say, for your sakes, that my major answered very nervously that we had not shot any spies for a very long time, and asked, did I really want him to carry out the order. I said, "Yes, of course", but if the names of the spies were Carter, he could use his discretion and let them go.'

At the end of his anecdote, the major-general smiled broadly.

Turkish humour, Carter was discovering, took time to understand and was clearly an acquired taste. What was more, it always had a point.

'As you have seen, there is nothing to hide in northern Cyprus, apart from those things which involve security which any country must keep secret,' Major-General Bitlis continued after a pause. 'But many journalists come here with their ideas already made up. If soldiers behaved like journalists, seeing only what they want to see and ignoring realities, they would lose their lives on the battlefields and cause the deaths of innocents.'

Cyprus was a place where journalists should be more aware of their responsibilities, the major-general said. He believed there was a danger to peace and stability if ill-considered opinions and inaccuracies were published; they fanned intolerance. He chose his words carefully, correcting a phrase here or there in Fikri's translation, suggesting that he had a better command of English than he cared to admit.

Carter had heard similar opinions from servicemen elsewhere, and these had been British. They, too, had been unimpressed by the way the media operated and always quoted examples of journalistic irresponsibility; there were no more sensitive animals than soldiers challenged and journalists criticized.

Major-General Bitlis finished his English sherry trifle, a pudding he had first sampled during a visit to an army camp in England. Now he wanted to quiz Carter. Lighting a Marlboro cigarette, he suggested that the BBC producer should be better informed on Cyprus than most people as he had travelled on both sides, visited the Sovereign Bases, and toured the Buffer Zone with UN soldiers. With the benefit of this background, how did Carter see the future of Cyprus?

Carter coughed and felt awkward. It was easier to put questions than provide answers. He agreed that he had moved widely about the island, but claimed he had not met the decision-takers. His tapes, he said, reflected the feelings of ordinary people. Therefore, he argued, he was too inexperienced in the currents of local politics to even navigate the present, let alone chart a course ahead.

But, replied the major-general, if Carter had met the people, then he must be in touch with the situation. Truth was in the streets of towns and in the village squares, but truth came in many forms, often contradictory yet still valid. That was the case in Cyprus and why journalists should take time and think deeply before they wrote or spoke their words; words which ordinary people believed and to which they reacted, sometimes in ways which did not serve their best interests. He apologized, if what he said was obvious.

'Now,' said Major-General Bitlis, 'tell me how you would settle the problem of Varosha.'

From the glint in the major-general's eye, Carter knew he did not expect an answer.

'Find a solution for Varosha,' Carter replied, 'and you are half-way to cracking the Cyprus dispute. Quite frankly, sir, I don't know.'

'Good.' The general stood up, looked at a nearby table which had been occupied by UN officers until a few minutes ago, and said, 'The evening is late and my wife and I have a long journey home.'

Outside the cool night carried the scent of jasmine.

By the side of his black limousine the major-general shook Carter's hand.

'Thank you, David, for a most enjoyable evening.'

'Thank you, sir, for sanctioning my visit to Varosha.'

'Don't thank me, thank Mr Denktaş. He is the President. It is his country,' replied Major-General Bitlis.

The door of the limousine was pulled shut and the major-general disappeared into the darkness with his escort of soldiers in their two Jeeps.

Midnight approached. The only sound was the call of an owl, hooting in the distance; was it a resident or had the bird crossed the 40 miles of sea from Turkey to settle on this northern shore of Cyprus?

Looking up at the abbey, silhouetted boldly in the light of a crescent moon, Carter thought about its builders, the Order of Premontre. They had ruled by strictness and austerity and they had provided a peace of sorts which gave this village its name.

Muslims had succeeded Christians; Turkish words had covered Greek slogans, but strictness, austerity, and a peace of sorts remained embedded in the life of northern Cyprus, as firm as the granite foundations of Bellapais itself.

Carter's seventh journey to Cyprus was over.

It was time to go home.

CHAPTER 26

AN IRISH VICTORY

THE first blizzard of the winter had brought the morning traffic to a full-stop in West Berlin on the day Rauf Denktaş astonished the international community by his address to the Turkish Cypriot parliament in Nicosia, the divided capital of Cyprus.

'We hereby declare before the world and before history the establishment of the Turkish Republic of Northern Cyprus as an independent state.'

One-hundred-and-sixty-thousand Turkish Cypriots had waited patiently for almost a decade to hear their leader's pronouncement, but even they were surprised when it came. For Greek Cypriots, all 450,000, it was the statement they had hoped would never be made, but feared would come one day.

That day was 15 November 1983.

All along the 150 mile-long cease-fire line of the partitioned island, UNFICYP contingents were immediately placed on full alert, the Greek Cypriot National Guard stood by for trouble, and the media rediscovered Cyprus. In northern Nicosia, crowds gathered in Atatürk Square. In New York, UN resolutions were drafted ready to condemn the Turkish Cypriots.

Somebody in *The World At One* offices at the BBC's Broadcasting House telephoned Carter's office at Radio London to find out if any of his Cyprus tapes contained material suitable for a programme to be broadcast in three hours' time.

But Carter was at the British Military Headquarters on the edge of Hitler's 1936 Olympic Stadium in Berlin. He was there to meet staff and plan other programmes. It was here that he heard the news of the Turkish Cypriots' declaration of independence. It came to him from Colonel Derrick Knight, calling from the Ministry of Defence in London.

'You were right after all, David,' Knight said, congratulating the BBC producer's predictions of a change in the status quo, made two months earlier.

Carter had suggested to all who cared to listen that something dramatic was bound to happen in Cyprus during the first two weeks of November. To support his belief, he had drawn attention to the Turkish mainland elections, aimed at restoring civilian government, which would be taking place at that time. These elections, he argued, could provide both sides, Turks and Greeks, with an opportunity to exploit the situation in Cyprus. He quoted various strong rumours that suggested Greek air force units would be flying to the new Paphos airport, which, by coincidence, was opening at the same time as the Turkish elections; others claimed that EOKA-B extremists might mount a series of rapid hit-and-run attacks in the area of Morphou with the aim of provoking the Turks to react militarily at an awkward time, thereby damaging the elections on the mainland and forcing the world to focus again on Cyprus.

Finally, the strongest rumour of all said Rauf Denktaş, frustrated by endless rounds of UN-initiated discussions about talks about talks, would feel the time was exactly right to declare an independent state in the north, which in reality it had been for years.

Carter's views had fallen on deaf ears. His photographs of the 'forbidden city' of Varosha, the first taken in ten years, had not been accepted by BBC Television news and current affairs' departments, even for file purposes.

Only Derrick Knight at the Ministry of Defence had taken Carter seriously.

Because Carter had been kept fully occupied with other matters, such as making jingles in Manchester, escorting a round-England cycle marathon in its latter stages and compiling swing band music shows for Radio London — all the things which paid his mortgage — he had been forced to temporarily set aside his interest in Cyprus matters.

Nevertheless, prior to leaving for Berlin, Carter had written to Alan Rogers, BBC Radio's Head of Current Affairs Magazine Programmes, at Broadcasting House. In his note, Carter said: 'I've recorded all sorts of interesting, ordinary people and secured promises that "the leaders" will talk happily to us in April '84 . . .'. He explained how he had entered Varosha and described his meetings with Rauf Denktaş and Major-General Bitlis, stressing he now had plenty of 'fresh' material to warrant a Radio 4 documentary along the lines discussed and agreed earlier in the summer. He suggested that Rogers should meet Greg Ainger, the Editor of Local Radio Services, to see if the resources of the two BBC departments could be usefully shared in the preparation of a single programme. He hoped that by the time he returned to London Rogers would have replied.

As one of the first people in Berlin to hear of the events taking place in Cyprus that morning, Carter passed Knight's information to his military colleagues. They reacted immediately by sending messages to all military units and the civilian authorities to keep a watchful eye on the Greeks and Turks in that divided city. Fortunately there were no incidents, as the so-called 'guest workers' had enough local problems with which to deal, without adding those of a place at the far end of the Mediterranean where their 'cousins' lived.

Meanwhile, at Radio London, Peter Champness, one of the station's producers, searched frantically for Carter's Cyprus tapes, hoping to pass them on to Broadcasting House. Not finding them, he telephoned Carter in Berlin. The latter told him the tapes were at his home in

Welwyn Garden City, held there for safety. Consequently none of this material was used, or lost; the first post-independence interview with President Denktaş in northern Nicosia was by a Canadian reporter, and this was used by *The World At One* programme on Radio 4.

By the time Carter returned to London Rogers had still not replied, but Carter felt it was best to leave the matter until the New Year before chasing him for his reaction.

Although it was now the start of the Christmas season, the mood was far from festive at Radio London. Because of an escalation in programme-making costs and a large deficit in the station's budget, Derrick Amoore, the manager, had been forced to take some hard decisions. Several producers and journalists had been told that their contracts would not be renewed. Union meetings were held to protest and threats of strike action echoed in the corridors of 35A Marylebone High Street.

Radio London had always been a highly competitive place, as Carter knew well, but tension was even more pronounced now. Personal survival, at almost any price, was uppermost in the minds of most people. Spirit was much in evidence, but seasonal goodwill was lacking.

While many were convinced that 1984 would live up to its Orwellian connotations, Tony Freeman, Radio London's news editor and expert on travel, believed Carter had the least to worry about. In any shake-up, he would fare best, Freeman claimed, but Carter did not share his colleague's optimism.

'Your trouble is that you're always so gloomy,' Freeman observed. 'Let's face it, you're a survivor. I told you so in '74 when you thought the end of your world was just around the corner, and you're still here.'

But the New Year opened grimly. In a remarkable letter mailed to him at home by the station manager, Carter was told that he was to be removed from his office and his current responsibilities. He would be given new ones; choosing music for an afternoon DJ. He was now the *former* Music Programmes Organizer of BBC Radio London.

Carter immediately protested at his downgrading of responsibility and status without cause. Protracted discussions took place but, in the end, BBC Local Radio chiefs came down on Derrick Amoore's side. They argued Carter would continue to be paid as a senior producer who still carried management responsibilities, but, in their view, the post of Music Programmes Organizer had never existed even if Carter had done the job for the past 14 years. As such, they could instruct him to do any work which they agreed fell within the normal duties of a producer. If he did not accept the situation, he could face possible 'termination of employment'.

Carter's doctor advised him to stay at home while the National Union of Journalists took up his case with the BBC.

Carter believed that the best way of resolving the dispute would be to persuade Radio 4 and Alan Rogers to formally commission his documentary on northern Cyprus. That way he could continue to work usefully for the BBC, and stay away from Derrick Amoore, Radio London and his Local Radio critics. Time and union resolve would cool tempers and lead to a common sense solution redefining his job in the corporation painlessly.

On 14 February 1984, Carter packed his Cyprus tapes and sent them to Rogers with a covering letter, which, in part, stated, 'During my time away from the office, I've leadered together some of the chats I recorded in northern Cyprus and I hope you or one of your staff will be able to find the time to listen to the material, so that you can take a decision on whether you wish to go ahead with the documentary.

'Of course, lots of political interviews will have to be recorded when I revisit the north. At the moment I'm trying to schedule this trip for mid-April and would very much enjoy going there with one of your producers to make certain that I'm objective. If you need any more information, please telephone me.'

Soon afterwards Carter received a telephone call from Maggie Redfern, one of the producers in Rogers's department. She said his tapes had been passed to her, but she held out little hope of their use as the Controller of Radio 4, David Hatch, had already bought *another* programme about Cyprus from a producer at Radio Ulster. Its provisional title was *John Bull's Other Island* and its aim was to compare the problems of Cyprus with those of Northern Ireland.

'But, Maggie, there's no direct comparison. It's a cute title, but the wrong premise,' Carter exclaimed, surprised to hear about Radio 4 commissioning this programme while his had been in the works for more than nine months. 'How come it's been set up by people in Belfast when Alan knew I was gathering material with his approval?'

Maggie Redfern did not have an answer, but promised she would battle on Carter's behalf at Broadcasting House and Radio 4.

'Look,' said Carter, 'get hold of David Hatch and tell him it's David Carter's programme which he's scrapping.' Because he had worked with Hatch in the past co-producing several series of mainstream programmes for the networks, he hoped the Controller would reconsider his decision in light of this new information. 'If it helps, tell him I'll work with the producer from Northern Ireland.'

By 25 April 1984 Carter had heard nothing further and his dispute with Local Radio continued. So he wrote another letter to Alan Rogers: '. . . some weeks ago Maggie Redfern telephoned to say that David Hatch had gone for a Cyprus programme called *John Bull's Other Island* rather than having the one relating almost exclusively to the Turkish Cypriot viewpoint. She promised to raise the matter again and see whether two Cyprus programmes could be made as the formats appear vastly different. She mentioned, too, that my tapes were being pushed in the direction of *Woman's Hour* to see if something could be salvaged or rebuilt.

'It would be one heck of a morale booster were I to hear from you that some part of our scheme could go ahead.'

Next day a letter arrived from Maggie Redfern. Dated 25 April 1984, it said: 'I am sorry not to be writing with better news, but since I have heard nothing further about *Cyprus, A View From The North* since I raised it again, I can only assume that CR4's decision stands. I believe you will by now have had a letter from Alan Rogers suggesting that you contact *Woman's Hour* about a possible alternative use for your material.

'I have your tapes safe in my new office. Do call by sometime to collect them, or if you prefer it, give me a ring and I will send them.

'I'm only sorry we aren't enjoying the Cypriot sunshine at the moment.'

On 1 May 1984, Rogers wrote: 'Many thanks for your letter — I believe Maggie Redfern has already been in touch. I will pass the word to *Woman's Hour* and tell Sandra Chalmers the background.'

Two weeks later, on 15 May 1984, Carter received another letter from Rogers: 'Your proposal is running into problems all along the line because I now find that *Woman's Hour* already have a feature planned on Cyprus (including the Turkish part). Had they known that you had material, they would have commissioned it from you, but it was only when the main documentary proposal fell down that I told them of your visits to the island.

'However, I do have an alternative suggestion which is to contact Ian Gilham, Head of World Service Productions. I spoke to one of his producers and he thought that your material may find a place in the World Service.

'I am sorry that your material has been dogged in this way on top of your health.'

Carter knew he was fighting a battle on two fronts: to retain a job in the BBC and to get his programme on the air. Neither was being won. What puzzled him was how all these various projects on Cyprus were going ahead without anybody in the Turkish Cypriot administration knowing. He feared his BBC colleagues were treading well-used paths, probably placing themselves firmly on the Greek side and only travelling briefly into northern Nicosia to record short interviews with officials there.

But Carter followed Rogers's advice and contacted Ian Gilham at the World Service, passing him copies of the correspondence between himself and Radio 4 during the previous 12 months.

Gilham replied swiftly. On 23 May 1984 he said: 'I think your material is more relevant to our Current Affairs Department, so I have passed it to them.'

On 29 May 1984, John Marshall, the Assistant Head of Talks and Features at the World Service, wrote Carter: 'Towards the end of last year our half-hour programme *Assignment* did a programme from the

Turkish-controlled sector of Cyprus. With regret, therefore, I must say that we would not be able to use your material in the World Service.'

Time was running out. The tenth anniversary of the Turkish intervention was only weeks away.

Carter's programme was not destined to reach the air.

On 20 July 1984, Radio 4 broadcast the programme David Hatch had bought from Radio Ulster. A network announcer said: 'In many ways the history of the troubled island of Cyprus is similar to that of northern Ireland. Mike McKimm reports from Cyprus, the place many refer to as *John Bull's Other Island*.'

During the next 45 minutes McKimm investigated the premise he had set himself, but in the end he concluded that the problems were very different. In fact, he said many aspects of the Cypriot dispute 'made the Irish problem pale into insignificance'.

Carter was disturbed by McKimm's statistics because they exaggerated the number of Turkish soldiers based in the north, increased the number of casualties suffered by the Greek Cypriot side in 1974, and decreased the size of the Turkish Cypriot population. McKimm did not reveal his sources, but his figures did not coincide with those of UNFICYP and, therefore Carter concluded they had been supplied by the Greek Cypriot PIO, probably Panayiotis Argyrides, who dealt with the foreign media.

Because McKimm had based himself in the south, his interviews were mainly with Greek Cypriots, all of whom talked about their losses in 1974, the maltreatment of prisoners of war by the Turkish army and their affection for Turkish Cypriots.

One said: 'The Turkish Cypriots are the first victims; they fell into the trap of the Turkish army.'

Another claimed the Turkish army brought to an end 'the life Turkish Cypriots had begun to enjoy before 1974'.

McKimm reported that during the 10 years since partition, the Greek Cypriot economy had boomed and unemployment was negligible, while the north suffered badly on both fronts.

Only two interviews with Turkish Cypriots were broadcast; one with President Denktaş, the other with a PR official.

It was the kind of programme which Greek Cypriots would have welcomed, but one which did nothing to reveal the true feelings and attitudes of the Turkish Cypriots.

McKimm ended his programme by asking President Denktaş to offer a solution to the Irish problem.

Carter switched off the radio.

Cyprus was, as McKimm said, an island where every family had suffered the loss of a relative.

One side had found the economic good life, while the other had military strength.

Greek Cypriots were internationally-recognized, their voice heard in the world's fora and their economy buttressed by foreign aid. Turkish Cypriots were recognized only by Turkey, their calls unheeded abroad, and their state underpinned by financial contributions from wherever they could get them.

New generations were growing up in the island, their emotions governed by the prejudice of their elders and the hearsay of others. If, as many said, history repeated itself, then something had to change and that would not necessarily be for the better.

Carter went to his study. On its shelves rested several large boxes. They held *The Cyprus Tapes*, his work from seven trips to the island. He shrugged his shoulders, sat down at his typewriter and drafted an application for another job outside the BBC. From his Turkish Cypriot friends, he had learned patience and the ability to survive.

Was Carter's odyssey at an end or only just beginning?

CHAPTER 27

THE END OF AN AFFAIR

CYPRUS became the focus of world media attention again on 17 January 1985 when a historic meeting took place at the United Nations' headquarters in New York between President Denktaş and President Spyros Kyprianou. The leaders of the two Cypriot communities stood side by side, flashing smiles around the world as TV cameras recorded what Mr Denktaş called 'the handshake of the century'. An end seemed to be in sight to the long-standing Cyprus dispute.

During the previous six months, the UN Secretary-General, Perez de Cuellar, had conducted a series of personal discussions with both Mr Denktaş and Mr Kyprianou. From the Turkish Cypriots he had wrung major concessions on the constitutional and territorial aspects of the problem. Despite severe criticism from his own supporters, Mr Denktaş had gone along with de Cuellar's wishes. On the basis of these talks, the UN Secretary-General had put together a 'draft agreement'.

However, when the moment came in New York for the 'draft agreement' to be signed, Mr Kyprianou refused. To the shock of everybody present, except perhaps the Greeks, he demanded further concessions. His change of attitude surprised the UN Secretary-General, who had been assured privately that the document met with the Greek Cypriot President's complete approval.

Mr Denktaş, looking his opposite number in the eye, warned that if the 'draft agreement' remained unsigned, Turkish Cypriots would not be bound in future to the concessions which they had agreed for the purposes of this document. Everything, he said, would return to 'square one'. Still Mr Kyprianou refused to pick up his pen to sign.

On 20 January the summit broke up with the Cyprus problem no nearer solution. Both leaders returned home. For the first time since 1974 world opinion edged towards the side of the Turkish Cypriots.

Back in Cyprus, Mr Kyprianou found his administration plunged into a political crisis; many Greek Cypriots had wanted a settlement, and this was their last chance. By contrast, Mr Denktaş was welcomed home by his people, most of whom were relieved that they would not have to make the promised sacrifices.

No longer prepared to allow northern Cyprus to function without a democratically-elected government, pending a settlement with the Greek Cypriots, Mr Denktaş and his Council of Ministers announced a date for a referendum on the draft Constitution of the Turkish Republic of Northern Cyprus, which had been declared 18 months earlier.

Referendum Day would be 5 May 1985.

If the Turkish Cypriots approved the draft Constitution, general elections would follow almost immediately. With eight political parties ready to field candidates from the extreme right to the extreme left, the campaign promised to be lively and the results could not be forecast with certainty.

Clearly, the more the foundations of the TRNC were laid, the more difficult it would become ever again to create a single state of Cyprus. This appeared to go unnoticed abroad. As far as most observers were concerned, Cyprus had returned to the status quo. Once again it could be ignored.

To the news-room staff at Radio London, Referendum Day was just another Sunday. Derrick Amoore, the station manager, was far away from the Marylebone High Street studios; he was on holiday in Greece. His news editor, Tony Freeman, and senior producer Frank Dawes, their roles unchanged over the years, were at home in the suburbs. They still churned out travel programmes at a rate of one a week.

None at the station, which claimed to serve all of London's ethnic communities, took account of the fact that more Cypriots lived in London than in any city in Cyprus; nor the thousands of Britons who had served on the island or who had been tourists there; people like Mr and Mrs Griffiths. They still lived in Ealing and remembered their 'memorable holiday' in 1974 which ended with them leaving on the last civilian aircraft to use Nicosia International airport.

Not only did Radio London and all the BBC's domestic services ignore the events taking place in the TRNC, they failed to report the results of the referendum.

Just as the Griffithses had never returned to Cyprus, Carter would never set foot again in Radio London, its output these days geared mainly to devotees of 'soul' music.

Carter had resigned from the BBC two weeks before the referendum. For the preceding 17 months the corporation had debated his future and paid his salary, but eventually he had decided to break the stalemate and try to build another career outside the world of broadcasting.

On holiday, for the first time without a Uher recorder on his shoulder and a microphone in his hand, he was as free as any other tourist in northern Cyprus. He had no deadlines to keep, no formal appointments to make, no worries of any kind. He could set out each day on his own terms, discover new friends, meet old ones and see how life had changed for them since they had contributed to his Cyprus tapes.

First he tracked down 'The Cave Ladies'. They no longer lived in Tjiklos, where they had witnessed at close quarters the events of summer 1974. Now their home was a small bungalow near the Turkish Cypriots' National Archive building in Kyrenia. Their front gate displayed a Union flag and the Cross saltire to mark their English and Scottish origins. Although neither was in good health, their zest for life and their generosity with a bottle of Scotch remained undiminished.

At The Dome Hotel, the management was ensuring that everything went smoothly for a party of British Members of Parliament on a fact-finding mission to northern Cyprus. It included the former actor Andrew Faulds, representing the Labour Party, and Keith Speed, a Conservative, once the Navy Minister in Prime Minister Thatcher's government.

None of the MPs was able to cash cheques in the Barclays bank opposite the hotel. On orders from London it had been closed permanently after the Turkish Cypriots' declaration of independence. Mr Sami had retired to enjoy his collection of Victor Sylvester records. Street trading in foreign currency continued, however. One of the first traders had been Sergeant Mustafa, an ex-policeman. He had done well. Today he ran a small *bureau de change*, highly respectable and profitable.

Nine miles west of Kyrenia, John Aziz, the owner of The Celebrity Hotel, was in happy mood on Referendum Day, even if one of the letters of the large electric sign above the entrance to his hotel was falling off. He knew his business was expanding rapidly. His travel agency was reporting heavy bookings for the holiday bungalows across the road. On the hotel's terrace overlooking the sea, more than a dozen British tourists were enjoying the spring sunshine.

In Famagusta, Arif Gürbüz remained with the water board and was not looking forward to the coming summer. He still contended with the problems caused by shortages and the threat of supplies being cut completely by the Greek Cypriots. He had voted early and planned to spend the rest of the day with friends, the members of the local folk music society.

Hüssein Herbsoy's Cyprus House restaurant was proving profitable, but Ali Özel's tourism agency 'in the shade of the Lala Mustafa Paşa Mosque' was yet to break even. He had suffered mixed fortunes. His father had died in January. Earlier, with the help of UNFICYP, Ali's mother had been able to leave Limassol in the south and, after 11 years, rejoin her family, now living in Famagusta.

For Carter, Referendum Day ended with him having dinner with Trevor Taylor at a Chinese restaurant in Kyrenia. Earlier they had spent half an hour in The Grapevine, where Allan Cavinder was again behind the bar, serving guests. Once a month he wrote a column in *Pan*, a magazine published in English and Turkish by Arman Ratip, who had performed jazz pieces with his trio on Radio London in 1972.

As they ate their Chow Mein and Peking Duck, Taylor, one of the British expatriate community's most visible personalities, talked about his plans for a wildlife park in northern Cyprus. To his donkeys in the fields outside his Ozanköy home, he had added some Cyprus bulls, a species on the verge of extinction. Taylor's dream would become reality only after his death. Within 18 months he would die of cancer, but a local trust would continue his work, secured through the bequest of an annual income.

The results of the referendum were published the next day. Seventy per cent of voters approved the draft Constitution. Now an election campaign would begin for the presidency and the seats of the legislature. While nobody predicted which party, if any, would achieve an overall majority, it was clear, in May 1985, that Rauf Denktaş would be returned as president.

There was also agreement amongst most politicians that the close links between Turkey and the TRNC had to be maintained, while leaving the door slightly ajar for a settlement one day with Greek Cypriots, if that were possible. Meanwhile there would be a determined effort to acquire more foreign investments, increase tourism and secure international recognition of the independent state.

Leading the way was the son of a Turkish Cypriot policeman from Famagusta who had fled Cyprus in 1961 amid Greek Cypriot terrorism. In London's East End he had started a new life and a clothes-making business. By 1985 his son had made it a multi-national conglomerate which employed a third of the workforce of northern Cyprus. Now three flags flew there. They represented Turkey, the Turkish Republic of Northern Cyprus and Asil Nadir.

Had Major Cedric Mercer or Major David Emmett remained in Cyprus, the former UNFICYP MPIOs would have noted the increasing signs of the TRNC's permanency. On the northern side of the Ledra Palace check-point, a Customs house was nearing completion. A new airport was under construction at Geçitkale. When it became operational, it would be able to handle the world's largest jet aircraft, military and civilian. And Saudi Arabia was funding a motorway cut between Nicosia and Kyrenia, where a new port was being developed.

Major Mercer had retired from the British army soon after completing his UNFICYP tour. Today he was the director of the Anglo-Israel Association in London. Major Emmett was serving NATO, not the UN; he was stationed at Heidelberg, West Germany. Major-General Eşref Bitlis of the Turkish army, too, had left. According to Fikri Direkoğlu, now the Under-Secretary of the Ministry of Tourism, the friendly major-general had taken up 'important duties elsewhere'. It would not be long before Fikri himself moved and the major-general died in a helicopter crash. Once the elections were over, changes would take place in every government agency, whichever party or coalition took over.

Across 'The Green Line' in south Nicosia, George Tsigarides's life had altered as well. Greek Cypriot tourism may have boomed, but he had not been the direct recipient of any of the benefits. He still held the same post in the CTO, but he no longer lived in the family home in Themistocles Dervis Street. When the area was designated an area for redevelopment, the old houses had been pulled down and George, with his mother, moved to a modern apartment in Araouzos Street, a turning off Archbishop Makarios III Avenue.

Before he left Cyprus on this occasion, Carter stood on the roof of the Saray Hotel in northern Nicosia. Looking south across the capital, he remembered many people whom he had met over the years on his trips to the island. Several felt he had let them down. Julia Sinclair came to mind.

Carter had used her diary which recorded life in Cyprus during the coup and months following the intervention; her recollections suggested only British residents had value, but she also believed the Greeks had the divine right to rule Cyprus. She had accused the former BBC producer of partiality, and she was correct in her assessment. He *was* biased; in favour of justice. Or so he liked to believe.

When Julia left Cyprus she did not give the island a second thought. Married again, she and her new husband settled in Auckland, New Zealand. He had been a civilian UN official. The exact whereabouts of Bill Sinclair were not known, although somebody mentioned they had seen him in the BBC Club in the Langham building, opposite Broadcasting House.

A light breeze carried the scent of citrus and the smell of wood-smoke from the charcoal grills somewhere below in the streets of Nicosia.

In the distance Carter saw Greek flags fluttering, UN flags nearer, and Turkish flags where he stood. As dusk came they would be pulled down for another day.

The orange light of evening turned to purple and then to black. Soon it became impossible to tell where 'The Green Line' wound its way through the ancient walled city. It would be a long time before Cypriots travelled freely again between the tavernas and kebab houses of the divided city.

In Carter's view, both sides must accept the right of the other to exist, secure and free. The more outside powers refused to recognize the Turkish Cypriot state, placed obstacles in the way of trade, quarantined the north by preventing direct flights, postal services and telecommunications, denied equal treatment to TRNC representatives at international conferences and sporting events, and questioned the validity of Turkish Cypriot passports, the longer it would take for trust to be established between the two peoples of the island.

Carter had conducted a love affair with Cyprus but few love affairs last forever. The island had been his mistress, warm, generous and exciting; she had also been frustrating.

He returned to the UK, and while Cyprus was never far from his thoughts, he saw little and read even less of what was taking place on the island. All of his time was used learning a new job in the defence industry, which would take him to the Gulf, Pakistan, India and Turkey.

CHAPTER 28

TIME TO MOVE ON

DURING the next 18 months Cyprus was quiet and remained outside the attentions of the international community. For the drama of violence the media looked to the Lebanon, Iraq, Iran, the Philippines and Nicaragua. Away from the glare of publicity, however, diplomatic activity continued to try to settle the differences between the Turkish and Greek Cypriots.

At the United Nations, Secretary-General Perez de Cuellar pressed both sides into making further concessions. On 29 March 1986 he once again submitted a 'draft agreement' for Mr Denktaş and Mr Kyprianou to consider. Just as before, the Greek Cypriot President balked at the terms as they stood.

In London, Keith Speed and a number of fellow Members of Parliament had formed an all-party pressure group to counter the Greek Cypriot supporters in the House of Commons, while Lord Willis, the award-winning playwright, was doing the same in the House of Lords. Then, in May, the Foreign Affairs Committee of the House of Commons announced its intention to undertake an inquiry into the Cyprus problem.

Less than a mile away at the TRNC's offices in Cockspur Street, members of staff were taking a more positive approach to public relations, led by Tansel Fikri. The drive for more British tourists was also being stepped up following the arrival in London of Fikri Direkoğlu.

In Nicosia, the reins of the Turkish Cypriot government were held by the new Prime Minister, Dr Derviş Eroğlu. His Foreign Minister was Dr Kenan Atakol.

Suddenly in November a battle of words broke out in London between the two sides. Three factors contributed to the verbal warfare. First of all, President Denktaş was invited to give evidence to the House of Commons Foreign Affairs Committee. Secondly, while in London, the Turkish Cypriot planned private meetings with British politicians, businessmen and media representatives; in addition Denktaş was due to address members of the Royal Institute of International Affairs at Chatham House. Lastly, the London representative of the TRNC had booked the Queen Elizabeth Conference Centre, a British government-owned building, to use as a venue for a party to celebrate the Republic's third anniversary. President Denktaş would be present.

On hearing this, Greek Cypriot political activists in London, especially those belonging to the Panhellenic Socialist Movement (PASOK) immediately put their propaganda machines into top gear.

They declared that Mr Denktaş's visit and 'the reception being accorded him at the heart of the British establishment' was 'an affront to democratic public opinion in England and in Cyprus'.

Simultaneously, but more discreetly, the British members of 'The Friends of Cyprus', an organization almost exclusively dedicated to supporting the Greek Cypriot side, expressed their opposition in loud whispers. Their opinions found space in the columns of certain influential newspapers.

On the rain-swept evening of 17 November, PASOK demonstrators and their left-wing British sympathizers gathered outside the Queen Elizabeth Conference Centre. They waved damp banners, shouted against the breeze and tried to hand pamphlets to the guests arriving at the TRNC's third birthday party. 'Stop Denktaş,' they chanted, the sound of their cries drowned by the falling rain and passing traffic.

Their actions only generated greater interest in the President's speech. His moderate approach contrasted sharply with the mood of hysteria outside the building.

Before long, heavy showers cooled the Greek Cypriot hot-heads much more effectively than the thin blue line of London policemen drafted to ensure 'the peace'.

Next day the scene was repeated outside Chatham House. Inside Keith Kyle, whose wife Susan had worked with Carter in the current affairs department of Thames Television, introduced Mr Denktaş to members and friends of the Royal Institute of International Affairs, some of whom were Greeks and Greek Cypriots. The discussion that took place was conducted with good manners and good humour.

The session over, the Turkish Cypriot leader was driven at speed to the House of Commons, where the Foreign Affairs Select Committee was preparing what Ian Mikardo MP called 'sharp and penetrating' questions. Because the meeting was to be held in public and on the record, a large crowd had gathered early in the corridor outside Committee Room 16. Everybody wanted a seat.

Greek Cypriots were there in force, stopping non-Cypriots and pleading that if they believed in 'justice' Mr Denktaş should be banned from speaking.

Carter, who had been invited to attend the Commons session, pulled a cloak of discretion around himself when people in the crowd approached. Asked who he represented, he answered that he simply had a tourist's interest in the UK's parliamentary process.

He carefully did not declare his support for the TRNC, nor that he had ever travelled to Cyprus. Instead he listened patiently as two elderly Greek Cypriots told him of 'the desert around Kyrenia' and 'the perfect harmony which we all enjoyed until the Turkish army occupied our beloved land'. One of them had lived in London since 1945, without once returning home.

EOKA and *Enosis* were words whispered by Carter, but they were brushed aside as having no importance in the context of today's events.

'Yes,' one of the Greek Cypriots conceded, 'we did have a few silly people, but they are in the past.' The other added, 'There were no problems before 1974. All my friends were Turkish people. Believe me.'

Yes, Carter believed them as much as the one-armed German, a former soldier from World War II, whom he had met in Berlin. That individual had insisted only a handful of people belonged to the Nazi party and absolutely nobody knew about concentration camps and the persecution of Jews, gypsies and homosexuals.

At 16.30 exactly, the Foreign Affairs Select Committee began its meeting. Mr Denktaş made an opening statement which was followed by a reminder from the chairman, Sir Anthony Kershaw MP, that the Turkish Cypriot 'administration' had accepted the UN Secretary-General's latest 'draft agreement'.

Then he asked: 'Is that really your preferred solution, or is it the solution which you think you could reasonably ask Mr Kyprianou to accept?'

'It is a compromise solution for the good of Cyprus,' Mr Denktaş replied. 'I think it is a solution which we can expect reasonable Greeks, who have no ulterior motives about the future of Cyprus, to accept.'

Each of Mr Denktaş's answers was filled with facts and figures. Everything he said contradicted the official Greek Cypriot submissions to the committee and appeared to surprise some members.

'If within a reasonable time-scale no constitutional solution appears possible, what will be your policy?' Sir Anthony asked. 'In particular, can you tell us whether you envisage maintaining your present independence, or will you seek some formal relationship with Turkey?'

Mr Denktaş was unambiguous in his reply. 'We cannot see that,' he said. 'I think the question means this: do you intend, do you think, do you want to be united with Turkey because there is no other solution? We have Turkey as a guarantor power. It is protecting us; it is helping us economically.

'There is no policy, no decision, no desire to unite the northern part of Cyprus with Turkey. Turkey does not want it, we do not want it.

'Turkey does not want it because it would open the door to Greece to unite the southern part of Cyprus, and Turkey does not want to be flanked all over by the Greek army, and, therefore, union with Turkey or double-union is out of the question.'

If two separate states were the eventual solution to the Cyprus problem, Robert Harvey MP wanted to know whether Mr Denktaş would consider any changes to the current boundaries.

Mr Denktaş: 'Naturally, if that would mean final peace.'

Mr Harvey: 'Would that also involve a shift of population?'

Mr Denktaş: 'According to what would be exchanged, it is a natural result.'

The select committee raised many other issues, including the question of satisfactory guarantees of protection for the Turkish Cypriots, the role of UNFICYP, and the future status of the British Sovereign Bases.

'I think Turkey should guarantee our rights,' Mr Denktaş told the committee. 'Greece should continue to guarantee Greek Cypriot rights, and Britain should guarantee her own interests, but we rely on Turkey.'

On the subject of the UN force, he said: 'UNFICYP is useful in the no-man's-land, but it is a fiction that UNFICYP has prevented war, and can prevent war. Our survival cannot be guaranteed by UNFICYP.' He described the UN soldiers as 'international witnesses', but he was prepared to have UNFICYP remain in Cyprus, until there was an agreed solution to the problem.

His comments on the Sovereign Bases were brief. 'All I would say for the time being is that you, the British, are in the south. Your problem is with the south.'

Nigel Spearing MP asked Mr Denktaş to suggest any diplomatic action which could be taken to break the current deadlock. 'I suggest, since the British government's policy is to back up Mr de Cuellar's initiative, this should be done not only in words but deeds. That paper treats us as political equals of the Greek Cypriots.

'Mr de Cuellar sees us as leaders of two communities, treats us equally on all issues. I say the British government should do the same, and stop bumping up Mr Kyprianou as the government of Cyprus.

'I am sure the British conscience, the British legal mind, the freedom of parliamentarians, cannot accept that in Cyprus, where legitimacy was handed to a bi-communal establishment, it can now be carried on by only one of the parties at the expense of the other, in the light of what has been done in Cyprus since 1963.

'If this is known, I am sure you will revolt against the idea that Greek Cypriots can speak for the whole of Cyprus, can speak for Turkish Cypriots, and that they are the legitimate speakers for our land.'

In December, the seven members of the Foreign Affairs Select Committee left for a 10-day tour of Athens, Cyprus and Ankara.

Despite Mr Denktaş's suggestion that they should enter Cyprus from one side and leave from the other to prove Mr Kyprianou could not 'dictate to the British government', the Members of Parliament chose not to.

While the Commons committee gathered evidence abroad, Cyprus was debated in the House of Lords on 17 December. Lord Willis opened. He, Lord Hanworth and Lord Broxbourne gave their support to the Turkish Cypriots. But their views were not shared by Lords Kennet and Stallard, both of whom believed that all the island's problems stemmed from the Turkish intervention in 1974.

Old age and ill health did not help to give Lord Caradon a clear memory. The last colonial governor of Cyprus blamed both communities equally. While arguing that Britain should not take sides, he failed to explain why, therefore, the government here continued to recognize the Kyprianou administration as the only authority in Cyprus and refused to approve the independence of the TRNC.

Later, one observer remarked: 'There is of course no point in argument for argument's sake, but if the British Parliament refuses to address the arguments which are made by both parties to the dispute, it cannot hope to understand the problem. Bitterness is not likely to be avoided by perpetuating the present situation.'

The debate ended with comment from Baroness Young, the Minister of State, Foreign and Commonwealth Office. Ignoring most of the points made by Lords Willis, Hanworth and Broxbourne, her speech was bland, misleading, and inaccurate.

'The present situation benefits nobody and brings enormous distress to many,' she said. 'Certainly the present situation is not in Britain's interests. We want a stable Cyprus. We know and respect its people and wish them well.'

She pointed out Britain made the largest annual contribution of any nation to UNFICYP: 760 men and more than £21 million. She expressed regret that 'one side' could not accept the United Nations Secretary-General's proposals for a unified federal Cyprus. This was a serious set-back for peace, she said, without stating that the fault lay with Greek Cyprus.

Baroness Young refused categorically to accept that the British government's policy was unfair to Turkish Cypriots.

She insisted: 'We maintain contact with their leaders in northern Cyprus. We continue to trade normally with them. They both benefit from the aid that we give Cyprus.'

Carter read the House of Lords Official Report (*Hansard*) with wry amusement. If what Baroness Young said were true why then was it that all his friends in northern Cyprus received their Christmas cards only after they had travelled through Mersin in Turkey? Why did his local travel agent still insist holidays in the TRNC were 'illegal'? Why were there no direct flights allowed between Ercan and London? These refuted her claims that 'we continue to trade normally with them'. Even parliamentarians travelling on official business were ordered to enter Cyprus from the south.

Nevertheless, in northern Cyprus the outlook for 1987 was far from gloomy.

The TRNC's Prime Minister, Derviş Eroğlu, signed an 'Economic Co-operation Agreement' with Turkey. It promised that Ankara would guarantee all investments in northern Cyprus. This augured well for local industry and business, but it was questionable whether it lessened the economic dependence of Turkish Cypriots on the 'Motherland'.

Meanwhile, in London, the Foreign Affairs Select Committee, to which Carter had submitted evidence, continued its inquiry, promising to publish its findings and conclusions by the spring. But with election fever in the air, it was unlikely that Members of Parliament would devote time to the committee's recommendations, whatever they were. Change in Britain's relations with either side in Cyprus was not an issue that stimulated any interest amongst the local electorate, except, possibly, in areas of north London where British Cypriots had settled in large numbers. There candidates could say anything and forget their promises immediately after the votes were counted.

Most MPs simply wanted Cyprus to remain exactly as it was, a comparative haven of peace and stability in the turmoil of the Middle East.

The Turkish Cypriot leadership accepted the political realities pragmatically, and concentrated their attentions on domestic issues which they could influence. President Denktaş's agreeable responses to the most recent 'draft agreement' and his willingness to be cross-examined in 'the mother of Parliaments' had helped him to take some of the political high ground away from the Greek Cypriot government of Kyprianou.

All this and more was discussed by Carter and his old friend, Derrick Knight. They were lunching at the Topkapı, a Turkish restaurant in Marylebone High Street, where they had met frequently in the past. Knight was now enjoying retirement in northern Cyprus, where he and his wife he lived in the village of Lapta. He played an active role in community life and was a prominent member of the British Residents' Association in Kyrenia. Twice-yearly he travelled to London. This was one of those visits. He had flown on a spanking new Airbus of Turkish Airlines from Ercan airport, touched down briefly at İzmir, and then continued on to Heathrow, without him or his wife having to leave the 'plane. It had been the nearest thing to a direct flight.

Northern Cyprus was on the move, Knight told Carter. A new generation of Turkish Cypriots was slowly taking over. These young people had been born after the 1960 republic had ceased to exist. They needed no reminding that their tiny island, throughout its history, had never been completely free to chart its own destiny. Because they were realists, their ideas were relevant to present conditions and they aimed to navigate a steady course through calm waters, unlike their elders who remembered 'the old days' when the weather outlook was always stormy and, therefore, chose to stay in harbour, protected but poor.

Knight remembered, too, that early morning in July 1974 when he had received confirmation that Turkish forces were landing on the island.

'Intervention' or 'invasion', it made no difference now. The map of Cyprus had been changed forever.

Young Turkish Cypriots today looked to what could be, rather that what might have been if . . . Their loyalty was to the future only and the state their parents had created against all odds.

'The next time we meet, it must be in *Girne*,' Knight shouted from his taxi as it drove away. 'Remember, bring the family with you. You'll be very welcome.'

Carter nodded. 'Yes. One day.' He stood for a moment trying to decide which direction to take for his journey home. He turned and walked northwards. Here, 10 years ago, on a summer's evening, his Cyprus tapes had begun . . . as a holiday assignment.

On the way to Baker Street tube station, he passed The Rising Sun on his left and BBC Radio London on his right.

A decade later, it seemed like only yesterday.

> *I have seen the old ships sail like swans asleep*
> *Beyond the village which men still call Tyre,*
> *With leaden age o'ercargoed, dipping deep*
> *For Famagusta and the hidden sun*
> *That rings black Cyprus with a lake of fire.*